KU-465-496

The Nature of the Universe

The
Nature
of the Universe

GUILD PUBLISHING
LONDON · NEW YORK · SYDNEY · TORONTO

Contributing Editors Patrick Moore, Iain Nicolson

Editor Peter MacDonald
Designers Ayala Kingsley, Niki Overy
Picture Editor Linda Proud
Picture Researchers Milly Trowbridge, Lynda Poley, Judy Aspinall, Anne Hobart (US)

Project Director Lawrence Clarke
Art Editor John Ridgeway

Advisors
Professor Jack Meadows, University of Leicester
Professor Martin Rees, University of Cambridge

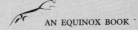

AN EQUINOX BOOK

Planned and produced by:
Equinox (Oxford) Ltd
Musterlin House
Jordan Hill Road
Oxford OX2 8DP

Copyright © Equinox (Oxford) Ltd 1989

This edition published 1989 by Guild Publishing by arrangemennt with Equinox (Oxford) Ltd

All rights reserved. No part of this publication may be reproduced, stored in a retrieval system or transmitted in any form or by any means, electronic mechanical, photocopying, recording, or otherwise, without the permission of the publishers.

CN 2768

Printed in West Germany by Mohndruck Graphische Betriebe GmbH. Gütersloh.

Introductory pictures (pages 1-6)
1 A typical spiral galaxy
2-3 A collection of nebulae
4-5 The "Horsehead" nebula
6 Star trails

Contents

Planets and Orbits

Earth, Sun and Solar System introduced...Describing the motions of the planets...The exceptional orbits of Mercury and Pluto...The terrestrial planets...The Jovian planets...Comparative planetary data...Their moons, or satellites...Eclipses of the Sun and Moon... PERSPECTIVE...Early speculation on Earth's shape and position...Copernicus, Galileo and other founders of modern astronomy...Later discoveries of planets

The Earth is a small planet traveling in its annual path, or orbit, round a very ordinary middle-aged star, the Sun. Nine planets orbit the Sun, and of these seven are themselves orbited by satellites known as moons. These planets and moons, together with a host of minor bodies and some gas and dust, make up the Solar System.

The Sun, a self-luminous globe of gas, is by far the biggest member of the system. Its diameter of 1,392,000km is 109 times that of the Earth and nearly ten times that of the largest planet, Jupiter. It is 330,000 times as massive as the Earth, and about 740 times as massive as all the planets put together. Because the Sun is so massive it exerts a powerful gravitational attraction, and this is the force that holds the system together, controlling the motions of all the planets and minor bodies within it.

The names of the planets (in order of increasing distance from the Sun) are Mercury, Venus, Earth, Mars, Jupiter, Saturn, Uranus, Neptune and Pluto. Some astronomers believe there may be a tenth planet far beyond Pluto's orbit. The largest minor bodies, the asteroids, lie mainly between the orbits of Mars and Jupiter. Each planet's orbital path is elliptical rather than perfectly circular, and its distance from the Sun therefore varies during its yearly orbit. The point of closest approach to the Sun is called perihelion and the farthest point aphelion. The average, or mean, distance between the Earth and the Sun is 149,597,870km, and this distance, known as the astronomical unit (AU), is a useful yardstick for comparing planetary orbits. The mean distances of the other planets range from 0·39AU for Mercury to 39·44AU for Pluto. The distance of Pluto varies between 29·6 and 49·2AU, and at perihelion it is closer than Neptune to the Sun.

◄ The Sun is shown orbiting the Earth between Venus and Mars in this stylized illustration of the Ptolemaic system, published in Nürnberg in 1493, 50 years before the idea of a centrally placed Earth was seriously challenged.

From flat Earth to round

Looking around him, a casual observer knowing nothing about science would assume the Earth was flat, allowing for local irregularities such as hills and valleys. It was quite natural for early civilizations to regard the world as not only flat, but also stationary, with the whole sky moving around it and completing one revolution every 24 hours.

Even the early Greek philosophers believed in a central, non-rotating flat Earth. Thales of Miletus (c. 624-537 BC), who is generally regarded as the first of the great Greek scientists, taught that the Earth was a flat disk, floating on water like a cork.

The eventual realization by the Greeks that the Earth must be a globe followed logically from observation. For instance, the bright star Canopus can be seen from Alexandria, but not from Athens, where it never rises above the horizon. And when the shadow of the Earth falls upon the Moon, producing a lunar eclipse, it is seen to be curved – so that the Earth's surface must also be curved. Acceptance of this was a major step forward, but the Greeks still could not dethrone the Earth from its position in the center of the universe.

The Earth-centered universe

A few of the philosophers did in fact challenge the concept of the Earth-centered or "geocentric" universe. Aristarchus of Samos (c. 310-230 BC) was bold enough to suggest that the Earth moved round the Sun in a period of one year. He could provide no proof, however, and the Sun-centered or "heliocentric" theory was disregarded for many centuries. Instead the Greeks developed a theory involving what were known as "epicycles". They thought that all celestial bodies must move in perfect circles, since the circle was the "perfect" form and nothing short of perfection could be allowed in the heavens. However, it was quite clear that the "wandering stars", or planets, which had been recognized from very early times, did not move smoothly and regularly against the starry background. The Greeks therefore assumed that although a planet moved round the Earth, it also described a small circle or epicycle, the center of which moved round the Earth in a perfect circle. As more and more irregularities came to light, further epicycles had to be added, until the whole system became a complicated cosmic maze.

The Ptolemaic system (named after Ptolemy, last of the great astronomers of the classical period, who lived around AD 150) survived for centuries in spite of its complexity, because it did not conflict with observed evidence, and there was no reason to reject it.

The Arab tradition

It was only with the rise of Arab civilization in the 7th century that systematic observation began once more, and then it was mainly for astrological purposes (until the 17th century, astrology was still regarded as a true science). The Arabs built improved measuring instruments and calculated the apparent motions of the known planets with impressive accuracy. Specialized observatories were built, the last and most elaborate by Ulugh Beigh at Samarkand in 1433.

The outer Solar System

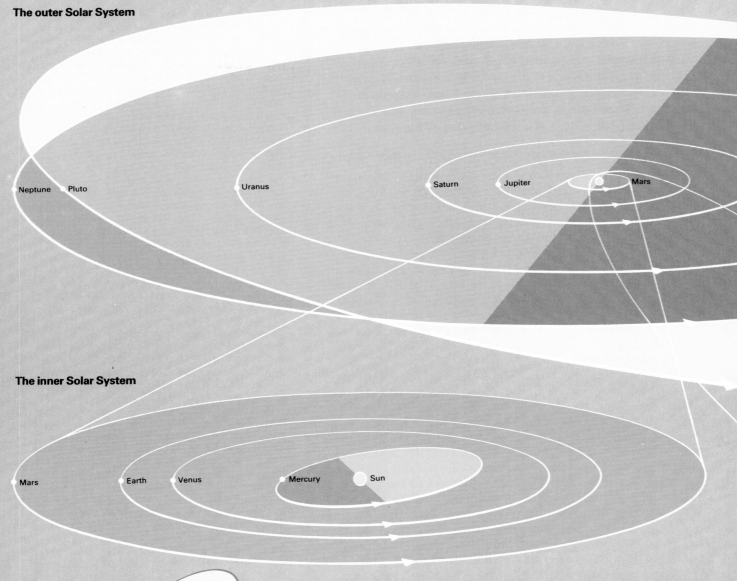

Neptune Pluto Uranus Saturn Jupiter Mars

The inner Solar System

Mars Earth Venus Mercury Sun

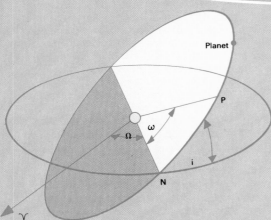

▲ *The orientation of a planetary orbit is described by three angles: i (inclination) – the angle between the plane of the Earth's orbit (the ecliptic) and that of the planet; Ω – the angle between a fixed direction in space (♈) and the point N where the orbit crosses from south to north of the ecliptic; and ω – the angle between N and perihelion P (the point at which the planet is closest to the Sun).*

Although the planets all move in elliptical orbits, most of these are nearly circular. The extent to which an ellipse is elongated – that is, its eccentricity – is given by a figure between 0 (for a circle) and 1 (for a parabola): the greater the eccentricity the flatter or more elongated the ellipse. Among the planets, Mercury and Pluto have distinctly elliptical orbits with eccentricities of 0·206 and 0·250 respectively. Most elliptical of all are the orbits of the comets, nearly all of which extend far beyond the outermost planets (most astronomers believe that there is a vast reservoir of comets with orbits extending to a distance of some 40,000AU from the Sun).

The planets all travel round the Sun in the same direction, and this motion is called direct. Most of their orbits lie within a few degrees of the ecliptic (the plane of the Earth's orbit). Again, Mercury and Pluto are exceptions, their orbits being tilted, or inclined to the ecliptic, by angles of 7° and 17° respectively. Some asteroids have more steeply tilted orbits, and the orbital inclinations of long-period comets range from 0° to 180°. Those with inclinations greater than 90° move in retrograde orbits (in the opposite direction to the planets).

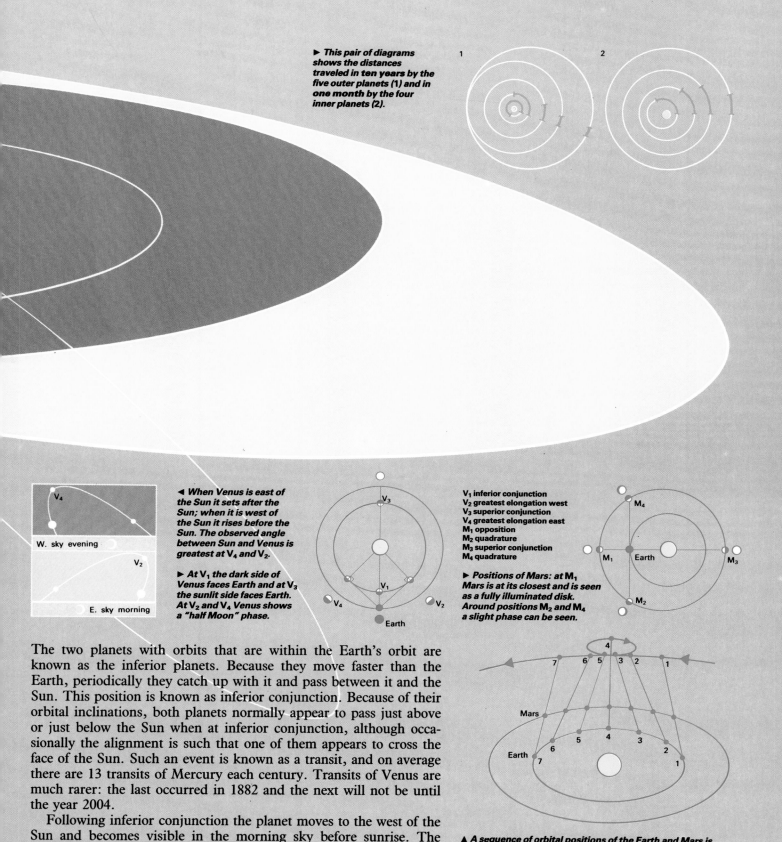

► This pair of diagrams shows the distances traveled in ten years by the five outer planets (1) and in one month by the four inner planets (2).

◄ When Venus is east of the Sun it sets after the Sun; when it is west of the Sun it rises before the Sun. The observed angle between Sun and Venus is greatest at V_4 and V_2.

► At V_1 the dark side of Venus faces Earth and at V_3 the sunlit side faces Earth. At V_2 and V_4 Venus shows a "half Moon" phase.

V_1 inferior conjunction
V_2 greatest elongation west
V_3 superior conjunction
V_4 greatest elongation east
M_1 opposition
M_2 quadrature
M_3 superior conjunction
M_4 quadrature

► Positions of Mars: at M_1 Mars is at its closest and is seen as a fully illuminated disk. Around positions M_2 and M_4 a slight phase can be seen.

The two planets with orbits that are within the Earth's orbit are known as the inferior planets. Because they move faster than the Earth, periodically they catch up with it and pass between it and the Sun. This position is known as inferior conjunction. Because of their orbital inclinations, both planets normally appear to pass just above or just below the Sun when at inferior conjunction, although occasionally the alignment is such that one of them appears to cross the face of the Sun. Such an event is known as a transit, and on average there are 13 transits of Mercury each century. Transits of Venus are much rarer: the last occurred in 1882 and the next will not be until the year 2004.

Following inferior conjunction the planet moves to the west of the Sun and becomes visible in the morning sky before sunrise. The angle between the Sun and the planet is known as the elongation, and increases to a maximum of 28° for Mercury and 47° for Venus. Thereafter the angle narrows until the planet passes behind the Sun at superior conjunction. It then reemerges on the east side.

▲ A sequence of orbital positions of the Earth and Mars is shown in this diagram, together with the apparent motion of Mars in the sky. Most of the time Mars moves directly – right to left – relative to the background stars, but near opposition, when the Earth is overtaking it, Mars appears to move backwards (in retrograde motion) and traces out a loop in the sky.

The planets which have orbits outside that of the Earth are known as the superior planets, and their behavior is somewhat different. Traveling more slowly than Earth, a superior planet is periodically overtaken by it. On such an occasion the Sun, Earth and planet lie in a straight line with the Earth in the middle. The planet is said to be at opposition and is then best placed for observation, because it is at its closest to Earth as well as being visible all night. After opposition the planet falls behind the Earth and eventually passes behind the Sun (superior conjunction) before emerging again to the west of the Sun and becoming visible from Earth in the morning sky.

The time interval between two similar alignments of Sun, Earth and planet (for example, between two conjunctions or two oppositions) is called the synodic period of the planet.

The terrestrial planets

The four innermost planets are collectively known as the terrestrial planets because they have some features in common with the Earth. All are small bodies of relatively high density, composed mainly of rocky minerals and metals. Mercury has just under 40 percent of the Earth's diameter. Its axial rotation period (the time it takes to rotate once on its axis) of 58·7 days is two-thirds of its orbital period of 87·97 days, and this leads to some interesting seasonal effects. Venus is almost the same size as the Earth, but is a hot and hostile world, permanently shrouded in cloud. It rotates on its axis in a retrograde sense once every 243 days. The third planet, Earth, has a surface largely covered in water and is the only planet on which life is known to exist. It has a large moon which is about one-quarter of the diameter of the planet. Mars has about half the diameter of the Earth and about one-tenth its mass. It is a chilly world with a thin atmosphere, but is nevertheless the least hostile of the planets apart from Earth itself. Even so, it now seems highly unlikely that Mars supports even the most basic forms of life.

The Jovian planets

The next four are giant planets, often called the Jovian planets because in some respects they all resemble Jupiter. They are much less dense than the terrestrial planets, and are composed mainly of hydrogen and helium. Jupiter has 11 times the diameter of the Earth and is 318 times as massive; indeed it is 2·5 times as massive as all the other planets put together. It has the shortest rotation period of any planet (9 hours and 50 minutes at the equator) and consequently spins so fast that it bulges at the equator and is flattened at the poles, the equatorial diameter exceeding the polar diameter by some 8,500km. Saturn is nearly twice as far as Jupiter from the Sun. It has 9 times the Earth's diameter and 95 times its mass. Less dense on average than water, it spins rapidly and bulges markedly at the equator. Its most remarkable feature, however, is its extensive and complex system of rings.

Uranus, the next planet, is 19 times the Earth's distance from the Sun, about four times the Earth's diameter, and pursues its lonely orbit in a period of some 84 years. Neptune is similar in size to Uranus, but slightly more massive and significantly denser. It is 30AU from the Sun and takes 164 years to complete each orbit.

Icy Pluto is the last of the known planets. Although smaller than the Moon, Pluto is accompanied by its own relatively large satellite, Charon. It takes 248 years to complete each circuit of the Sun.

Scientific Revolutionaries

▲ *Copernicus: a 16th-century woodcut.*

▼ *The Sun-centered Copernican system as published in 1543, shortly before Copernicus himself died. Martin Luther declared that "this fool seeks to overturn the whole art of astronomy". His words typified the reaction of the Church.*

Copernicus and Tycho Brahe break the Ptolemaic mold

Tycho Brahe

Copernicus

It was not until some fourteen centuries after the death of Ptolemy that his geocentric theory was seriously questioned – by a Polish cleric, Mikolaj Kopernik (1473-1543), always known by his Latinized name of Copernicus. Early in his career he had begun to doubt the Ptolemaic theory, and he realized that many of the objections could be overcome simply by removing the Earth from its position in the center of the Solar System and replacing it with the Sun. His great book "De Revolutonibus Orbium Celestum" was probably more or less complete by 1530, but he was reluctant to publish it, because he knew that the Church would be bitterly hostile to any idea that the Earth was not the most important body in the universe. The book finally appeared in 1543, and even then the publisher, Osiander, added a preface – without Copernicus' authorization – to the effect that the theory was not intended to be taken literally, and was merely offered as an aid to mathematical computations of the movements of the planets. There was indeed strong opposition, and it is also true that Copernicus made many mistakes. In particular, he retained the concept of perfectly circular orbits, making his theory almost as cumbersome as the one it replaced.

Tycho Brahe

The next important figure was the Danish astronomer Tycho Brahe (1546-1601), one of the most colorful characters in the history of science. In his student days he fought a duel and lost part of his nose, which he replaced with "gold, silver and wax". He was first drawn to astronomy in 1572, when he observed a supernova (an exploding star) in the constellation of Cassiopeia. Tycho established an observatory at Hven, an island in the Baltic, with support from the Danish court. He had no telescopes, but his measuring instruments were much the best of their time, and between 1576 and 1596 he drew up an accurate star catalog as well as measuring the movements of the planets with remarkable precision. He paid particular attention to Mars, which was fortunate because Mars has an orbit which is rather less circular than those of the Earth or Venus.

Tycho realized that the old Ptolemaic system simply did not work. Yet he did not believe that the Earth was in motion, and he worked out a compromise system according to which the planets moved round the Sun, while the Sun itself moved round the Earth. He died suddenly in 1601, leaving his observations to his last assistant, a German named Johannes Kepler.

▲ Tycho's observatory at Hven, where most of his important work was carried out. After Tycho left Denmark in 1596 the observatory was never used again.

▼ One of Tycho's instruments was this zodiacal armillary sphere, used for sighting and following the motions of the stars, as well as the planets.

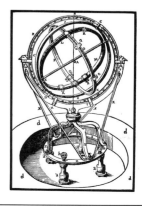

All but two of the Solar System's nine planets are accompanied by moons

	Mean distance (AU)	Mean distance (millions of km)	Eccentricity	Inclination to ecliptic	Sidereal period (days)	Equatorial diameter (km)	Polar diameter (km)	Equatorial rotation	Mass (kg)	Density (water = 1)
Sun	—	—	—	—	—	1,392,530	1,392,530	24.6d	1.9891×10^{30}	1.41
Moon	—	—	0.0549	5°09'	27.322	3,476	3,476	27.32d	7.3483×10^{22}	3.34
Mercury	0.3871	59.91	0.2056	7°00'	87.969	4,878	4,878	58.65d	3.3022×10^{23}	5.43
Venus	0.7233	108.21	0.0068	3°23'	224.701	12,104	12,104	243d	4.8689×10^{24}	5.24
Earth	1.0000	149.60	0.0167	—	365.256	12,756	12,714	23.93hr	5.9742×10^{24}	5.52
Mars	1.5237	227.94	0.0934	1°50'	686.980	6,794	6,759	24.62hr	6.4191×10^{23}	3.94
Jupiter	5.2028	778.34	0.0485	1°18'	4332.59	142,800	134,200	9.8hr	1.899×10^{27}	1.32
Saturn	9.5388	1,427.01	0.0556	2°29'	10,759.20	120,000	108,000	10.2hr	5.684×10^{26}	0.70
Uranus	19.1818	2,869.6	0.0473	0°46'	30,684.8	51,800	49,000	16.3hr	8.6978×10^{25}	1.27
Neptune	30.0580	4,496.7	0.0086	1°46'	60,190.5	49,500	47,400	18.2hr	1.028×10^{26}	1.77
Pluto	39.44	5,900.0	0.250	17°12'	90,465.0	2,500	2,500	6.3d	1.6×10^{22}	1-2

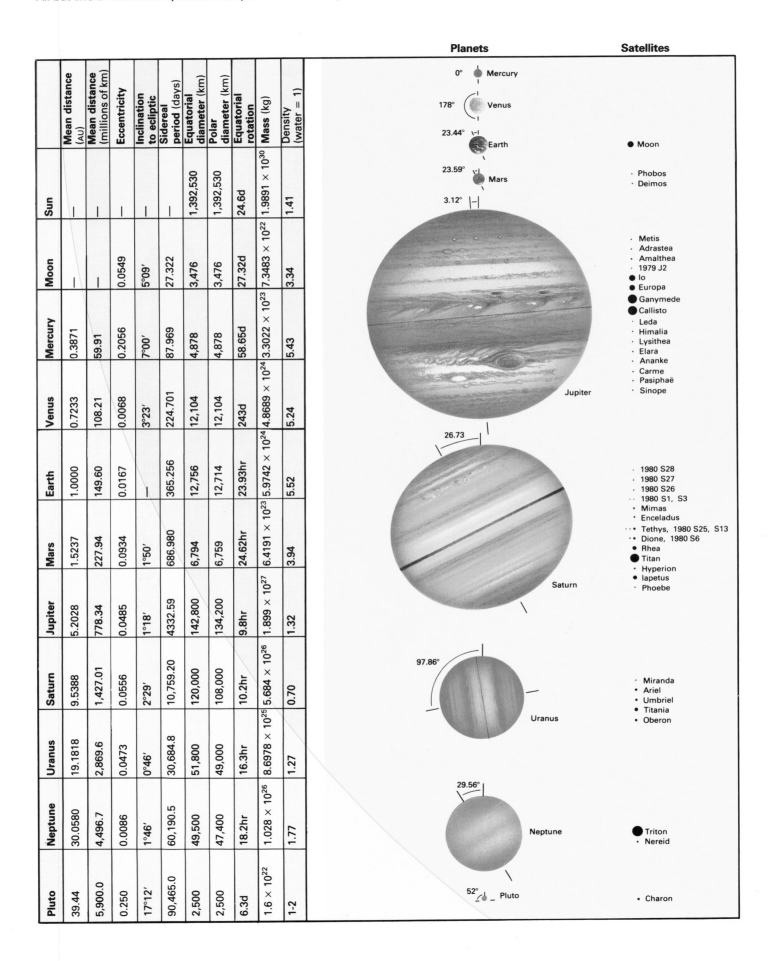

The Earth's satellite

The Moon, a barren, airless, cratered world, lies at a mean distance of 384,392km from Earth and has an orbital period of 27·3 days. Its orbit is elliptical, the distance from Earth varying between 356,410km at perigee (closest point) and 406,680km at apogee (farthest point). This is a variation of over 10 percent, and there is a corresponding variation in the Moon's apparent size. It rotates on its axis in the same period of time as it takes to travel round the Earth, so that the same face is always turned towards the Earth. This phenomenon is known as "captured" or "synchronous" rotation (◗ page 55).

Because the Moon shines by reflecting sunlight, at any instant one hemisphere is lit while the other is dark. When it is "new" the Moon lies in line with the Sun, and the hemisphere that faces Earth is dark. After New Moon it moves to the east of the Sun and as the angle between Sun and Moon increases, more of the illuminated hemisphere becomes visible and the appearance of the Moon changes from a thin crescent to a fully illuminated disk (Full Moon) when it is opposite the Sun. Thereafter the Moon again begins to approach the Sun in the sky, returning eventually to New Moon in 29·5 days.

Eclipses of the Sun and Moon

Since the Moon's orbit is inclined to the ecliptic by about 5°, the New Moon usually passes above or below the Sun. However, if the new phase occurs when the Moon is close to one of the nodes of its orbit (the points where its orbit meets the ecliptic) it crosses the face of the Sun, giving rise to a solar eclipse. If the alignment is exact, the Sun is completely covered and there is a total eclipse. (By coincidence the Sun and Moon appear virtually the same size in the sky. Although the Sun is 400 times the diameter of the Moon, it is also 400 times farther away.) Outside the narrow region from which a total eclipse can be observed, partial eclipse occurs. If the Moon is near apogee the solar disk is not completely covered and a ring of sunlight remains round the dark lunar disk. This event is called an annular eclipse.

A lunar eclipse occurs when the Full Moon passes into the shadow cast by the Earth instead of passing above or below the shadow.

Eclipses

▲ If the Moon covers the whole disk of the Sun, a total eclipse (1) is seen from the umbra (area of deepest shadow) and a partial eclipse (2) from adjoining areas. When the Moon is at apogee an annular eclipse (3) occurs.

▲ When the Moon enters the Earth's penumbra its brightness is reduced. If it brushes the umbra it will be partially eclipsed and the Earth's shadow can be seen. At total eclipse the Moon lies completely within the Earth's umbra.

▼ The upper diagram shows how at New Moon and Full Moon the shadow of the Moon usually passes above or below the Earth, and vice versa. If New or Full Moon occurs when the Moon is near one of the nodes of its orbit, then its shadow falls on the Earth, causing an eclipse of the Sun; alternatively it passes into the Earth's shadow, when an eclipse of the Moon is seen (lower diagram).

Phases

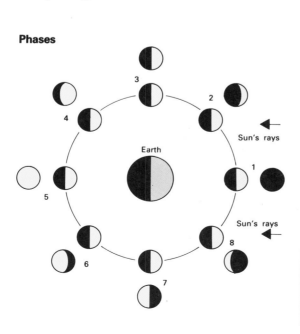

▶ The phase of the Moon – the part of its disk which is illuminated as seen from the Earth – depends on the angle between Sun, Earth and Moon. The Earth-facing hemisphere is dark at New Moon (1). Thereafter the phase goes through the following sequence: (2) crescent, (3) first quarter, (4) gibbous, (5) Full Moon, (6) gibbous, (7) last quarter and (8) crescent before returning to New Moon.

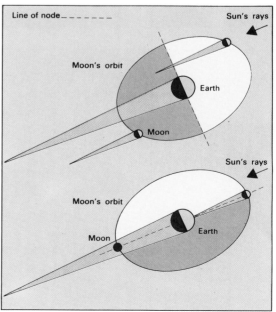

The growth of the Solar System: Uranus...

It came as a distinct surprise to scientists when, in 1781, William Herschel discovered a new planet moving well beyond the orbit of Saturn, and taking 84 years to complete one circuit of the Sun. Indeed, Herschel himself did not immediately recognize it as a planet – he believed it to be a comet.

Records showed that the new planet had been observed earlier, although without being identified as a planet. The first Astronomer Royal, John Flamsteed, had seen it in 1690 and had taken it for a star, designating it No. 34 in Taurus (The Bull) – which is why 34 Tauri is no longer to be found on star maps. A Frenchman, Pierre le Monnier, had seen it eight times in December 1768 and January 1769, but overlooked its gradual movement, and thus missed his chance of immortality.

...*Neptune*...

However, Uranus did not move quite as expected. It deviated from its computed path, and as early as 1834 an amateur English astronomer, the Rev. T. J. Hussey, suggested that the cause might be perturbations by another, more distant planet. He even wrote to Sir George Airy, who was later to become Astronomer Royal. But Airy did not believe that, even if Hussey were right, it would ever be possible to track down an unknown planet.

In 1841 the problem was taken up by John Couch Adams, a Cambridge undergraduate. By 1845 Adams was fairly sure that he had calculated the position of the planet which was perturbing Uranus, and he sought an interview with Airy, by then

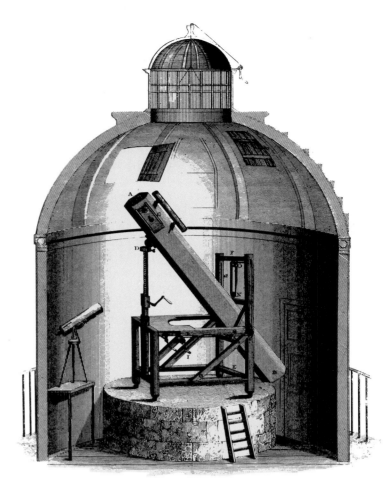

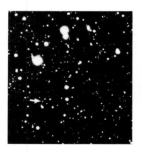
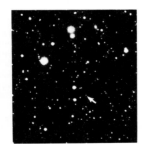

▲ **William Herschel discovered Uranus in 1781 with this telescope.**

◄ **Pluto (arrowed) was identified from these photographic plates.**

▼ **Le Verrier discovers Neptune and Adams observes Le Verrier, according to one French cartoonist.**

Astronomer Royal. This proved so difficult to arrange that Adams became discouraged, and nothing was done.

Meanwhile, Urbain Le Verrier, a French astronomer and mathematician, had turned his attention to the same problem, and come to much the same conclusion. One of his memoirs reached Airy in December 1845, and finally Airy asked James Challis, Professor of Astronomy at Cambridge, to search in the position indicated. Challis, however, had no good star chart of the region, and he began his task by laboriously plotting all the stars. In fact, he recorded the planet twice almost as soon as he began observing, but did not check his results. In Berlin, Johann Gottfried Galle and Heinrich Louis d'Arrest, using Le Verrier's results, identified Neptune on their first observing night.

Neither Adams nor Le Verrier took much part in the acrimonious controversy that ensued over who should claim the credit for the discovery, and they are today recognized as co-discoverers of the planet.

...*and Pluto*

The discovery of Neptune still did not completely satisfy astronomers, however, and there were suggestions that there might be yet another planet awaiting discovery. Percival Lowell, founder of the Lowell Observatory at Flagstaff, Arizona, worked out a possible position for "Planet X" but failed to find it, despite a careful search. It was finally located by Clyde Tombaugh on photographic plates taken at the Lowell Observatory in 1930, fourteen years after Lowell's death.

Inside the Planets

2

Overview...Interior of the Earth...How such information is obtained...Interiors of the terrestrial planets – and the Moon...Planetary magnetic fields and their possible cause...An unexplained anomaly... Bulging equators, flattened poles...Liquid interiors of the gaseous giants...The iceberg planet... PERSPECTIVE...Indirect evidence...Early notions about planetary interiors

Each planet has a distinct chemical composition and physical structure. The four low-density giants contain large amounts of hydrogen and helium, differing fractions of "ices" and small fractions of rocks and metals. The four terrestrial planets consist almost entirely of rocky materials and metals – such as iron and nickel – in differing proportions. Each planet contains several distinct concentric layers.

The terrestrial planets

The interior of the Earth consists of three main layers. On the outside is a crust, only 10-40km thick and composed of relatively light rocks, which sits on top of a denser rocky "mantle", 2,900km thick. Below the mantle is a dense iron-nickel core, 3,400km in radius. Temperature increases with depth from about 290K at the surface to 700K at the base of the crust, and to more than 4,000K in the core. The principal source of the Earth's internal heat is energy released by the radioactive decay of elements such as uranium and thorium. The heating and melting of the interior, early in the Earth's history, allowed the heavy metals to sink to the center and the light rocks to rise to the surface, hence the present structure. The mean density of continental rocks is 2,670 kilograms per cubic meter, compared with about 13,600 kilograms per cubic meter at the center of the core.

The core consists of a solid center and an outer liquid region. The mantle contains three regions. The outermost layer, or lithosphere, is rigid and less than 100km thick. Below this lies the more plastic asthenosphere. The deepest mantle layer, the mesosphere, is more rigid than the asthenosphere.

Each of the other terrestrials has a similar structure but there are important differences. Mercury has the largest core in proportion to its radius, Venus has a slightly smaller core than the Earth, and, apart from the Moon, Mars seems to have the smallest, least dense core.

What shock waves reveal

More detailed analysis of planetary interiors is possible if any seismic activity can be studied. This includes shock waves that travel along the surface and through the interior of a planet as a result of internal events such as earthquakes, and external events such as meteoritic impacts or man-made explosions. Two types of waves, known as P- and S-waves (primary and secondary waves), travel through the body of the planet and yield information about its deep structure from the way in which they are refracted or reflected as they reach layers of different densities. The fact that P-waves travel through both solids and liquids but S-waves can only pass through solids reveals whether or not all or part of a planet's interior is liquid in nature. The study of these waves by a global network of seismic stations has yielded a detailed model of the Earth's interior. A similar, although less detailed, analysis of the Moon was made by seismometers left on its surface by the Apollo astronauts. The only other planet to receive such instruments is Mars. However, only one Viking seismometer worked and the results were inconclusive, except to show that Mars is rather quiet seismically.

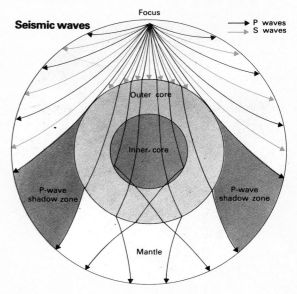

Seismic waves

Focus

→ P waves
→ S waves

Outer core

Inner core

P-wave shadow zone

P-wave shadow zone

Mantle

▲ P- and S-waves pass through the Earth's interior from the site, or "focus", of an earthquake or man-made explosion. Their speeds vary with depth, and they follow curved paths. S-waves travel only in solids: they cannot pass through the liquid core so there is a "shadow zone" at the surface where they are not received. P-waves can travel through liquids but they are refracted as they cross the boundary of the core, and this creates a smaller shadow zone within which these waves are not detected by seismometers.

Clues to composition

There is a simple technique by which astronomers are able to deduce the chemical composition of a planet. The first clue is its mean density, a figure obtained by dividing the mass by the volume. Mean density depends on chemical composition and on the extent to which material is compressed by gravity. The greater the mass of a planet, the greater the compression in its interior.

If the mean density is similar to that of the Earth (5,500kg/m^3 – that is, 5·5 times the density of water), the composition is probably similar too, which means primarily metals (iron and nickel) and silicates (rock-forming minerals). On the other hand, if a massive body has a mean density similar to that of water (1,000kg/m^3), then, taking compression into account, it must be composed mainly of the lightest chemical elements. The mean density of the Sun is 1,400kg/m^3 and its composition by mass is probably about 73 percent hydrogen, 25 percent helium and 2 percent heavier elements. Jupiter and Saturn (with densities of 1,300kg/m^3 and 700kg/m^3 respectively) are also composed mainly of hydrogen and helium but the less massive giants, Uranus and Neptune, contain proportionally more "icy" materials such as water, methane and ammonia.

Mercury, Venus and Earth have similar mean densities, but Mars, with a mean density of 3,940kg/m^3, resembles the Moon (3,340kg/m^3) in this respect, and must differ structurally from the other terrestrial planets.

The dense core of Mercury is probably larger than the whole globe of the Moon

The Earth

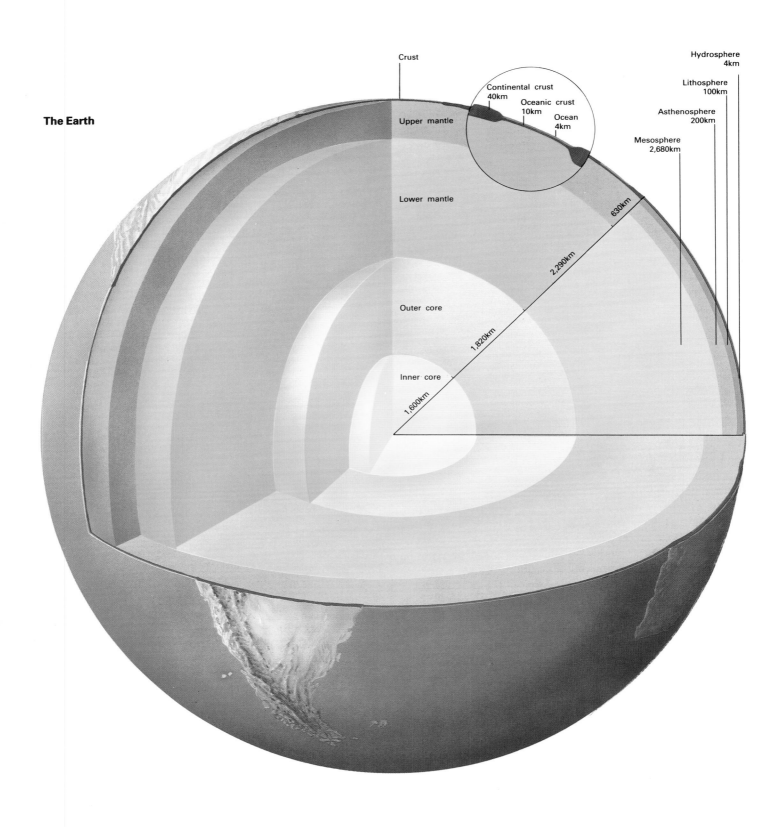

Crust

Continental crust
40km

Oceanic crust
10km

Ocean
4km

Upper mantle

Lower mantle

Outer core

Inner core

630km

2,290km

1,820km

1,600km

Hydrosphere
4km

Lithosphere
100km

Asthenosphere
200km

Mesosphere
2,680km

*The basic structure of the Earth reveals a core, mantle and crust, on
top of which lies the hydrosphere (surface water and oceans). The
region outside the core may be subdivided according to the rigidity
of its material into mesosphere, asthenosphere (which is weaker
and more plastic) and lithosphere, or according to composition and
density into lower mantle, upper mantle and (least dense) crust.*

Moon

Mercury

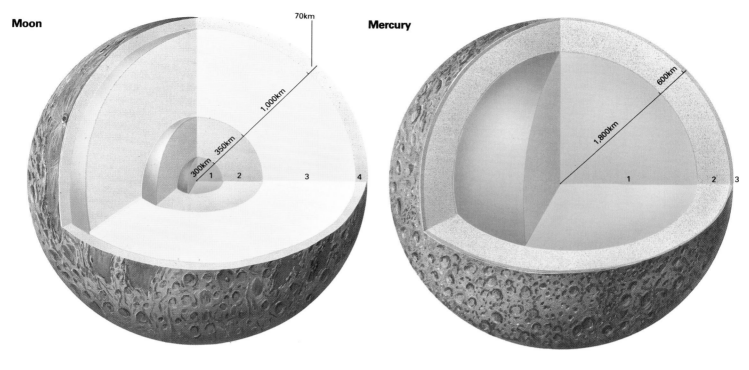

▲ The Moon may contain a small iron-rich core (1) surrounded by a partially molten zone (2). The rigid mantle (3) is about 1,000km thick, while the crust (4) varies in thickness from about 60km to some 75km. Deep-seated moonquakes occur in the lower part of the mantle. The lava which filled the surface basins came from a depth of several hundred kilometers.

▲ Despite its small size, Mercury has nearly the same density as the Earth, and this suggests that it must be about twice as rich in iron as the Earth. The iron-nickel core (1) probably extends to a radius of about 1,800km – about 75 percent of the radius of the planet – and contains nearly 80 percent of its mass. Above this is a rocky mantle (2) and a lighter crust (3).

Venus

Mars

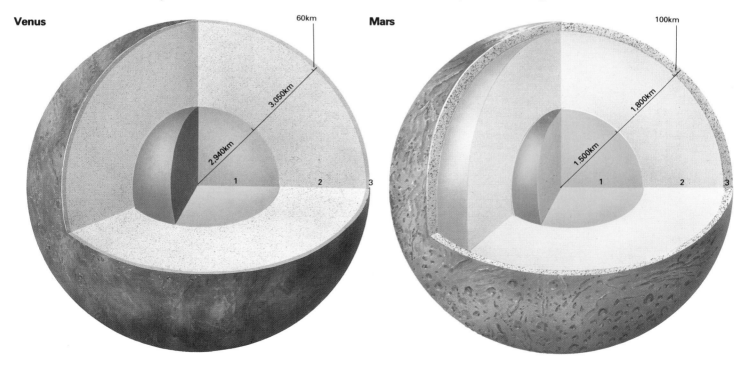

▲ The composition and internal structure of Venus is probably broadly similar to that of the Earth. Astronomers believe that the partially molten metallic core (1) is slightly smaller than its equivalent in the Earth, with a radius of some 2,940km. Above this lies the mantle (2) and a crust (3) some 60km thick – at least twice the thickness of the Earth's crust.

▲ The mean density of Mars is about 30 percent lower than that of the Earth, and therefore the planet cannot have a large metallic core. Many alternatives have been suggested. The one illustrated here has a core (1) of iron and iron compounds some 1,500km in radius, a silicate mantle (2) about 1,800km thick, and a crust with a thickness of about 100km (3).

The structure of the Moon

The lunar interior has been investigated in some detail by means of heat flow experiments and seismometers placed on the surface during the Apollo missions. The heat flow experiments showed that the interior is hot, reaching as high as 1,500K. The seismometers measured natural moonquakes and the tremors produced by meteorites and man-made impacts. The crust consists typically of a 20km layer of basalt on top of a 20-40km layer of rock; it is about 15km thicker on the side which faces away from the Earth. The rigid lithosphere extends down to about 1,000km. Below this lies a partially molten asthenosphere and a core which may or may not be molten and probably comprises a mixture of iron and iron sulfide.

Planetary magnetic fields

The Earth has a magnetic field with a strength at its surface of between 3×10^{-5} and 6×10^{-5} tesla. It is a dipole field – one which behaves like a simple bar magnet – and compass needles line up along the lines of force connecting the north and south magnetic poles. The direction of the magnetic field changes with time, and at present the north magnetic pole lies at a latitude of 78·5°N, in northwest Greenland.

Of the terrestrial planets, Venus and Mars have exceedingly weak fields, but Mercury has a field strength at its surface of nearly one percent of the Earth's field. Although the presence of a large metallic core is conducive to the presence of a magnetic field, the planet's slow rotation seems to rule out a dynamo mechanism, and the origin of Mercury's field remains a mystery. Jupiter and Saturn have powerful and extensive fields, while the magnetic field of Uranus is unusual in that the magnetic axis is inclined to the rotational axis by about 60°.

The significance of a magnetic field
The conditions necessary for a planet to have a magnetic field include the existence in the interior of a fluid, electrical conductor kept in a state of circulation by the effects of planetary rotation and convection currents. Theory suggests that if planetary material initially had a weak magnetic field (for example, a galactic magnetic field that permeated the material from which all the planets formed), the motion of the conducting fluid through the magnetic field would generate an electrical current which would sustain and amplify the original weak field. For as long as the circulation continued, the magnetic field would remain, being sustained by a dynamo-like process operating in, for example, a liquid metallic core. The presence or absence of a magnetic field thus gives a further clue about the nature of planetary interiors.

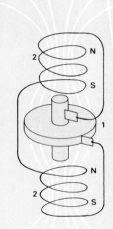
◄ *If a metal disk rotates in a magnetic field, the resulting force pushes electrons towards the center of the disk or along a wire attached at the center. Unlike an ordinary dynamo with two magnets, a simple self-exciting dynamo uses a coil (2) with the metal disk (1). Once the disk starts spinning, the flow of electrons sets up a current through the coil. The resulting system generates a magnetic field as long as the disk remains spinning.*

Rotation periods	
Mercury	58.65d
Venus	243d
Earth	23.93hr
Mars	24.62hr
Jupiter	9.8hr
Saturn	10.2hr

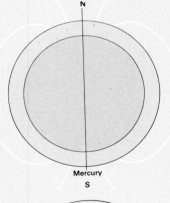
Mercury

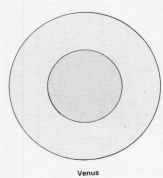
Venus

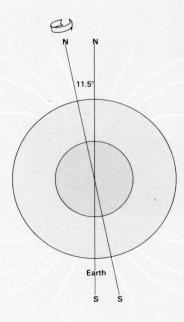
Earth

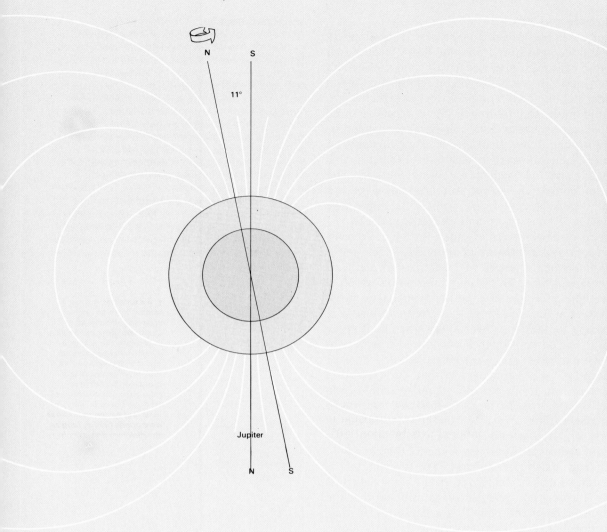

Jupiter

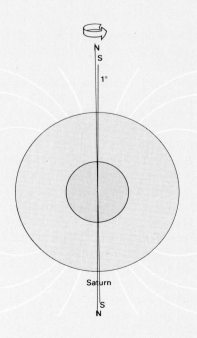

Saturn

Mars

The Earth's magnetic axis (the line passing through north and south magnetic poles) is inclined to the axis of rotation by about 11·5°. Mercury has a weak field closely aligned with its rotational axis. Jupiter and Saturn have powerful fields tilted at the angles shown; both are directed in the opposite sense to that of the Earth, each having its south magnetic pole in the northern hemisphere. The field strength at the cloud tops on Saturn is similar to that at the Earth's surface, while the strength at the Jovian cloud tops is 20 times greater. Since both planets are much larger than the Earth, their overall fields are much more powerful. The electrical currents needed to sustain a magnetic field are carried by the circulation of a conducting material such as iron in the Earth and "metallic hydrogen" in Jupiter and Saturn. Mars does not have a suitable core, while Venus rotates too slowly to carry an electrical current at the core. Although Mercury has a large metallic core, it rotates slowly; its measurable magnetic field remains a mystery.

The giant planets – Jupiter and Saturn

Jupiter, the largest and most massive of the planets, is completely different in structure and composition from the Earth. Composed primarily of hydrogen and helium, it does not have a solid surface like that of the terrestrial planets. Beneath the visible cloud tops lies a hydrogen-rich atmosphere about 1,000km thick, below which there is a deep ocean of liquid molecular hydrogen. At a depth of some 25,000km, where the pressure is about 3 million Earth-atmospheres, hydrogen molecules are broken down, their electrons moving around and conducting heat and electrical currents easily. Hydrogen in this state behaves like a metal, and is known as metallic hydrogen. The bulk of Jupiter's interior consists of liquid metallic hydrogen, but there is probably a central rocky-metallic core, similar in composition to the Earth's, with a mass of between 10 and 30 Earth-masses.

Jupiter radiates into space about twice as much heat as it receives from the Sun and has a central temperature of about 30,000K. Astronomers do not fully understand the source of Jupiter's internal heat, but it may be heat generated during the planet's formation which is still leaking into space. The presence of a powerful magnetic field, more than 10 times stronger at the cloud-tops than the Earth's field at ground level and extending its influence over a vast volume of space (◀ pages 18-19), is readily accounted for by a dynamo-like process in the metallic hydrogen zone of this rapidly rotating planet.

Saturn has a significantly lower mean density than Jupiter and is flattened to a greater extent, but it has a broadly similar composition and structure. Estimates of the mass of its rocky-metallic core range from 3 to 20 Earth-masses. This core is probably surrounded by liquid metallic hydrogen which, at a radius of some 28,000km, gives way to an ocean of liquid molecular hydrogen some 32,000km thick, on top of which is a hydrogen-rich atmosphere. Like Jupiter, Saturn emits about twice as much heat as it receives from the Sun. Saturn is much less massive than Jupiter, however, and it is unlikely that the heat source is left-over heat from the planet's formation. The most plausible theory is that droplets of helium, formed in Saturn's cooler atmosphere, sink towards the core, releasing energy as they do so.

The farthest planets

Uranus and Neptune are similar in several respeects but there is still some uncertainty about basic data such as diameter, mean density and rotation period for Neptune. Uranus seems to be marginally the larger of the two, but Neptune is the more massive and has the higher mean density. Each planet is likely to have a rocky-metallic core of about 3 Earth-masses, surrounded by a deep envelope of water, methane and ammonia "ices", and a deep atmosphere composed mainly of hydrogen, helium and methane. By mass, the relative proportions of core to ices to atmosphere are probably about 20:65:15. A puzzling discrepancy between the two planets is that Neptune, like Jupiter and Saturn, emits about twice as much heat as it receives from the Sun, but as yet Uranus has shown no evidence of a similar internal heat source.

The last of the known planets, enigmatic Pluto, with a diameter of only 2,500km, is significantly smaller than the Moon. Its mass, deduced from the orbital motion of its satellite Charon, is only about one-fifth of the Moon's mass. The mean density of Pluto is similar to that of water, and it seems likely that both planet and satellite are cosmic icebergs made mainly of frozen water, ammonia and methane.

Shape and structure

The oblateness, or flattening, of a planet provides another clue about its composition and structure. This is a measure of the extent to which a planet's rotation causes it to "bulge" at the equator. The degree of flattening depends on the rate of rotation, the fluidity of the planet, and the extent to which mass is concentrated towards its center. The dense, slowly rotating terrestrial planets show little polar flattening, but Jupiter and Saturn, low-density bodies each with a rotation period of about 10 hours, are conspicuously oblate, the equatorial radius exceeding the polar radius by 6 percent and 10 percent respectively.

The shape of a planet and its distribution of mass distorts its gravitational field, which affects the motion of any orbiting satellites. The greater the concentration of mass towards the center of the planet, the less the flattening and the less the effect on satellite orbits.

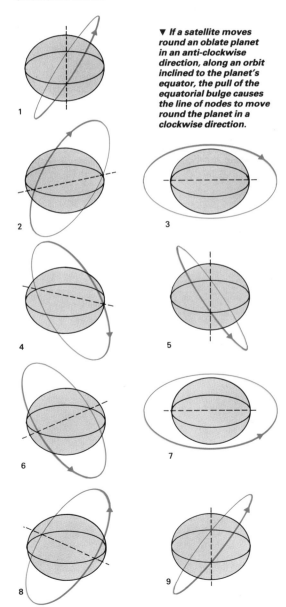

▼ *If a satellite moves round an oblate planet in an anti-clockwise direction, along an orbit inclined to the planet's equator, the pull of the equatorial bulge causes the line of nodes to move round the planet in a clockwise direction.*

Jupiter

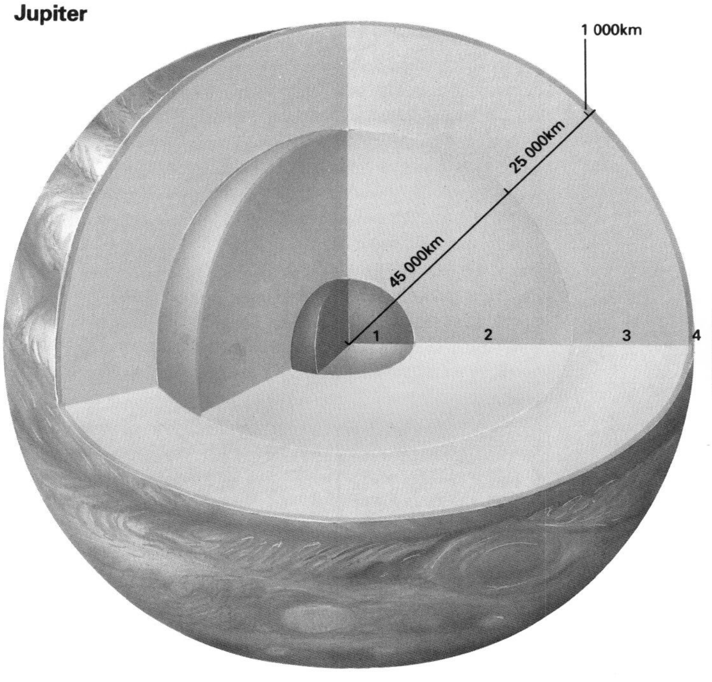

Saturn

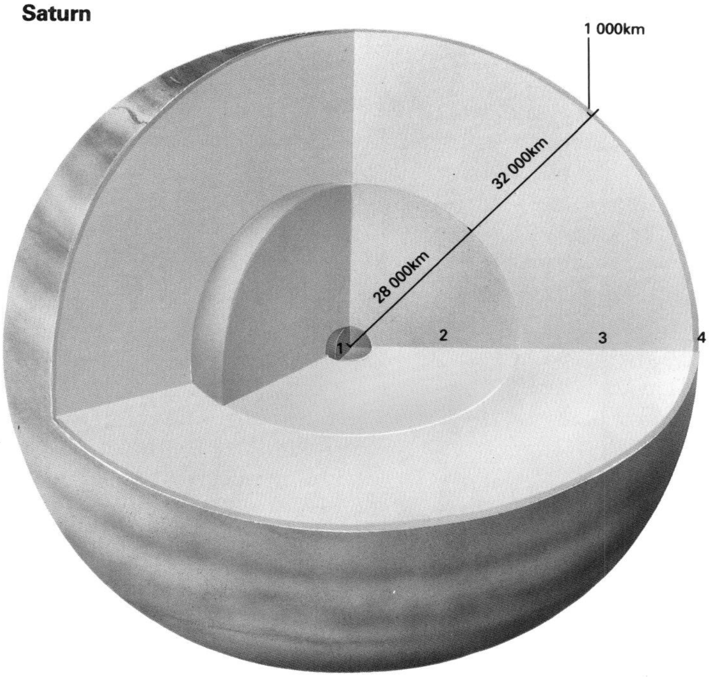

▲ *Jupiter may contain a compact iron-silicate core (1) in a zone of liquid metallic hydrogen (2) which extends to a radius of about 45,000km. Above this there is a layer of liquid molecular hydrogen (3) some 25,000km thick, then the 1,000km deep hydrogen-rich atmosphere (4). Temperature at the center is about 30,000K and pressure is 100 million atmospheres.*

▲ *Like Jupiter, Saturn may contain a compact iron-silicate core (1) embedded in a liquid metallic hydrogen zone (2) extending to a radius of some 28,000km. The liquid molecular hydrogen zone (3), probably 32,000km deep, lies below the hydrogen-rich atmosphere (4). Saturn's core temperature may be 12,000K and pressure 8 million atmospheres.*

Uranus

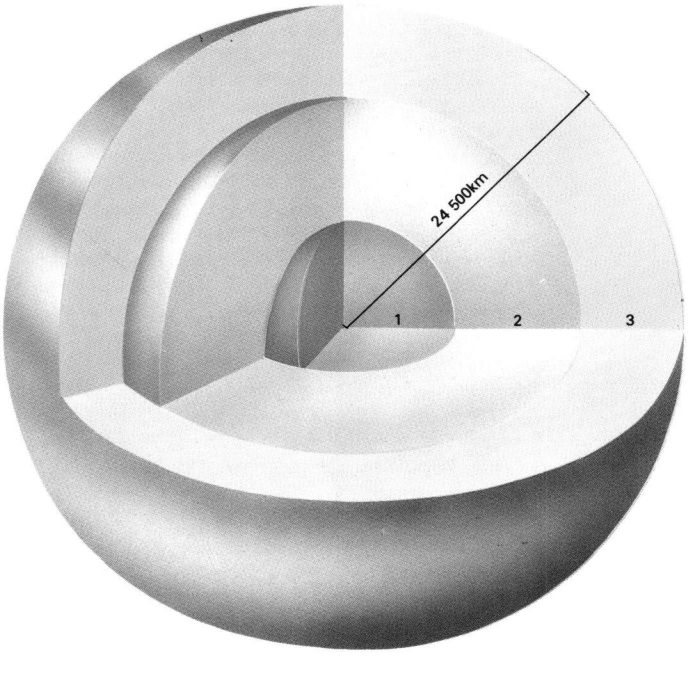

Neptune

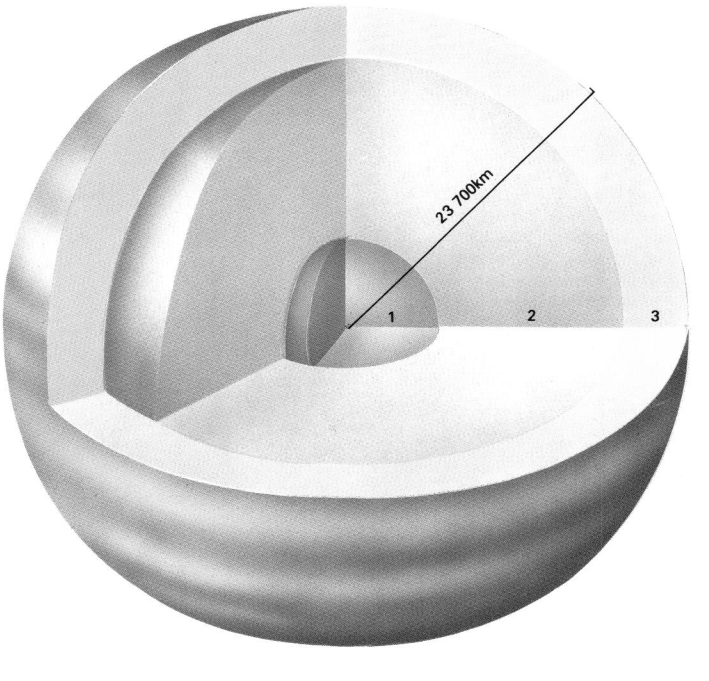

▲ *Planetary geologists think that Uranus has an iron-silicate core (1) of about three Earth-masses which is somewhat larger than the Earth itself. This is probably surrounded by a mantle (2) of water, ammonia and methane ices extending to a radius of some 18,000km, and by a deep atmosphere (3) of hydrogen, helium and methane. The interior may be partly fluid.*

▲ *Neptune is denser than Uranus but probably has a similar general structure, with an iron-silicate core (1), an "icy" mantle (2) and a deep atmosphere (3) rich in hydrogen, helium and methane. Although the core is believed to be solid the planet emits sufficient heat to suggest that the mantle may be fluid, and that motions within it may generate a magnetic field.*

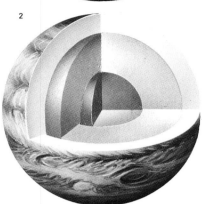

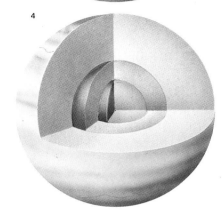

▲ **Early theories about the giants.** Jeffreys proved that the giant planets were cold, not hot as was widely believed. His 1923 model of Jupiter (1) consisted of a large core and a thin atmosphere, while Wildt in 1934 suggested a smaller, denser core and a deep atmosphere of condensed gases (2). Jeffreys' 1923 model of Saturn (3) was also modified by Wildt in 1934. Wildt gave the planet a rocky and metallic core surrounded by frozen water and carbon dioxide, then by solid hydrogen (4).

▶ **Mr Richard Anthony Proctor, B.A., F.R.A.S., was one of Vanity Fair's "Men of the Day" in the issue of 3 March 1883.**

Cold water on a hot theory

Spacecraft can now study the surfaces of the planets directly but, as far as the interiors are concerned, scientists can still only theorize, based on other physical data obtained from Earth, the Moon or spacecraft.

It was always assumed that the terrestrial planets would have compositions not unlike that of the Earth. However, until less than 50 years ago many astronomers believed that the giant planets must be hot worlds, not only on the inside, but also on their gaseous surfaces – rather like primitive suns. Richard Proctor (1837-88), an English astronomer and author, summed up this view in a book published in 1882. With regard to Jupiter and Saturn, he wrote that:

"Over a region hundreds of thousands of square miles in extent, the glowing surface of the planet must be torn by subplanetary forces. Vast masses of intensely hot vapour must be poured forth from beneath, and, rising to enormous heights, must either sweep away the enwrapping mantle of cloud which had concealed the disturbed surface, or must itself form into a mass of cloud".

But were, in fact, the surfaces of the giant planets hot, as Proctor thought? The lengthy investigation carried out in the 1920s by the great British geophysicist Harold Jeffreys (b. 1891) showed conclusively that in the case of the largest planet, Jupiter, the "miniature sun" theory was incorrect.

Early theories about the giants

There is no doubt that the Jovian planets are hot at their cores, but Jeffreys showed that their surfaces were extremely cold. Jeffreys proposed a model in which a giant planet had a rocky core about 46,000km in radius, a mantle of water ice and carbon dioxide 18,000km thick, and an extremely tenuous atmosphere composed largely of hydrogen and extending for about 6,000km.

This theory was modified in 1934 by Rupert Wildt, who was German by birth but worked in America. Since hydrogen is the most abundant element in the universe, it was natural to assume that the giant planets contained a great quantity of it. This was supported in 1932 when T. Dunham, at the Mount Wilson Observatory, used the spectroscope to detect methane and some ammonia in the atmospheres of the giants – both of these are hydrogen compounds. As a result Wildt was able to propose a dense rocky core surrounded by a thick layer of ice, which was in turn overlain by a deep atmosphere of condensed gases.

More recent theories

A new modification was introduced in 1951 by W. Ramsey in England and W. DeMarcus in the US. This time the core had a radius of 61,000km, was made up of hydrogen and was so compressed that it assumed the characteristics of metal. Around this was a layer of liquid hydrogen about 8,900km in depth lying below a relatively shallow atmosphere. The latest view resembles the previous model in some respects, but incorporates a solid central core of rocky materials (silicates).

Planetary Landscapes

Surfaces of the solid rocky planets...How their landscapes were formed...The Moon's dark lava plains and cratered highlands...Formation of the lunar surface...The Earth: plate tectonics and erosion... Mercury's Moon-like landscape...Venus and its searing plains...Mars: ice-caps and massive volcanoes... PERSPECTIVE...Moon-men – a hoax...Mapping the Moon...The Martian "canals"...Life on Mars?

Cratering

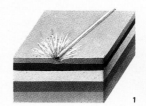
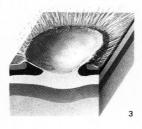

A body striking a planetary surface at high speed (1) blasts a conical stream of matter (ejecta) away from the site of the impact, excavating a bowl-shaped crater (2). Surface matter is ejected before deeper matter. Where ejecta lands to form the crater rim (3) it produces inverted strata.

Volcanism

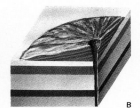

Volcanism brings molten material to the planetary surface with various results. The lunar basins (A) were once filled with lava to form smooth plains – the maria. Highly fluid lava spread (B) to form gently sloping "shield" volcanoes, while less fluid lava (C) built up steep-sided cones.

Of the nine major planets only Mercury, Venus, the Earth and Mars have solid rocky surfaces. Pluto probably has an icy surface. The Moon is included here because it has been explored quite thoroughly and, though a satellite, is large enough to be treated as a planet. From Earth the surfaces of Mercury, Mars and the Moon are directly visible, but that of cloud-covered Venus can be studied only by radar.

The terrestrial planets and the Moon display a fascinating variety of surfaces, with the Moon and the Earth contrasting most sharply. The Moon is a dead world whose surface was sculpted by cratering and volcanic activity billions of years ago, and has changed hardly at all since then, while the Earth is an evolving planet continually building up and breaking down its surface features. Mercury is close to the Moon in appearance, Mars is intermediate between the Moon and the Earth, and Venus is yet more Earth-like.

Surface-shaping processes

The surfaces of planets and satellites have been molded by a number of processes, both internal and external. The principal internal process is volcanism – activity that brings molten subsurface material (magma) to the surface (as lava) to build cones, gently-sloping "shield" volcanoes and lava plains. Also important are movements of the mantle due to convection which may fracture the surfaces of planets into distinct plates (◆ page 28).

The major external process is cratering, produced by the impact of bodies such as meteorites, asteroids and the nuclei of comets. The amount of energy released by an impact is enormous. A rocky body about 1km in radius, for example, striking a planet at 20 kilometers per second, would produce a blast comparable to the detonation of more than 500,000 one-megaton nuclear bombs. An impacting body excavates a bowl-shaped crater and throws out a blanket of material, or ejecta, which covers much of the neighboring surface and builds up the crater rim. Larger lumps hurled out by the blast may produce secondary craters. Small craters retain their simple bowl shape but larger ones, depending on the surface gravity of the planet, may slump to produce a series of terraced walls. They may also have mountain peaks in the center. Sometimes magma flows into larger craters and basins to give smooth, lava-floored features.

Astronomers now believe that all the planets and satellites suffered a heavy bombardment soon after their formation. This cratering record is well preserved on the Moon, Mercury and, to a lesser extent, Mars. Venus has a number of large shallow craters, but the Earth bears the scars of only a few relatively recent impacts, the rest having been obliterated by erosion. Wind, water and ice wears down surface features and the eroded materials are deposited and eventually compacted into sedimentary rocks.

Clues to the nature of a planet's surface
An important clue to what the planet's surface is like is given by the proportion of sunlight it receives that is reflected back into space. This reflecting power is known as the albedo and is expressed as a number between 1 (for a perfect reflector) and 0 (for a totally matt black surface which absorbs all radiation that falls on it). Atmospheric effects can be considerable. Ice-coated or cloud-covered bodies have high albedos while those with dark, rocky or dusty surfaces have low albedos; thus Venus has an albedo of 0·76 (that is, it reflects 76 percent of the sunlight that falls on its cloud-covered globe), while Mercury and the Moon have albedos of 0·06 and 0·07 respectively. The albedos of Mars and the Earth fall between these two extremes. Measurements of reflectivity are made at a range of wavelengths and angles of illumination.

Other clues as to whether a surface is rocky or dusty, rough or smooth, are given, for example, by infrared measurements of daily temperature changes (dust cools faster than rock) and by radar measurements (rough and smooth surfaces reflect radar pulses differently).

The lunar surface

The surface of the Moon is dominated by two kinds of landscape: the dark lava plains with relatively few craters, known for historical reasons as "seas" or maria (mare in the singular); and the lighter-colored, heavily cratered highlands. Craters range in size from microscopic pits to huge walled depressions up to 250km in diameter. Craters up to about 20km in diameter are bowl-shaped, but larger ones are more complex, many having terraced walls and central peaks. The dark maria cover a large proportion of the Earth-facing hemisphere but are mostly absent from the far side of the Moon, perhaps because the crust is thicker on the far side, which may have inhibited the flow of magma to the surface there.

The lunar surface is overlain by the "regolith", a layer of soil made up of pulverized rocks. Lunar rocks are broadly similar in nature to terrestrial rocks. The maria consist of basalts (dark, fine-grained volcanic rocks) and the highlands of lighter-colored older rocks such as anorthosites, which are richer in aluminium and calcium than the basalts. Many of the highland rocks are breccias – shattered fragments of various types of rock which have become welded together – testifying to the heavy bombardment that the highlands have suffered. The principal difference between terrestrial and lunar rocks is that the latter are richer in refractory elements (those with a high boiling point, such as titanium) and depleted of volatiles (those with a low boiling point). In particular, lunar rocks contain no water or hydrated material. As for their age, rock samples, brought back from the Apollo and Luna missions, date from 3·1 to 3·8 billion years ago in the case of mare basalts and 3·8 to 4·5 billion years ago (older than any terrestrial samples) in the case of highland rocks.

▲ *This lunar crater – Eratosthenes – shows the classic structural features of an impact crater.*

▼ *Harrison H. Schmitt, one of the last men on the Moon, examines a huge split lunar boulder.*

▲ The Moon, seen from Apollo 11 at a distance of 16,000km. The Mare Crisium is near the center of the picture; to its left is the bright ray-crater Proclus. To the left, near the edge of the disk, is the Mare Serenitatis, and below this the Mare Tranquilitatis, where the Apollo 11 astronauts landed. The regions to the right are on the side of the Moon which is always turned away from the Earth.

◄ Samples have now been obtained from different parts of the Moon – from the Apollo landings and unmanned Russian probes. The rocks are essentially volcanic, with little meteoritic material. These are a lunar basalt (left) and an anorthosite (right). Some of the basalts are rich in rare-earth elements and potassium and phosphorus. No unfamiliar elements had been expected and none were found.

No large craters have been formed on the Moon for at least a thousand million years

Mapping the Moon

The Moon is the only body in the Solar System whose surface features can be clearly observed from Earth with a small telescope. The first Moon map was drawn in 1609 by an Englishman, Thomas Harriot (1560-1621), one-time tutor to Sir Walter Raleigh. The Italian astronomer Galileo Galilei (1564-1642) attempted to measure and map the heights of lunar mountains in 1610, and his results were quite accurate. In the mid-17th century larger maps of the Moon were produced: in 1651 an Italian Jesuit, Giovanni Riccioli (1598-1671), drew a map based on observations by his pupil Francesco Grimaldi (1618-1663), and introduced the system of naming lunar features after prominent people.

The first really good lunar map was drawn in the 1830s by two Germans, Wilhelm Beer (1797-1850) and Johann von Mädler (1794-1874). Though they used only a small telescope, their map was a masterpiece, and was not surpassed for decades. When it was published, many astronomers felt that, since the Moon was changeless and Beer and Mädler had mapped it so precisely, there was little point in studying it farther. However, the German astronomer Julius Schmidt (1825-1884) continued to observe the Moon, and in 1866 he announced that a small crater, Linné, had disappeared. The effect of this improbable announcement was to revive interest in the Moon, and new maps were produced.

In 1878 Schmidt drew an elaborate map, but this was soon followed by the first photographic atlases. One, in 1904, by the American astronomer William Pickering (1858-1938), showed each region of the Moon under several different illuminations. The last elaborate lunar map before the Space Age was that of Welsh amateur observer Hugh Wilkins (1896-1960). The original, which first appeared in 1946, was 7·6m in diameter, and was accompanied by a detailed description of the entire lunar surface.

A lunar chronology

During the first 200 million years of its existence, the Moon was molten, but the outer part cooled rapidly, becoming solid about 4·4 billion years ago. Over the next few hundred million years, the entire lunar surface suffered heavy bombardment by Solar System debris. The last of the major periods of bombardment, which excavated the mare basins, probably occurred about 3·8 billion years ago and thereafter the cratering rate declined rapidly. Between 3·8 and 3·2 billion years ago the mare basins were flooded by lava. These regions are now made up of rocks that are similar in nature to terrestrial ocean-floor basalts. Parts of the rims of these basins remain in the form of mountain chains such as the Apennines which border the Mare Imbrium.

Since 3·2 billion years ago there have been few substantial changes to the Moon's surface apart from a few impacts which produced conspicuous features such as Tycho and Copernicus. The thickness of the lithosphere, together with the limited amount of mantle convection, has ensured that there is no plate tectonic activity (◆ page 28). Apart from occasional minor gaseous emissions and meteorite impacts, the Moon is a dead and unchanging world.

▲ *The imposing Mare Orientale contains little dark lava. It is similar to basins on Mercury, Mars and Jupiter's Callisto.*

▶ *This condensed history of the Moon shows how the surface probably appeared before the volcanic phase (1) when magma filled in many of the great basins (2). Later cratering produced the present-day appearance (3).*

1

2

3

Moon men

The first observers to use astronomical telescopes believed the Moon to be a world with large oceans on its surface. The lunar "seas" were soon found to be dry – there has, in fact, never been any water on the Moon – but the idea of lunar inhabitants was curiously slow to die. German-born William Herschel (1738-1822), one of the greatest astronomical observers of all time who spent much of his life in England, believed that the ability of the Moon to support life was "an absolute certainty". Later, in 1822, the German observer Franz von Paula Gruithuisen (1774-1852) announced the discovery of a true lunar city, with "dark gigantic ramparts". This turned out to be no more than a completely normal arrangement of low, haphazard ridges.

Some years later, the Danish mathematician Peter Hansen (1795-1874), who was famous for his work on the Moon's movements, put forward a strange idea about the far side which is never visible from Earth. Hansen suggested that the Moon's center of mass might not coincide with its center of figure, so that all the air and water had

been drawn round to the hidden side, which might well, therefore, be inhabited. The idea never gained much favor; for one thing, it would certainly have led to an appearance of "twilight" at the cusps of the crescent Moon, and needless to say, nothing of the sort was observed. It was not until 1959 and the round trip of Luna 3 that the far side was seen to be as barren as the Earth-facing side.

The celebrated Moon Hoax

In 1835 John Herschel (1792-1871), son of William, was in South Africa to survey the southern sky. Communications in those days were slow and uncertain, and R. A. Locke, a reporter on the "New York Sun", realized that it would take time to disprove anything outrageous that he published. Accordingly the "Sun" was issued with a series of articles describing how Herschel, using a plausible-sounding though practically impossible method of observing the Moon in great detail, had discovered remarkable forms of life, including bat-men and even "a strange, spherical creature which rolled with great velocity across the pebbly shore". Many people were taken in, though only briefly.

▲ The original caption to this absurd illustration, published in 1835 in the "New York Sun", read as follows: "Lunar animals and other objects, discovered by Sir John Herschel in his Observatory at the Cape of Good Hope and copied from sketches in the Edinburgh Journal of Science. For description, see pamphlet published at the Sun Office." The hoax, perpetrated by a reporter, succeeded – for a while!

The Earth

The main features of the Earth's surface are continental land-masses (about 30 percent) and oceans (about 70 percent). Other striking features are the great mountain chains, and cracks and rifts in the surface such as the San Andreas fault in California and the Great Rift Valley in Africa. Geologists believe that the dominant process shaping the large-scale structures of the Earth's surface is plate tectonics. This is the mechanism whereby convection currents in the molten mantle have broken the lithosphere (upper mantle and crust) into about a dozen rigid plates which drift slowly over the globe.

Where two plates are drifting apart, as in the middle of the Atlantic Ocean, molten mantle material rises at a mid-oceanic ridge and spreads out to form new ocean bed composed of basalt. At present Europe and North America are drifting apart at a rate of about 2cm a year. When two continental plates collide, the crumpling and buckling of crustal material may throw up great ranges of mountains. Where an oceanic plate meets a continental plate, the heavier oceanic plate descends below the lighter continental plate. This process, known as subduction, results in the melting of oceanic plate material, the thrusting up of long mountain chains and the production of deep ocean trenches such as the one running parallel to the Andes off western South America. Volcanic and earthquake activity frequently occurs along plate boundaries.

Plate tectonics and volcanic processes build new landscape features, but there are many erosive processes at work to wear them down and to transport material to new locations. The Earth is thus a dynamic, changing planet.

▼ *This computer-generated relief map shows areas lying within the same 500m altitude band. The difference between highest mountain and deepest ocean is about 8km.*

▲ *The Earth, seen from the weather satellite Meteosat 1.*

▶ *The Chilean Andes as seen in winter from the land survey satellite Landsat.*

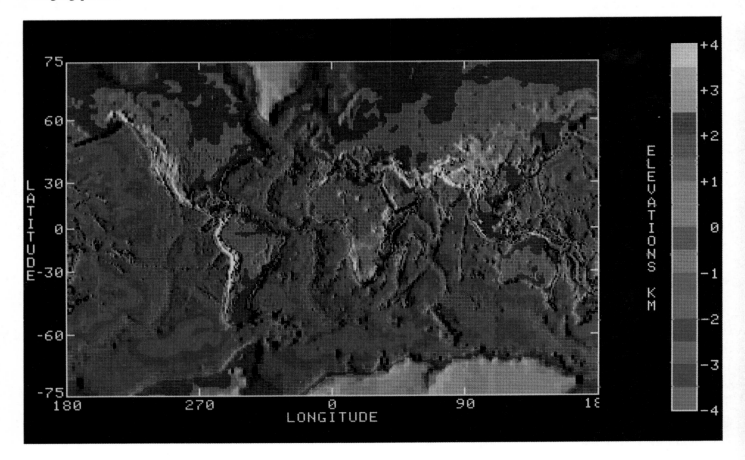

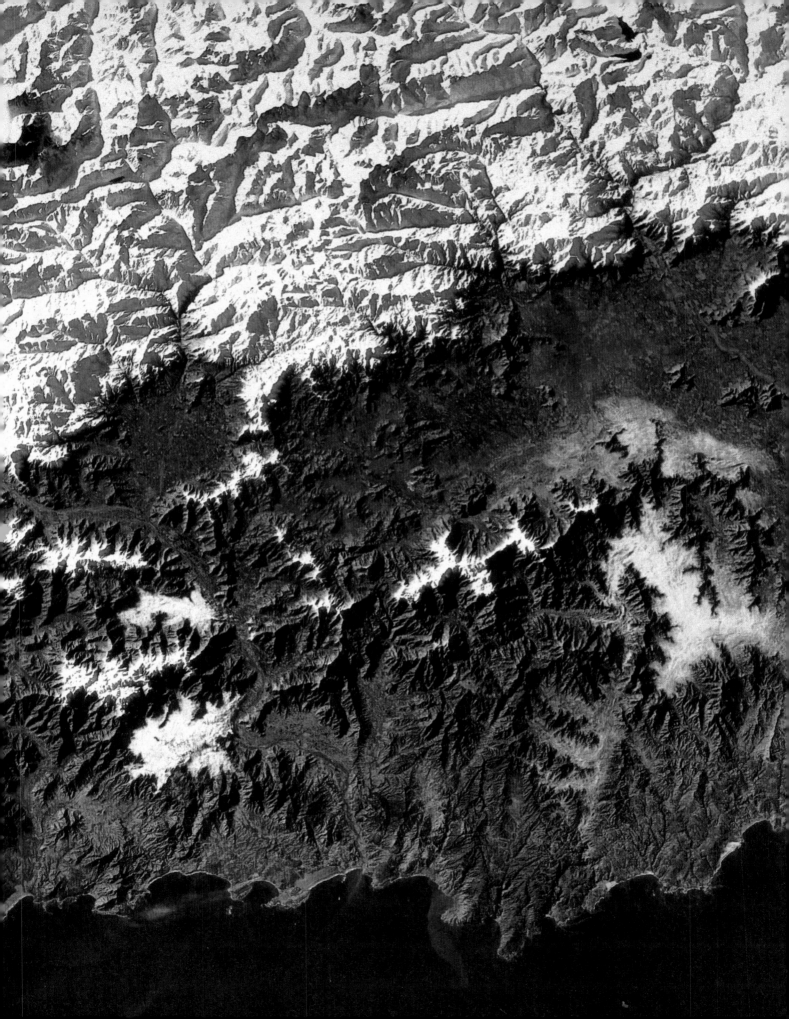

On Mercury temperatures are either extremely hot or cold – there is no "twilight zone"

Mercury

The smallest of the terrestrial planets and the closest to the Sun, Mercury receives about six times as much solar radiation per square meter as the Earth. The daytime temperature is high, 600K (about 330°C) on average, reaching a maximum of about 750K (about 480°C), whereas at night it drops down to 90K (about -180°C). There are two regions of the surface which are most strongly illuminated at alternate perihelia, giving rise to what are termed "hot poles".

The surface of Mercury, like that of the Moon, has cratered highlands and smoother volcanic plains. Intermediate in type between these two regions are the "intercrater" plains, ancient moderately-cratered plains quite unlike the lunar maria. There is one giant concentric ring-shaped basin, the Caloris Basin, some 1,400km across, which is similar to the Mare Orientale on the Moon and was presumably also caused by a giant impact. Lava flows are also visible on Mercury, and the hills and plains are covered in pulverized dust. The planet's history seems to have been similar to that of the Moon, with saturation bombardment and lava flows occurring during the first billion years of its existence. There is no evidence of plate tectonics, but the long lines of cliffs and scarps may be due to wrinkling of the surface as the planet cooled down.

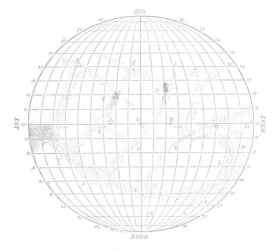

▼ *This is how Mercury appeared to the onboard television cameras of Mariner 10, (left) six hours before and again (right) six hours after the spacecraft flew past the planet in 1974.*

▲ *The first map of Mercury was made by Giovanni Schiaparelli (1835-1910) in Milan. He found the dark patches difficult to distinguish and they later proved illusory*

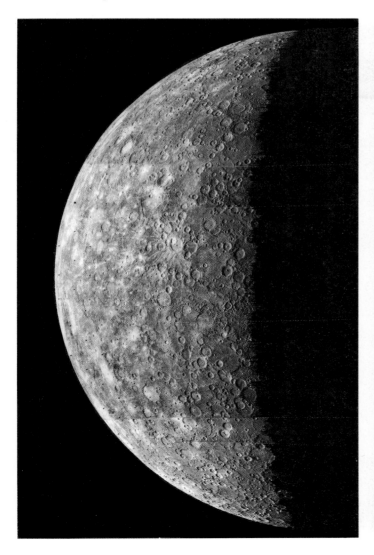

◄ *This ridge, known as Discovery Scarp, was photographed by Mariner 10. More than 300km long and in places 3km high, it cuts straight through the crater Ramsan. It was probably formed by compressive forces acting on the crust.*

▼ *The Caloris Basin, a huge impact crater on Mercury's surface, has a diameter of 1,400km and shows many similarities with the Mare Orientale on the Moon. Between the ridges and more recently formed craters are large areas of smooth floor – presumably the heat generated by the impact caused the rock to melt.*

Observing the cloudy planet

Venus presented major problems to the early observers, who did not at first realize that all they could see was the top of a cloud layer. In 1726, the Italian astronomer Francesco Bianchini (1662-1729) went so far as to draw a map of the surface showing oceans and continents. In 1789, the German astronomer Johann Schröter (1745-1816) observed what he thought was the top of a mountain, several kilometers high. This led to a dispute with his great contemporary William Herschel, who correctly claimed that Schröter's "enlightened mountain" was non-existent.

The Ashen Light mystery

The Ashen Light is the faint visibility, probably electrical in origin, of the unlit region of the planet when Venus is in the crescent stage. In the pre-space age it gave rise to some imaginative theories. The German astronomer Franz von Paula Gruithuisen (1774-1852) believed that it was due to vast forest fires lit on Venus by the inhabitants to celebrate the accession of a new ruler. It was later suggested that the light could be due to phosphorescent oceans. However, when it became clear that the surface of Venus is always hidden by clouds, theorists came into their own. Particularly notable was the Swedish scientist Svante Arrhenius (1859-1927), who believed that Venus today is in much the same state as the Earth was more than 200 million years ago. He pictured hot swamps with luxuriant vegetation and, quite possibly, amphibious life forms and insects such as giant dragonflies. This led to the attractive conclusion that Venus might evolve in the same way that the Earth had done, so that it would eventually become habitable.

▼ *Illustrations such as this, depicting a weird and exotic flora on the surface of Venus, were common in the 19th century.*

On Venus, there is almost constant lightning beneath an orange sky

The surface of Venus

Despite the similarity in size and mass of Venus and the Earth, surface conditions on Venus are much harsher. Searingly high temperatures of 750K (about 480°C) are maintained by a dense atmospheric blanket (♦ pages 40-1).

Radar mapping has been carried out by Pioneer and Venera orbiters and by Earth-based radio telescopes. Pioneer results showed that about 70 percent is made up of undulating rolling plains, just under 20 percent is isolated depressed lowlands, and 10 percent is mainly of highland "continents", typically 4 or 5km above mean surface level. There are also many shallow craters up to about 1,000km in diameter, some huge volcanoes, and a number of rift valleys and trenches.

The rolling plains appear to be ancient crust, heavily cratered. The lowlands are smooth and apparently crater-free. They may be basaltic lava flows reminiscent of lunar maria and terrestrial ocean beds. The largest is Atalanta Planitia, a roughly circular depression some 2,500km in diameter and 1·6km deep at its lowest point. Although there is no water on Venus now, there is some evidence to suggest that at a much earlier period in the planet's history there may have been oceans which subsequently evaporated.

The two largest upland areas, or "continents", are Ishtar Terra in the northern hemisphere, and Aphrodite Terra, which lies on and south of the equator. Ishtar, which is about the same size as Australia, rises steeply from the rolling plain and boasts the Maxwell Mountains which, at 11·1km above the mean surface level, are the highest feat-

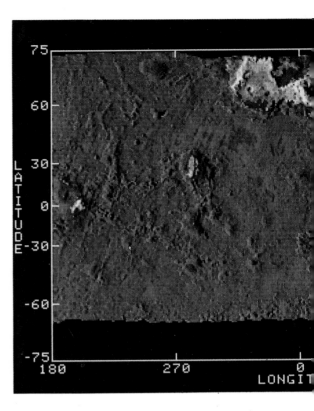

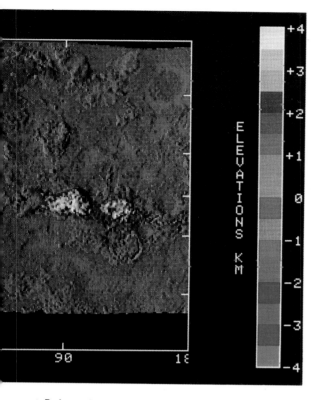

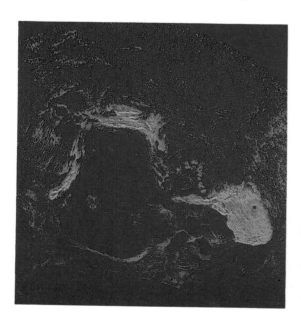

ures on the planet. Aphrodite Terra is about the size of Africa – about 10,000km long. Another smaller, but interesting upland area is Beta Regio, which has two massive shield volcanoes (Theia Mons and Rhea Mons) and several smaller ones. Volcanic eruptions may be responsible for the dramatic changes which have occurred in the sulfur dioxide content of the atmosphere since Pioneer arrived in 1978.

Mantle motions do not seem to have fractured Venus' thick lithosphere into separate plates. There are, for example, no spreading ridges of material like the mid-oceanic ridges on Earth. However, considerable internal activity is evidenced by giant rift valleys, continents, and the massive volcanic structures. The large volcanic shields are probably located over rising currents of hot mantle material. By sitting over these hot spots for long periods of time they have grown far larger than terrestrial volcanoes (which are carried away from their magma source after a time by plate motion).

The surface rocks investigated by the Venera spacecraft show interesting variety. Granitic rocks were found at the Venera 8 site, and elsewhere other types of basalts, reddish-brown in color, were found. At some locations the rocks were sharp and angular, with little sign of weathering, while at other sites smoother, more eroded rocks and finer soils were found. Also seen were some layered rocks which may be sedimentary. It is not yet clear what erosive forces are at work on Venus, for there is no running water, nor are the temperature changes large, and surface winds appear to be too gentle to produce effective sandblasting.

▲ **Radar equipment on the Venus Pioneer Orbiter produced this color-coded relief map of the planet's surface. Areas of each color lie within the same 500m altitude band.**

◄ **The Russian spacecraft Veneras 13 and 14, working in conditions of crushing pressure and intense heat, performed the astonishing feat of transmitting color pictures from Venus.**

► **Mariner 10 flew past Venus on 5 February 1974 en route for Mercury. The onboard television cameras recorded this view of the cloudy planet one day and 720,000km later.**

▼ **In this radar image from Arecibo Observatory yellowy areas are rough and blue areas smooth terrain. The distinctive patch to the right is the Maxwell Mountains.**

The surface of Mars

The Martian surface contains both lunar and terrestrial types of terrain. The dominant features are craters, lava plains, giant volcanoes, immense canyons, winding river-like valleys, and polar ice caps which expand and contract with the seasons (◆ pages 44-5). Surface temperatures range from an equatorial maximum of about 300K (27°C) to a minimum of about 135K (−138°C) over the winter pole. The mean value is about 230K (about −40°C).

Heavily cratered older terrain, 1-3km above the mean surface level, is found mainly in the southern hemisphere. It includes a number of large circular basins, the largest of which, Hellas, is some 2,000km in diameter. The region is not as heavily cratered as the Moon, however, and most of the craters are shallower than their lunar counterparts; they have flatter floors, and appear to be partially filled with wind-blown dust and seem to be quite well eroded. The northern hemisphere consists largely of smooth, depressed plains. Some of the smoother plains look like basaltic lava flows and show similar wrinkled "flow fronts" to those found in, for example, the Mare Imbrium on the Moon.

Although no liquid water exists on the Martian surface now, there is ample evidence to suggest that there must have been some, if only for short periods, in the past. There are features that look like dried-up river beds, and teardrop-shaped deposits of material around obstacles are similar to the effects produced by a heavy flow of sediment-laden liquid. Sudden brief periods of flooding may have occurred when the volcanoes were active in the past. Water vapor and other gases poured out by the volcanoes may have increased the density of the atmosphere sufficiently for rain to fall and surface water to flow.

The Martian surface contains about 1 percent by weight of water, and water is also present in the permanent polar ice caps and probably in a subsurface layer of permafrost, like that found in arctic regions on Earth. The thickness of the water-ice caps is uncertain, but a great deal more water probably lies beneath the surface of the planet. The seasonal changes in the extent of the ice caps are due to the melting and freezing of a thin layer of carbon dioxide over the ice.

At the Viking landing sites the surface was dusty and rock-strewn. Analysis of Martian soil by the landers revealed no traces of organic material and, although some of the results are open to question, it does seem that even the most elementary micro-organisms are absent from the dust-strewn surface of the red planet.

▲ This impressive vista appears when the Martian dust-storms abate. Viking 2 was leaning 8° from perpendicular, which is why the horizon appears to slope.

◄ The north polar cap on Mars consists primarily of water-ice. The distant view (far left) shows the cap shrinking as summer approaches. The closer view shows bands of water-ice separated by ice-free slopes at the top, and irregular ice patches below.

▲ Argyre Planitia, the large plain in the center, is an ancient impact basin surrounded by heavily cratered terrain. A thin haze, probably of carbon dioxide, highlights the horizon.

▼ This "river" is convincing evidence that a fluid once flowed on Mars. The channel is 573km long and 5-6km wide, and resembles terrestrial watercourses. The small tributaries are typical of run-off channels found elsewhere.

▼ This Martian dune field measures about 130km by 65km. The wind blows both ways across the dunes — hence the rounded crests.

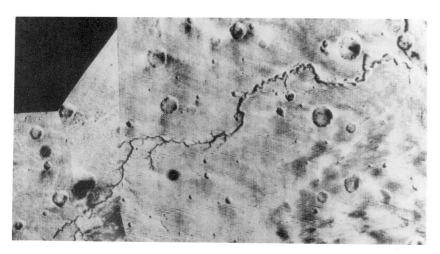

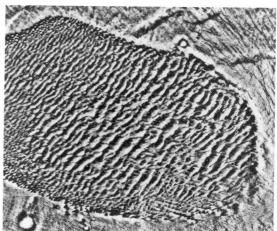

The loftiest volcano on Mars is three times as high as Earth's Mount Everest

Spectacular scenery on Mars

The largest volcano on Mars, named Olympus Mons, is a huge, gently sloping shield volcano, 25km high and some 600km across the base, with a summit caldera (volcanic crater) 80km in diameter. The gentle slopes of this feature and the surrounding lava sheets indicate that the lava from which it was formed must have been highly fluid. The largest comparable feature on Earth, Mauna Kea in Hawaii, stands a mere 9km above the floor of the Pacific Ocean and measures 225km across the base. About 1,000km southeast of Olympus Mons is the Tharsis Ridge, 2,000km long and 9km high; on top of this is a line of three massive shield volcanoes, Arsia Mons, Pavonis Mons and Ascraeus Mons. This ridge marks the edge of a great bulge in the Martian crust which was probably pushed up some 10km above the mean surface level by convection in the mantle.

An enormous canyon system, Valles Marineris, runs along the surface of Mars, just south of the equator for some 4,000km, reaching a maximum width of several hundred kilometers and a depth of 6km. It has numerous tributaries, and massive landslides beneath its cliffs. At the eastern end is a region of collapsed ground, littered with great blocks of rock; this is probably the result of the melting of subsurface ice. Valles Marineris may be a rift valley system which arose in conjunction with the uplifting of the neighboring Tharsis bulge. The mantle motions that produced this were probably too weak to fracture the 200km-thick Martian lithosphere into plates like those on Earth, and the shield volcanoes – like those on Venus – grew to their immense size because they remained stationary over reservoirs of magma.

The striking reddish color, seen in these photographs of the Martian surface, is due to a rust-like iron oxide material known as limonite, which is a hydrated rock.

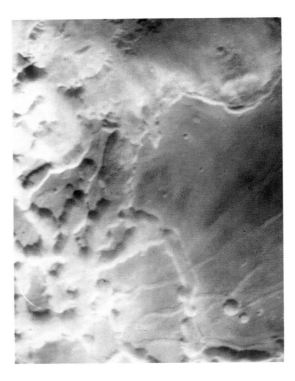

▲ As the Sun rises over the Noctis Labyrinthus area, bright clouds of water-ice become visible in the canyons (lower left). The picture was taken by Viking Orbiter 1 in October 1976.

▼ This contour map of Mars, compiled from information provided by ground-based radar and spacecraft, shows the vertical relief. Each color denotes a 500m altitude band.

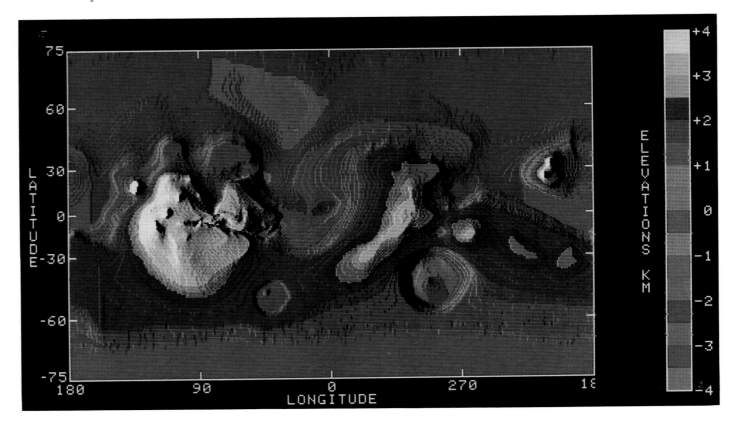

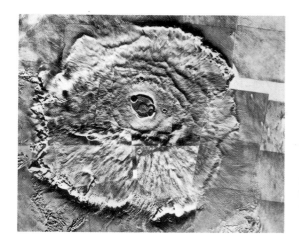

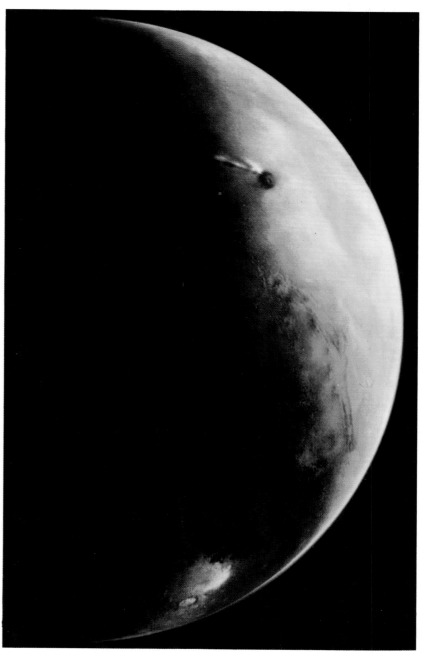

▲ Three photographs were combined to give this 200° Martian panorama. The surface material is highly reflective, and this has caused flare to degrade the center image.

▼ Olympus Mons, the largest mountain on Mars, is far larger than any comparable feature on Earth. It is a giant shield volcano, 25km high, with a base width of 600km.

▲ Slight variations of hue in the lava material suggest that the formation of the Olympus Mons shield took place over a long period of time. The photograph is in false color.

► The clearest features in this picture of Mars are Ascraeus Mons (near the top), the Valles Marineris canyon system (center) and the crater basin Argyre (near the bottom).

▶ *"Sunrise over the canals of Mars", a 19-century artist's impression. The idea that a network of artificial canals existed on Mars was completely dispelled by the 1964 Mariner 4 flyby.*

▼ *G. V. Schiaparelli of Milan drew a new chart of Mars in 1877, and this is a Mercator projection of his drawing. The straight lines which he called "canali" (channels, not canals) are numerous and striking, but Schiaparelli never committed himself to the belief that they were artificial. Percival Lowell, on the other hand, who drew the lower map, was fully convinced that the canals were part of an elaborate irrigation system.*

The origins of Martian "life"

Mars, unlike Venus, has a tenuous atmosphere, and usually there is no veiling of the surface, although at times there are planet-wide dust-storms which conceal all surface details, even the polar caps. During the 19th century various maps were produced, showing bright ocher-colored regions and dark areas which were at first thought to be seas. When it became clear that the Martian atmosphere is too thin and too dry to allow the presence of oceans, it was suggested that the dark patches might be old seabeds infilled with primitive organic matter. This theory was not finally disproved until the flight of the first successful Mars probe, Mariner 4, in 1965. Mariner also put an end once and for all to the long-standing controversy about the existence of Martian "canals".

Schiaparelli and the "canals"

The so-called canals were first drawn in detail in 1877 by Giovanni Schiaparelli (1835-1910), a skilled Italian astronomer. Schiaparelli drew long, narrow lines across the Martian "deserts", and called them canali. This is Italian for "channels", but it was inevitably translated as "canals", and before long came the suggestion that they might be artificial in origin. Schiaparelli kept an open mind throughout the great debate, but recorded

that he was "very careful not to combat this suggestion, which contains nothing impossible". An American astronomer, Percival Lowell (1855-1916), who built an observatory at Flagstaff in Arizona specially to observe Mars, was much less cautious, and wrote: "That Mars is inhabited by beings of some kind or other is as certain as it is uncertain what those beings may be." His beliefs met with considerable skepticism, however, even during his lifetime.

Talking to the Martians

The idea that Mars was inhabited was not new. As long ago as 1802 the great German mathematician Carl Gauss (1777-1855) had suggested signalling to the Martians by drawing vast geometrical patterns in the Siberian tundra. In 1874, the French astronomer Charles Cros (1842-1888) put forward a scheme to focus the Sun's heat onto the Martian deserts by means of a huge burning-glass, swinging the glass around so as to "write" messages in the desert. In 1901, a prize of 100,000 francs was offered in France to the first person to establish communication with extraterrestrial beings. Mars was excluded from the competition because it was thought too easy to contact Martian inhabitants!

What the Vikings found

By the start of the Space Age the canal network had been relegated to the realms of science fiction. Space-probe photographs confirmed that canals do not exist in any form, and that they were due simply to tricks of the eye.

Other established ideas about conditions on Mars were also found to be wrong. Contrary to expectations, the terrain proved to be mountainous and cratered, with giant volcanoes, of which the highest, Olympus Mons, rises to three times the height of Mount Everest on Earth, and has a base 600km in diameter. A number of scientists expected the Viking spacecraft to find evidence of primitive life-forms, but the experiments all proved negative.

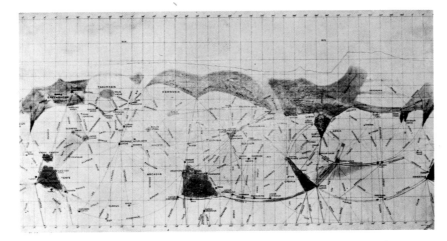

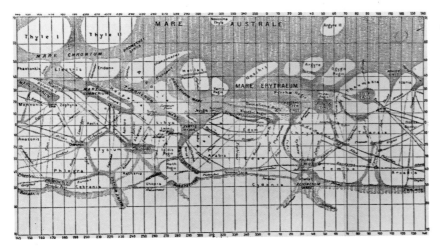

Planetary Atmospheres

4

Which planets have atmospheres?...Earth's unique features...Venus and its acid rain...Mars and the vestiges of atmospheric water...The giants and their helium rain...Jupiter's spectacular storms...Uranus and Neptune, their curious differences...PERSPECTIVE... The "greenhouse" effect and the terrestrial planets... Seasons and atmospheric engines...Jupiter's mysterious "Great Red Spot"

All the planets apart from Mercury and Pluto have significant atmospheres, although those of Venus, Earth and Mars are much less substantial than the deep envelopes surrounding the giant (Jovian) planets. The Jovian atmospheres are essentially the original gaseous blankets that those planets acquired at the time of their formation, but the terrestrial planets could not hold down atmospheres of this kind. Theirs were produced by outgassing – the release of gases from their interiors by, for example, volcanic activity.

Whether or not a planet retains an atmosphere depends on a number of factors, notably temperature, the chemical composition of the atmosphere, and escape velocity. If a particle in the outer regions of an atmosphere is moving faster than the planet's escape velocity, it can escape into space. The higher the temperature, the faster the speeds at which the atoms and molecules travel; but at any particular temperature the heavier atoms and molecules move more slowly than the lighter ones. Massive planets have higher escape velocities than less massive ones. The Jovian planets, being both cooler and more massive, have retained much of their hydrogen and helium, while the terrestrial planets have lost these gases.

By a process known as photodissociation (literally "separating by light"), ultraviolet radiation from the Sun breaks down molecules in the upper layers of an atmosphere into their constituent atoms. A molecule of water, for example, could break down into hydrogen and oxygen, and the hydrogen might then escape even though the original water would not have done so.

The mass of an atmosphere is important in several respects. The heavier the atmosphere, the greater the pressure it exerts at ground level – and pressure, together with temperature, determines whether a substance will exist in solid, liquid or gaseous form. The mass of an atmosphere, and its ability to retain heat, also affects its response to changes in the input of energy from the Sun. Both Venus, which has a much more massive atmosphere than the Earth, and Mars, which has a much less massive one, reflect this: the daily temperature variations on Mars are very large, while there is almost a complete absence of any differences between the day and night hemispheres of Venus. The temperature differences between equator and poles (which are responsible for driving global wind systems) on Venus, Earth and Mars are 2 percent, 16 percent and 40 percent respectively.

The greenhouse effect

A planet's atmosphere acts like a blanket, helping to conserve heat and thus to maintain a higher temperature at the surface than would be the case in the absence of an atmosphere. The process is known as the "greenhouse effect" because in some respects it resembles the action of a greenhouse.

Most of the solar energy reaching a planet is in the form of short-wavelength (visible or near-visible) radiation. This penetrates to ground level, where it is absorbed and so heats up the surface. The warmed surface emits infrared radiation, which cannot readily escape into space because it is strongly absorbed in the atmosphere by substances such as water vapor and carbon dioxide. The atmosphere radiates part of this heat back to the ground, so raising the surface temperature further.

The efficiency with which an atmosphere can do this depends upon its chemical composition and its mass. The massive atmosphere of Venus contains a high proportion of carbon dioxide and water vapor, and the greenhouse effect is much greater there than on the Earth. By contrast the Earth's greenhouse is more efficient than that of Mars, where the atmosphere is very thin and has little influence on surface temperatures, despite its high carbon dioxide component.

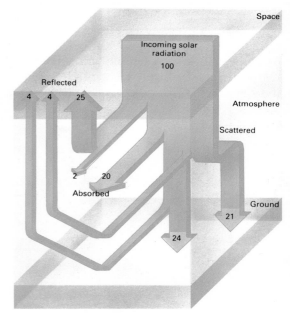

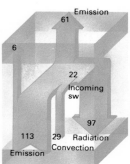

These diagrams show how the atmosphere helps to maintain a balance between incoming and outgoing radiation. The upper diagram represents the distribution of incoming solar radiation, the lower one that of long-wave (infrared) radiation from the Earth. The figures are summarized in the table (left). Gains and losses both total 183 units, so the average surface temperature remains stable.

Atmospheric gains		Atmospheric losses	
Short wave absorbed	22	Short wave scattered to space	4
Short wave scattered	25	Short wave scattered to ground	21
Long wave absorbed	107	Long wave radiated to space	61
Evaporation/latent heat	23	Long wave radiated to ground	97
Conduction/convection	6		
Total	183	Total	183

The Earth

The Earth's atmosphere consists mainly of nitrogen (78 percent by volume) and oxygen (21 percent). Of the other constituents the most abundant are water vapor, argon and carbon dioxide. Average pressure at ground level is 1013 millibars (mb) – equivalent to the weight of a column of mercury 0·76m high, or that of a 10m column of water – and this pressure is termed "one atmosphere".

The greenhouse effect maintains the mean surface temperature at about 290K (17°C), some 35K higher than it would be if there were no atmosphere. It ranges between a maximum of about 313K (40°C) near the equator to a minimum of about 233K (−40°C) at the poles.

It is convenient to divide the atmosphere into a number of layers. The lowest of these is the troposphere, which extends to an altitude of some 12km and contains most of the atmospheric water vapor, clouds and weather phenomena. Because the greenhouse effect is greatest near the ground, the temperature drops with altitude, reaching a minimum of about 217K at the tropopause (the upper boundary of the troposphere). Above this level is the stratosphere, which extends to an altitude of some 50km, and in this layer the temperature increases with height because of the absorption of ultraviolet rays from the Sun (mainly by ozone, which plays a vital role in protecting living creatures from the harmful effects of exposure to these rays).

In the next layer, the mesosphere, the temperature falls again to a minimum of 180K at an altitude of some 85km. Thereafter the rarefied gases of the thermosphere are heated by sunlight to typical values of 1,200K by day and 800K by night. At around 500km this layer merges with the exosphere, from which light atoms such as hydrogen can escape. At heights above about 70km, electrons are knocked out of some of the atoms by solar ultraviolet and X-rays. This produces the layers of electrically-charged electrons and ions which make up the ionosphere – the layer which reflects some radio waves.

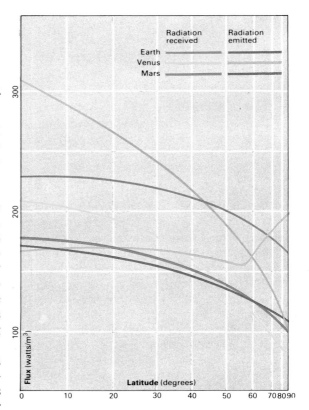

▲ At low latitudes the input of solar radiation exceeds the output of infrared; at high latitudes output exceeds input. To balance the sums, heat travels from equatorial to polar regions.

▼ The temperature increase found in the Earth's stratosphere is absent from the atmospheres of Venus and Mars due to a shortage of ozone, which absorbs solar ultraviolet radiation.

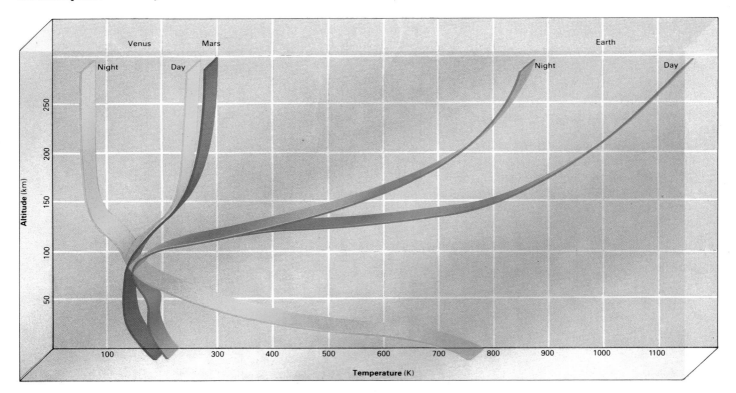

Venus

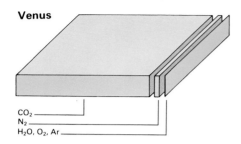

CO₂
N₂
H₂O, O₂, Ar

▲ The atmosphere of Venus consists almost entirely of carbon dioxide (96 percent).

▼ As on the Earth, the troposphere is heated by infrared radiation from below, while absorption of solar ultraviolet raises the temperature in the thermosphere. The main cloud layer lies between the altitudes of 45 and 60km, with a maximum density at 49-52km. Haze layers lie above and below the clouds.

Earth

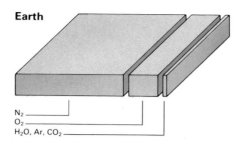

N₂
O₂
H₂O, Ar, CO₂

▲ Nitrogen and oxygen together make up 97 percent by volume of the Earth's atmosphere.

▼ The lowest atmospheric layer, the troposphere, which contains most of the clouds and water vapor, is heated by infrared radiation from the ground; its temperature falls with increasing height. The stratosphere is heated by incoming ultraviolet light, as is the thermosphere, where the ionized gases of the ionosphere are formed.

Mars

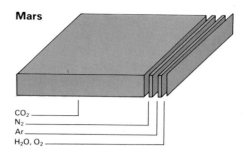

CO₂
N₂
Ar
H₂O, O₂

▲ The atmosphere of Mars consists largely of carbon dioxide (95 percent), but is very tenuous.

▼ In the thin Martian troposphere, temperature falls with increasing height, while absorption of solar ultraviolet produces only a slight warming in the thermosphere. Clouds of water droplets occur at low levels, where dust is also always present. At a height of tens of kilometers there is a thin haze of water and carbon dioxide crystals.

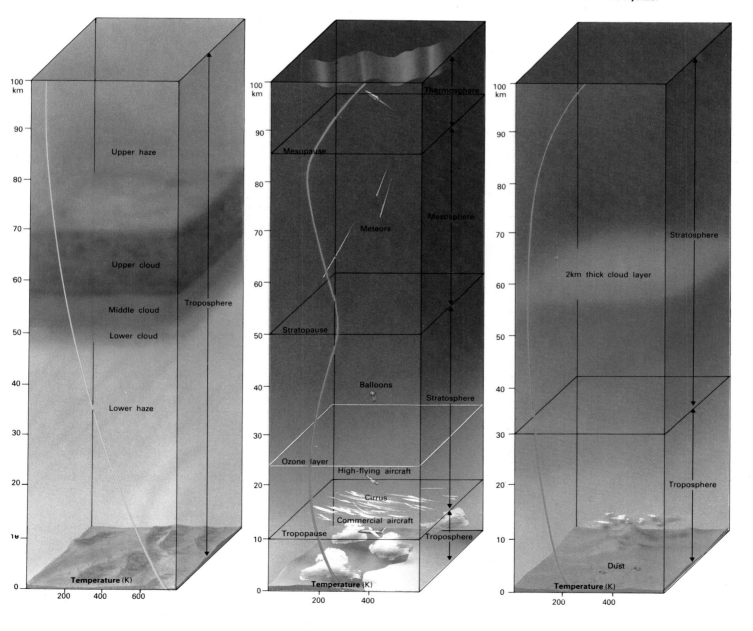

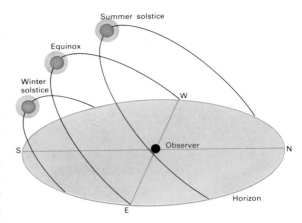

Venus

The dense atmosphere of this hostile world is composed mainly of carbon dioxide (which makes up 96 percent of the total) and exerts a pressure of over 90 atmospheres. The main cloud layer, which consists largely of droplets of sulfuric acid, spans a range of altitudes from about 45km to 60km. A given thickness of Venusian cloud absorbs less light than the same thickness of terrestrial cloud, but the Venusian cloud layer is so much thicker that only about two percent of incoming sunlight reaches the surface of the planet.

The Venusian "greenhouse" traps outgoing infrared radiation so effectively that the surface temperature remains about 750K – nearly 500K higher than it would be in the absence of an atmosphere. Many astronomers believe that at a much earlier period Venus had water on its surface, but that an increase in the luminosity of the Sun raised the temperature enough to start evaporating the oceans, increasing the quantity of water vapor in the atmosphere. Since water vapor is a good absorber of infrared, the greenhouse effect was enhanced, further raising the temperature and speeding up evaporation.

As a result of this "runaway" greenhouse effect, the temperature soared and the oceans evaporated completely. Sunlight must then have broken down the water vapor in the upper atmosphere into hydrogen, which escaped, and oxygen, which combined with surface rocks. The proportion of water vapor in the atmosphere is now only 0·005 percent, but even so it accounts for about 25 percent of the present Venusian greenhouse effect. The other major contributors are carbon dioxide, sulfur dioxide and clouds and haze.

The temperature falls with altitude in the troposphere to a minimum of 180K at 100km. Above this, on the daylight side, solar radiation heats the thermosphere to about 300K, but over the dark hemisphere the temperature of the upper atmosphere drops to about 100K.

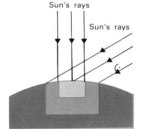

▲ *The apparent track of the Sun in midwinter, spring and autumn, and midsummer, shows how the noon elevation and the duration of daylight vary with the seasons.*

◄ *When the Sun is at a low angle its energy is diluted over a wide area. At a high angle it is concentrated.*

Seasons on Earth...
Seasonal effects arise because the tilt of the Earth's axis (23·4°) combined with the motion of the planet round the Sun causes periodic variations in the amount of sunlight reaching the northern and southern hemispheres.

...on Venus...
The Venusian "greenhouse" is so efficient that at the surface and in the lower levels of the atmosphere there are no significant temperature differences between equator and poles, nor between day and night. Because the tilt of the planet's axis is negligible there are no seasonal effects either – the "weather" is uniformly torrid at all times.

...and on Mars
Because the axial tilt of Mars (24°) is almost identical to that of the Earth, the Martian seasons follow the same pattern. However, the orbit of Mars is more elliptical than Earth's, and the input of solar energy is 40 percent greater at perihelion (closest approach to the Sun) than at aphelion (farthest point). This exaggerates the seasonal effects on Mars. A Martian year is almost twice as long as an Earth-year, so each season also lasts much longer than its terrestrial equivalent.

At each pole there is a permanent cap of water ice, but in the winter hemisphere the temperature over the cap is well below the freezing point of carbon dioxide (148K) which, therefore, forms a seasonal layer of frost and ice that extends over and beyond the permanent cap. About 30 percent of the atmospheric carbon dioxide is frozen out in the winter hemisphere, and this causes a drop in atmospheric pressure. With the coming of "spring" and "summer" the cap shrinks and the carbon dioxide returns to the atmosphere.

The seasons

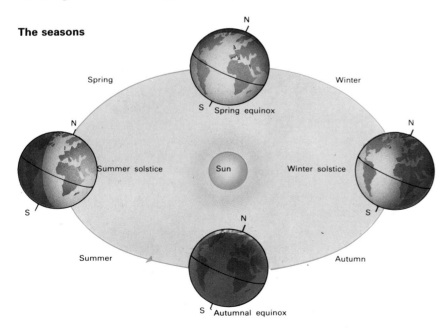

As the Earth orbits the Sun, the tilt of its axis gives rise to the seasons. Spring equinox: the Sun is overhead at the equator. Summer solstice: the Sun is overhead at the Tropic of Cancer (23·4°N). Autumnal equinox: the Sun crosses the equator again. Winter solstice: the Sun is overhead at the Tropic of Capricorn (23·4°S).

Atmospheric circulation on Earth

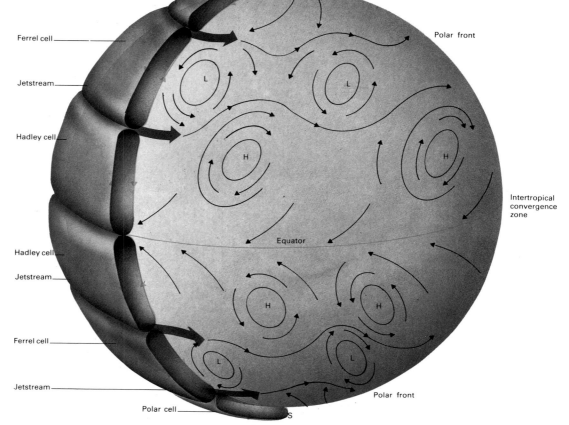

Polar cell

Jetstream

Ferrel cell

Jetstream

Hadley cell

Hadley cell

Jetstream

Ferrel cell

Jetstream

Polar cell

N

Polar front

Intertropical convergence zone

Equator

Polar front

S

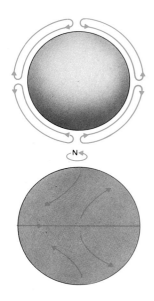

▲ The simplest form of atmospheric circulation is a Hadley cell, in which rising warm air moves polewards and sinking cool air returns to the equator (top). The effect of rotation is to deflect air parcels to the right in the northern hemisphere and to the left in the south.

▶ The Earth's circulation broadly contains three cells in each hemisphere. It breaks up into turbulent eddies in middle latitudes.

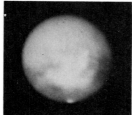

▲ The visible face of Mars can alter dramatically when violent dust storms sweep the planet. These pictures were taken at the Lowell Observatory in August 1971 (left) and October 1973.

▼ The north polar ice cap of Mars dwindles at a variable rate through spring and summer. Vertical scale is latitude of the cap edge; horizontal scale gives longitude of the Sun.

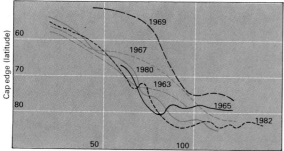

Cap edge (latitude)

60

70

80

1969
1967
1980
1963
1965
1982

50   100

Celestial longitude of Sun as seen from Mars

Mars

The rarefied Martian atmosphere consists mainly of carbon dioxide (95 percent) with nitrogen and argon making up most of the rest. There is a small proportion of water vapor – about 0·03 percent – but even if it were possible to liquefy it all, it would produce a surface water layer only a few tens of micrometers thick. The atmospheric pressure is less than 0·01 atmospheres. The surface is so uneven that pressure ranges from 9mb in deep depressions to about 1mb on high mountain tops, but a typical value is 6-7mb.

This tenuous atmosphere raises the surface temperature by less than 10K above the value it would have without an atmosphere. Mean temperature is about 220K, but it ranges from as low as 132K at the winter pole to as high as 300K at the equator. The variation between daytime and night-time temperatures can be as much as 60K.

At one time the atmosphere could well have been sufficiently thick to allow liquid water to exist. The volcanoes must have been a major source of atmospheric water, but the low escape velocity of Mars (5 kilometers per second) allowed gases to leak away quite rapidly.

Atmospheric engines on the terrestrial planets

It is the temperature difference between equator and poles that drives atmospheric circulation. Warm equatorial air flows towards the pole and cooler polar air flows towards the equator. The flow is very complex, particularly on Earth where, in the middle latitudes, it breaks up into turbulent eddies and wedges of cool and warm air intermingle.

Cloud and wind systems on Earth...

Two unique features of the Earth are the presence of oceans of water, and the existence of large quantities of free oxygen in the atmosphere. The oceans act as immense reservoirs of heat which smooth out global temperature variations. Energy is continually exchanged between the oceans and the atmosphere, within which clouds play a major role in the distribution of water vapor. Created by atmospheric motion, large-scale cloud systems reflect the movements of air masses and winds. The intensity of the winds often produces cyclones of up to 240 kilometers per hour.

...on Venus...

Winds at the surface of Venus are sluggish (a few kilometers per hour) but they rise sharply in the cloud deck to around 400 kilometers per hour. The uppermost clouds circle the planet in a period of about four days (60 times faster than the planet itself rotates), and this rapid rotation, combined with the flow of high-altitude air from the equator to the poles, produces characteristic Y- and C-shaped cloud patterns and raised polar "collars".

...and on Mars

The large temperature differences between the Martian equator and poles drive a strong atmospheric circulation. In both hemispheres the contrasts are reduced in summer (when the pole is tilted towards the Sun) and enhanced in winter. In spring the large temperature differences across the boundary of the retreating polar cap can produce particularly strong winds, which raise large quantities of dust high into the atmosphere. The dust absorbs sunlight and this heats the atmosphere, which in turn amplifies the winds and whips up yet more dust. Winds of up to 300 kilometers per hour can arise and spread the dust out to envelop the entire planet, so that it takes months to settle again. Atmospheric dust gives the Martian sky its pinkish hue.

Although cloud cover is generally small, clouds of water, water ice and carbon dioxide occur. Banks of cloud and haze lie over the poles in winter, and mists and hazes form at night in low-lying regions.

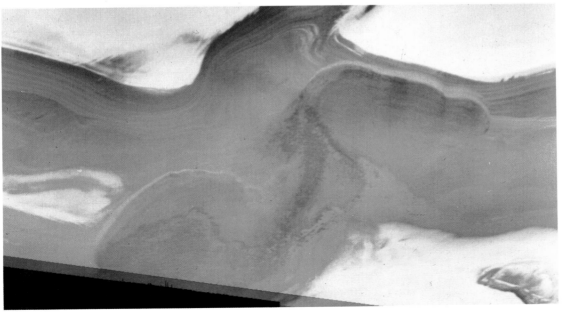

◄ *Part of the Martian north polar region, taken by Viking Orbiter 2, reveals the water ice and layered terrain that emerge in midsummer, when the carbon dioxide cap has retreated.*

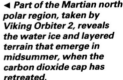

▶ *The irregular orange mass at the top and just left of center is a Martian dust cloud blowing around in Argyre Planitia. It is more than 300km across, and appears to be moving east.*

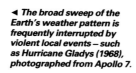

▲ Cloud vortices such as these over Guadalupe Island are rare on Earth, even in the tropics. These were photographed from Skylab in 1973.

◄ The broad sweep of the Earth's weather pattern is frequently interrupted by violent local events – such as Hurricane Gladys (1968), photographed from Apollo 7.

◄ Characteristic dark "Y" and "C"-shaped cloud forms encircle Venus. This picture shows the tail of a "Y", the arms of which spanned the planet two days earlier.

▼ The north pole is at the center of this infrared photograph of Venus. Blue areas are cold and red areas hot. The Sun was at the six o'clock position.

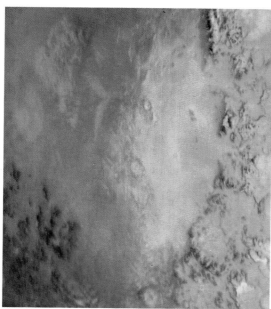

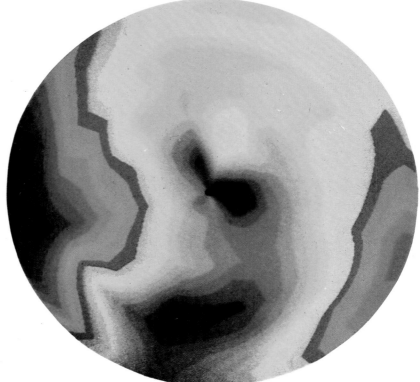

Temperature gradient

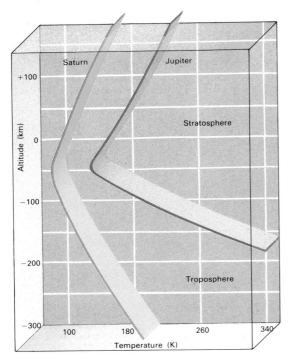

▲ The graph shows the vertical variation in temperature through the upper atmospheres of Saturn and Jupiter. Because neither planet has a solid surface from which to measure altitude, heights are referred to the level at which the atmospheric pressure is 100mb (0·1 Earth atmospheres).

Cloud layers

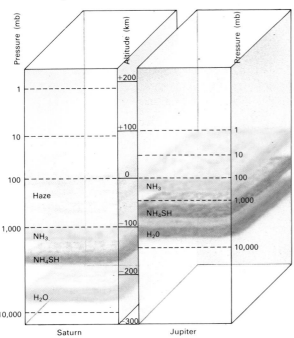

▲ From highest to lowest, the three main cloud layers are believed to contain crystals of ammonia (NH_3), ammonium hydrosulfide (NH_4SH) and water (H_2O). Saturn's atmosphere is cooler than Jupiter's and its atmospheric pressure increases more slowly with increasing depth.

Jupiter

Besides differences of composition, mass and temperature, the Jovian atmosphere contrasts sharply with those of the terrestrial planets in that Jupiter itself has no solid surface with which it can interact, and the planet also emits twice as much heat as it receives from the Sun. Internal heating is a major contributor to the forces which drive the circulation of the Jovian atmosphere. The temperature of the planet is the same all over, the polar regions emitting the same amount of heat as the equatorial regions.

The yellowish flattened disk of Jupiter is crossed by alternating bright zones and darker bands of cloud, the belts and zones being labelled according to their latitudes. There is considerable structure, with waves, plumes and eddies testifying to the turbulence of the clouds. Longer-lasting oval spots also appear, the most famous of these being the Great Red Spot, which measures 30,000-40,000km long by about 14,000km wide and is centered on latitude 22° south.

Since Jupiter has no rigid surface, the planet does not behave in the same way as a solid body: its rotation period varies with latitude, being about five minutes shorter at the equator than at the poles.

Composition and structure

The atmosphere of Jupiter consists mainly of hydrogen and helium, by volume 90 percent and 10 percent respectively, together with hydrogen compounds such as ammonia and methane. Within the troposphere the temperature decreases with altitude at an average rate of 2K per kilometer, reaching a minimum of 105K at the tropopause, where the pressure is about 0·1 atmospheres. The top of the main cloud deck lies about 30km below the tropopause. Seventy kilometers further down, at the base of the cloud layer, the temperature is about 300K and the pressure about 5 atmospheres. At a depth of 1,000km, where the atmosphere meets the liquid interior, the temperature may reach about 2,000K. Above the tropopause there is a stratosphere in which the temperature rises with altitude, mainly because the methane absorbs sunlight. Above this layer the temperature falls at first, then rises to about 1,000K.

Saturn

The composition of Saturn's atmosphere is broadly similar to that of Jupiter except that there is less helium (6 percent compared to 10 percent). Because it is less massive than Jupiter, Saturn has cooled more rapidly, and this has allowed droplets of helium to condense. These fall like rain into the deep interior, depleting the atmosphere of helium and heating the interior as they descend. This probably explains why Saturn emits just over twice as much heat as it receives.

The atmospheric temperature drops with increasing height, reaching a minimum of about 90K at the tropopause. Thereafter methane absorbs sunlight, producing a slight warming in the stratosphere.

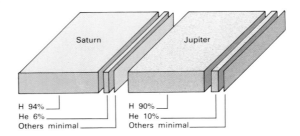

◄ The proportions by volume of the main atmospheric constituents of Saturn (left) and Jupiter (right) are compared. Hydrogen and helium are most abundant, but Saturn appears to have significantly less atmospheric helium than Jupiter.

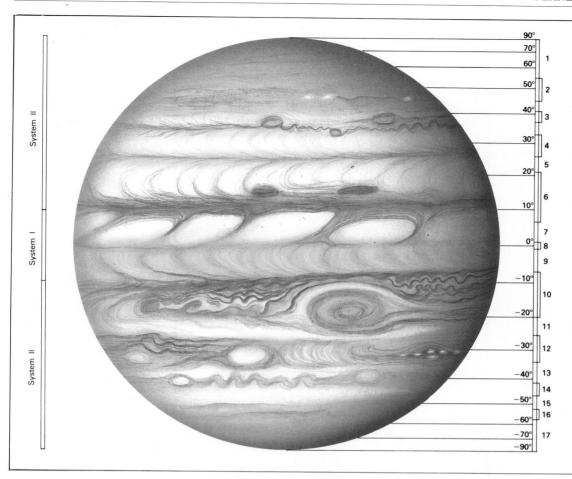

◀ **Jupiter's zones and belts.**
For convenience, observers have assigned three different rotation periods, or systems. System I, a period of 9 hours, 50 minutes and 30·003 seconds, applies to features within about 9° of the equator. System II, a period of 9 hours, 55 minutes and 40·632 seconds, is assigned to the slower-moving clouds farther from the equator. System III is based on measurements of Jupiter's radio emissions, which give a period of 9 hours, 55 minutes, 29·7 seconds.

1 **North Polar Region**
2 **North North North Temperate Belt**
3 **North North Temperate Belt**
4 **North Temperate Belt**
5 **North Tropical Zone**
6 **North Equatorial Belt**
7 **Equatorial Zone**
8 **Equatorial Band**
9 **Equatorial Zone**
10 **South Equatorial Belt**
11 **South Tropical Zone**
12 **South Temperate Belt**
13 **South Temperate Zones**
14 **South South Temperate Belt**
15 **South South South Temperate Zone**
16 **South South South Temperate Belt**
17 **South Polar Region**

◀ **Saturn's zones and belts.**
The same system of rotation periods has been assigned to Saturn. The rotation period at the equator – System I – is 10 hours, 15 minutes. The period at higher latitudes – System II – is 10 hours 38 minutes. Like Jupiter, various definite features, such as well marked spots, have rotation periods of their own, so that they drift about in longitude. Saturn's features are far less marked, however, although the two main belts – the North Equatorial and the South Equatorial – can always be distinguished. System III, based on radio emissions, is 10 hours, 39·4 minutes. Like Jupiter, the radio emissions are linked to Saturn's magnetic field, and since this is tied to the interior of the globe, System III is taken to be the "true" rotation period of the planet.

1 **North Polar Region**
2 **North Temperate Zone**
3 **North Temperate Belt**
4 **North Tropical Zone**
5 **North Equatorial Belt**
6 **Equatorial Zone**
7 **South Equatorial Belt**
8 **South Tropical Zone**
9 **South Temperate Belt**
10 **South Temperate Zone**
11 **South Polar Region**

Jupiter's Red Spot, once believed to be an active volcano, is now known to be a vast, rotating storm

▶ *Jupiter and three of the four Galilean satellites (Io crossing the face of the planet, Europa on the right and Callisto in the lower left hand corner), as seen by Voyager 1.*

◀ *The Great Red Spot as it appeared when Voyager 1 approached Jupiter in February 1979.*

▼ *Five months later Voyager 2's similar view shows changes in the white cloud regions, a different white oval, and cloud vortices forming from the wave structures to the left.*

Jupiter's distinctive features

Observers have distinguished three main levels of cloud in the Jovian atmosphere. The white zones are the highest and coldest, with temperatures of around 140K. They probably consist of crystals of ammonia ice. The brown clouds of the belts are warmer – about 230K – and lie 30-40km below the ammonia cloud tops. It is likely that they contain ammonium hydrosulfide, a compound of ammonia and hydrogen sulfide which turns brown when exposed to sunlight. The deepest clouds appear bluish and may consist of water ice and dissolved ammonia.

The bright zones are regions where convection is driving warm moist air upwards, and the belts are regions were cool dry gases are descending. As a result of the rapid rotation of the planet, the north-south flow of gases spilling out from the zones is diverted into strong east-west jetstreams with speeds of about 360 kilometers per hour along the boundaries between belts and zones. Astronomers are not sure what sustains the belt-zone pattern. According to one theory, in a rapidly rotating fluid body, concentric cylindrical convection cells will form round the axis of rotation. Where these meet the atmosphere, the belts and zones will appear. On the other hand, computer simulations can reproduce the Jovian belt-zone pattern quite well simply by scaling up the Earth's weather systems and taking account of the very rapid rotation. Perhaps very similar basic processes are at work.

The Great Red Spot seems to be an anticyclonic high-pressure feature rotating anticlockwise in a period of 6 days. The presence of phosphine may account for the color. Scientists believe that convection dredges the phosphine up from a great depth, and that ultraviolet radiation from the Sun breaks it down to release red phosphorus.

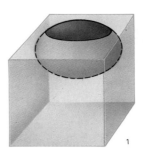
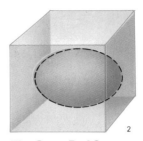
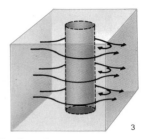

◄ *Early theories of the Red Spot. The "floating raft": a solid or semi-solid body floating in Jupiter's atmosphere (1). When the body sank, the Spot would be covered up and vanish temporarily (2). The "Taylor column": the spot was the top of a column of stagnant gas formed above a surface obstruction interrupting the atmospheric flow (3).*

The Great Red Spot: early theories

Considerable surface detail is visible on Jupiter, even in a small telescope, and from the early days of telescopic astronomy there had never been any serious doubt that the surface was gaseous rather than solid. However, there were many outstanding problems, one of which concerned the nature of the Great Red Spot. Unlike the smaller spots which are short-lived, it has been under observation for several centuries. It sometimes disappears for a few months or a few years, but it always returns.

Early suggestions that it might be a red-hot volcano rising above the clouds were soon rejected, and there was considerable support for a theory proposed by Bertrand Peek (1891-1965), an English amateur astronomer who was one of the best planetary observers of his time. Peek drew an analogy with the behavior of an egg dropped into a tall vase of water. The egg will sink to the bottom, but adding salt to the water increases its density and causes the egg to rise. Peek suggested that the Great Red Spot was a solid or semisolid body floating in Jupiter's outer gases. If the gases became denser, the Spot would rise; if they became less dense, the Spot would sink out of view. This theory was quite plausible, but the close-range results from spacecraft missions have recently disproved it.

Recent discoveries

The Pioneer and Voyager missions have now shown the Great Red Spot to be a whirling storm. Its longevity seems to be due to its exceptional size. It may not be permanent, and there is evidence that it is smaller now than it used to be. It has certainly grown smaller since 1878, in which year it became exceptionally prominent.

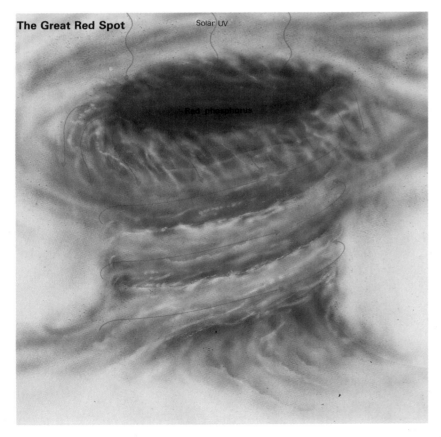

The Great Red Spot

Solar UV

Red phosphorus

◄ *The Great Red Spot seems to be a high-pressure region, its top standing about 8km above the surrounding cloud layer. The material within it circulates in an anticlockwise direction, which would be normal for a high-pressure system in the southern hemisphere. It seems likely that material flows up from lower atmospheric levels to the top of the Spot, then spreads out and descends at its edges.*

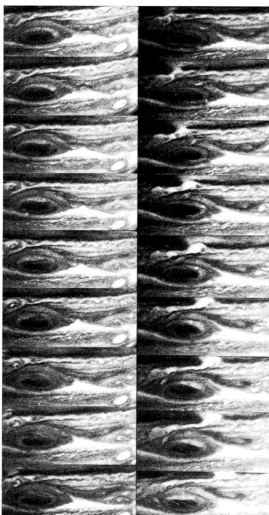

Saturn's muted appearance

The appearance of Saturn itself is blander and more muted than the dramatic panorama presented by Jupiter. The belt-zone pattern is present, but much less conspicuous, and large cloud features are scarce. Circulating spots are there too, but on a smaller scale. Because of the planet's weaker gravitational attraction its atmospheric layers are less compressed than those on Jupiter, and the various cloud layers are more widely spaced in altitude. The clouds which comprise the dark belts lie at a greater depth than those in the Jovian atmosphere and, therefore, may be less conspicuous because they are more heavily obscured by haze. The lower temperature affects the types of chemical reactions which occur, and the rates at which they proceed. Consequently, the more conspicuous coloring agents may be absent from the Saturnian atmosphere.

Saturn has zonal winds which are much stronger than those on Jupiter. The equatorial jet, in particular, blows at a speed of 1,800 kilometers per hour – four to five times faster than the Jovian equivalent. The jets are broader than those on Jupiter and, curiously, do not seem to bear any close relationship to the less well-defined belt-zone boundaries. Their most notable feature, however, is that they are completely symmetrical about the equator, the winds in the southern hemisphere being a mirror-image of those in the north. A possible explanation for this is that the jets may extend down through the planet as a series of concentric cylinders, rather than being confined to the atmospheric layers. The fierce winds, eddies, waves and interacting spots which are present in the Saturnian atmosphere bear witness to the powerful convection of heat from the interior of this intriguing world.

Atmospheric structure of the giants

◄ A time-lapse sequence of photographs reveals the flow of material around the Great Red Spot. Circulating currents to the left and wave-like regions to the right are clearly seen.

► The liquid molecular hydrogen zones of Jupiter and Saturn may consist of concentric cylindrical cells which cause belts, zones and zonal winds where they meet the atmosphere.

*The belts and zones on Saturn are much less striking than those on Jupiter,
because there is more overlying "haze"*

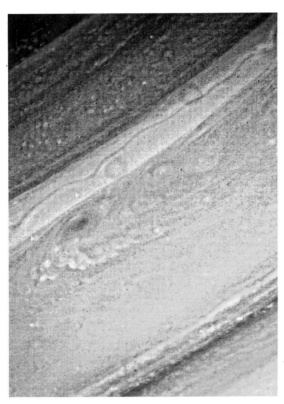

◄ *Saturn's northern
hemisphere in false color,
taken by Voyager 2 in
August 1981, the first (far
left) from a range of 7·1
million kilometers, the
second from 63,000km. Both
contain evidence of vigorous
activity within the
atmosphere, including fast-
moving wavelike features
and convective zones among
the stable ovals.*

► *Saturn as seen by
Voyager 2 from distances of
21 million kilometers (top)
and 43 million kilometers.
The small white disks in the
top picture are three of the
planet's moons, and the dark
spot is the shadow of one of
them (Tethys). Both pictures
clearly show the oblateness,
or flattening, of the planet.
The lower picture is in
false color.*

▼ *This view of Saturn's
northern hemisphere shows
a convective cloud with a
dark ring (light brown zone)
and a longitudinal wave
(light blue zone).*

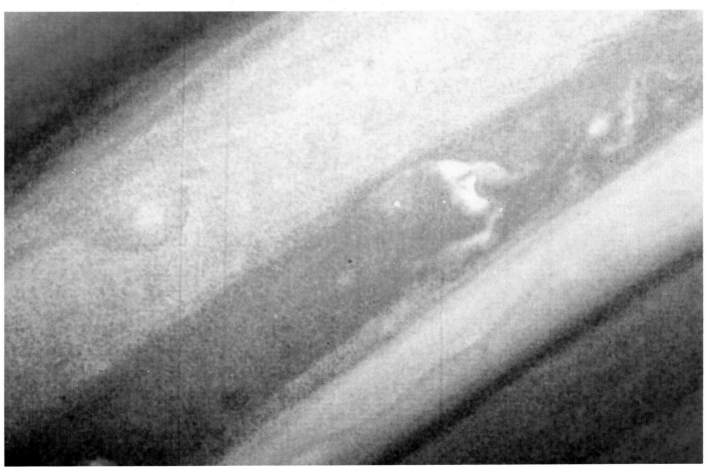

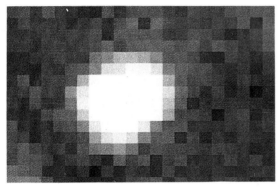

The atmospheres of Uranus and Neptune

To an Earth-based observer both Uranus and Neptune appear as small, rather featureless disks, greenish in the case of Uranus and bluish in that of Neptune. Spectroscopic observations have revealed the presence of hydrogen (the most abundant constituent) and methane in both atmospheres, and Voyager 2 has shown that helium comprises about 12 percent of the Uranian atmosphere. The effective temperatures of the two planets are very nearly the same – about 60K – despite the fact that Neptune is half as far again from the Sun as Uranus is. Neptune emits twice as much heat as it receives from the Sun and, like Jupiter and Saturn, must have an internal heat source which is an important driving force for atmospheric phenomena.

The lack of an internal heat source, together with its curious axial tilt, sets Uranus apart from the other Jovian planets. Because the axis is inclined by 98°, the Sun is almost directly over one of the poles at each solstice. Each pole, in the course of a Uranian year, receives a greater input of solar radiation than does the equator, but there appears to be little difference between the equatorial and polar temperatures. The atmospheric circulation on Uranus is much weaker than on Jupiter and Saturn and there is no obvious sign of the familiar belt-zone structure. A few individual cloud features were seen in Voyager images, and the motion of these revealed strong atmospheric currents. There is a general deck of methane ice crystals.

The atmosphere of Neptune is hazier and cloudier than that of Uranus, and infrared images reveal a dark equatorial band due to absorption of infrared by methane. The planet is shrouded in a haze of aerosols (fine particles) and ice crystals – a haze which varies with the level of solar activity. A plausible explanation is that variations in the solar output of particles, X-rays and ultraviolet radiation affect the atmospheric chemistry in an as yet unknown way.

▲ **Neptune, photographed from Arizona (top): the disk is brightest in the south. Taken in infrared by D. A. Allen and J. Crawford at Siding Spring, Australia (above), the planet appears extended along its polar axis, possibly by brightening from hazes at high latitudes.**

▼ **Uranus photographed in 1976 (below) shows no surface markings; the limb brightening results from high-altitude haze. Photographed by D. A. Allen and J. Crawford (right) methane absorption has dimmed the planet, making the rings visible.**

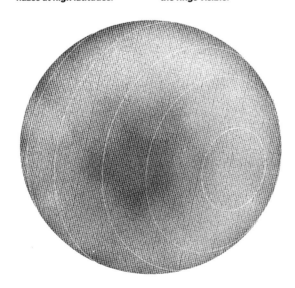

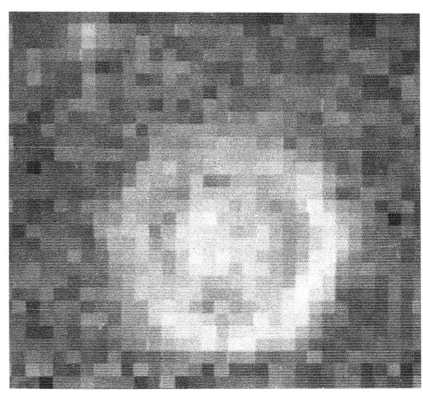

Moons and Ring Systems

5

Comparison of the planets' satellites...The Moon: its tidal effect on Earth...Jupiter's dramatically differing moons, and modest rings...Saturn's giant moon Titan and its smaller companions...Saturn's dramatic complex ring system...Rings and moons of the outer planets...PERSPECTIVE...The tiny Martian moons... Galileo's discovery of Jupiter's four largest moons... Early theories about Saturn's rings

All the planets, with the exception of Mercury and Venus, have natural satellites, or moons, which revolve around them. These range in size from planet-sized bodies, comparable with Mercury, to tiny irregular bodies like asteroids, a few kilometers in diameter. The Earth's Moon has been explored more thoroughly than the others (◀ pages 24-7). It is a rocky, cratered world, the surface displaying both the scars of bombardment by meteorites and the effects of volcanism. Other planetary satellites show a marvellous diversity of structure and form, ranging in composition from rock to ice and in appearance from heavily-cratered to glassy-smooth.

Three of the four giant planets have ring systems made up of small to moderate-sized particles and lumps of matter in orbit above their equators. Saturn's magnificent system is striking even through Earth-based telescopes. Jupiter and Uranus have thin faint rings on a much more modest scale; although not visible in optical telescopes, they can be detected from Earth at infrared wavelengths.

Satellites interact with their planets in various ways, an important one being the generation of tides. The Moon is mainly responsible for the ocean tides which rise and fall twice daily on Earth. A particle of water on the Moon-facing hemisphere is closer to the Moon than the center of the Earth's globe is, so it experiences a slightly stronger gravitational attraction and is accelerated towards the Moon, thus flowing into a bulge in the ocean arising on that side of the Earth. Conversely, a particle on the far side of the Earth experiences a weaker force of attraction than the body of the planet, and "falls behind", away from the direction of the Moon and into a second oceanic bulge. In this way the surface of the ocean assumes an ellipsoidal shape. Although the height of the bulge in mid-ocean is only about one meter, the situation in coastal water is complicated by local factors and a much greater tidal range can occur. The Sun exerts a weaker tide-raising force. When the Sun and Moon are in line (at New Moon and Full Moon) higher "spring" tides are raised. When Sun and Moon are pulling at right angles (First and Last Quarter) lesser "neap" tides arise.

Orbital and rotational effects

It is not only the Earth's oceans that experience tidal effects. The Earth raises tides in the body of the Moon. In the past the effect of the Earth's gravitational attraction on the tidal bulges raised in the Moon was to slow down the Moon's axial rotation until – as now – the Moon rotates on its axis and revolves around the Earth in the same period of time, so keeping the same hemisphere turned always towards the Earth. This phenomenon of synchronous, or "captured", rotation is common to most planetary satellites.

Similarly, the effect of the Moon's gravitational attraction on the Earth's tidal bulges is to slow down the Earth's rotation. The effect is small, between 10 and 15 parts in 100 billion per year, and is equivalent to a lengthening of the Earth-day by about 0·02 seconds per century. Nevertheless, the length of the day will eventually be equal to the period of the Moon's orbital revolution. The energy of rotation lost by the Earth is transferred to the motion of the Moon, and as a result the Moon is gradually receding from the Earth at a rate of some 4·5cm per year.

Satellite-to-planet ratios

Tidal interactions are complex and usually affect the satellite far more than they do the planet. Only where the mass of the satellite is a significant fraction of that of the planet does its effect on the planet become significant. In proportion to the planetary masses, the most massive satellites are the Moon (⅛₁ that of the Earth) and Charon (¹⁄₁₀ that of Pluto). By contrast, the most massive satellite of Jupiter is less than ¹⁄₁₀,₀₀₀ of that planet's mass.

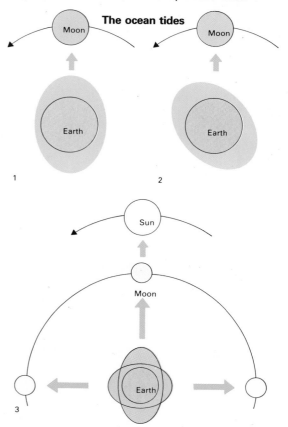

The ocean tides

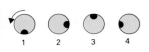

▲ In one complete rotation of the Moon on its axis, a point on its surface turns through an angle of 360°. The Moon revolves around the Earth in the same time as it takes to spin on its axis so that a point initially facing the Earth will always face towards the Earth.

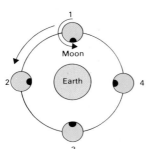

▶ 1 The Moon's attraction distorts the ocean surface into an ellipsoidal shape. The Earth's rotation carries a point on its surface past the two tidal bulges twice daily. 2 Frictional effects due to the Earth's rotation drag the tidal bulges ahead of the Earth-Moon line. 3 Tidal bulges are highest when Sun and Moon are in line and least when they are at right angles.

Most satellites follow a near-circular orbit close to the plane of their planet's equator

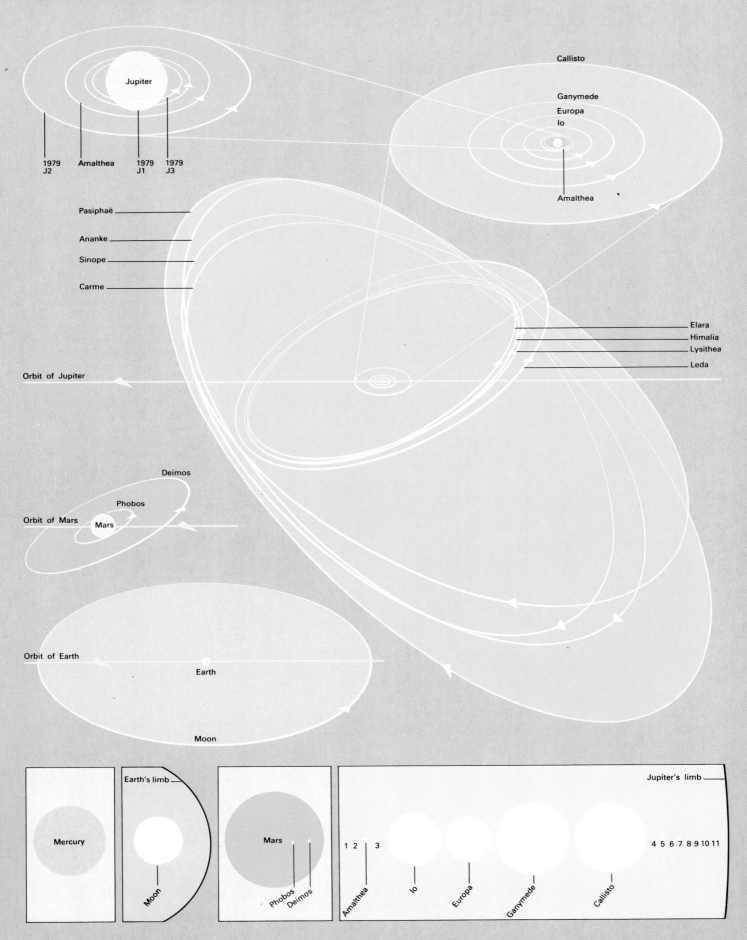

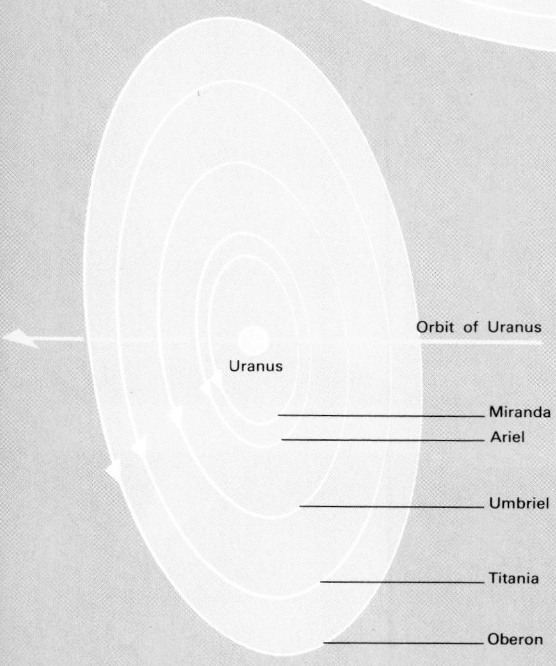

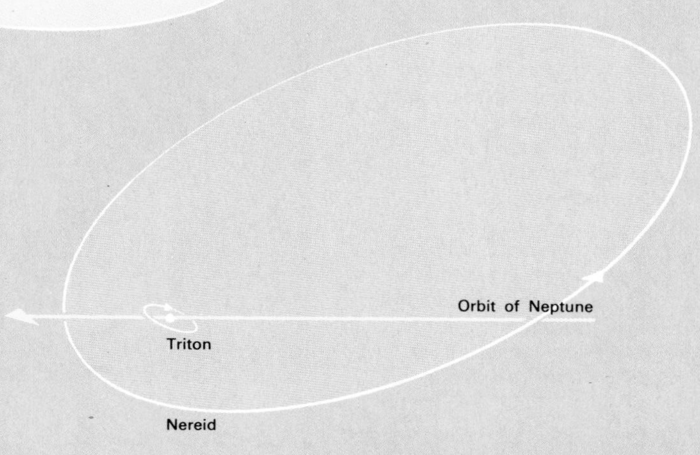

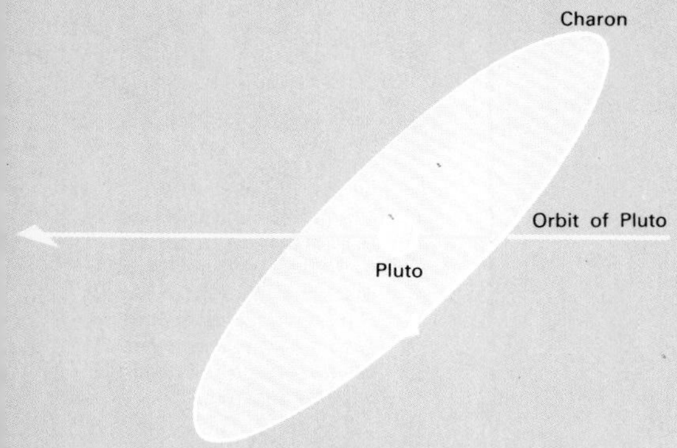

Hyperion

Titan

Tethys
Enceladus
Mimas

Rhea
Dione

Hyperion

Iapetus

Phoebe

Orbit of Saturn

Orbit of Uranus

Orbit of Neptune

Uranus

Triton

Miranda

Ariel

Nereid

Umbriel

Titania

Oberon

Charon

Orbit of Pluto

Pluto

The relative spacing and orientation of the orbits of the various planetary satellites are shown. The diameters of satellites are compared with their parent planets (below), but many of the smaller satellites are too tiny to be shown accurately to scale. The Earth has one large Moon and Mars has two tiny satellites which follow near-circular orbits above its equator. The largest of Jupiter's 16 moons is Ganymede, with about 1/27 of Jupiter's diameter. The innermost 8 satellites follow near-circular orbits in the plane of the planet's equator, the next 4 have more inclined elliptical orbits, and the outermost 4 have retrograde orbits. Saturn's collection of 21-23 satellites includes one giant moon, Titan, which has about 1/23 of Saturn's diameter. They mostly follow near-circular orbits close to the plane of the planet's equator, but the orbit of Iapetus is significantly inclined, and that of Phoebe is retrograde. Most of the minor satellites are omitted from the diagram as they either share orbits with the largest satellites or lie inside the orbit of Mimas. Uranus has 15 satellites in all, including 10 tiny ones which lie within the orbit of Miranda and are omitted here. The largest, Titania, has about 1/50 of the diameter of Uranus. Neptune's inner satellite, Triton, may be as large as 1/8 of the planet's diameter, and follows a retrograde orbit; the other, Nereid, has an extremely elongated orbit. Pluto's satellite, Charon, has about 1/3 of the planet's diameter.

Jupiter's minor satellites
1 1979 J3
2 1979 J1
3 1979 J2
4 Leda
5 Himalia
6 Lysithea
7 Elara
8 Ananke
9 Carme
10 Pasiphaë
11 Sinope

Saturn's minor satellites
12 1980 S28
13 1980 S27
14 1980 S26
15 1980 S3
16 1980 S1
17 Mimas co-orbital
18 1980 S25
19 1980 S13
20 Tethys co-orbital
21 unnamed
22 unnamed
23 1980 S6
24 Dione co-orbital
25 unnamed

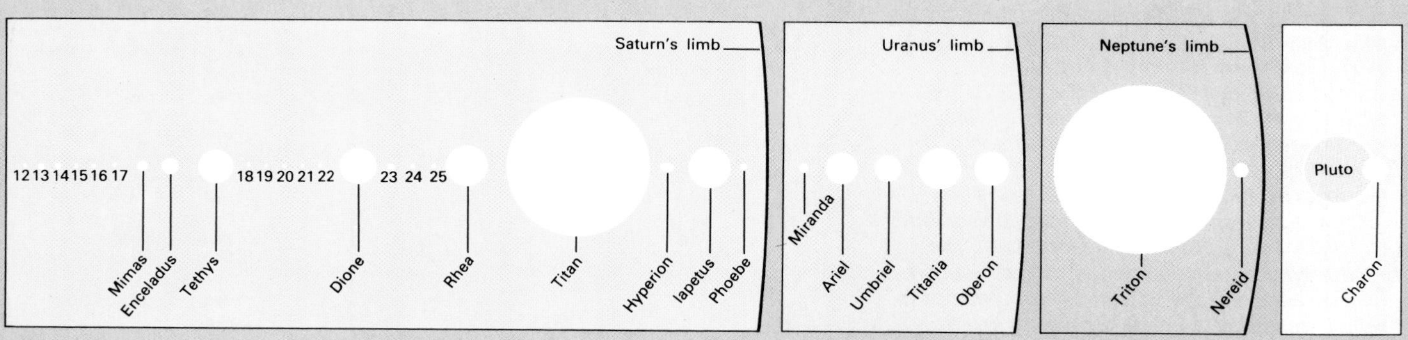

Saturn's limb

Uranus' limb

Neptune's limb

12 13 14 15 16 17   18 19 20 21 22   23 24 25

Mimas
Enceladus
Tethys

Dione

Rhea

Titan

Hyperion
Iapetus
Phoebe

Miranda
Ariel
Umbriel
Titania
Oberon

Triton
Nereid

Pluto

Charon

To an observer on Mars, the outer satellite, Deimos, would appear like a large, dim star

A pair of Martian moons

Both Martian moons are tiny. Phobos, the larger of the two, is an irregular ellipsoid with a maximum diameter of about 28km. At a mean distance from the center of the planet of 9,270km, it revolves round Mars in only 7 hours 39 minutes. It is thus the only satellite known to have an orbital period shorter than its planet's axial rotation period, so that it moves from west to east across the Martian sky. Deimos, with a maximum diameter of 16km, lies at a mean distance of 23,400km from Mars and has an orbital period of 30 hours 21 minutes. It moves slowly from east to west across the sky, remaining above the horizon for up to 2·5 Martian days.

The moons are both rocky bodies, apparently similar in nature to a class of carbon-rich asteroid (◊ pages 72-3) found in the outer part of the asteroid belt. It seems likely that Phobos and Deimos are asteroids which, long after their formation, became trapped in the Martian gravitational field.

Both satellites are heavily cratered, and Phobos has one crater, Stickney, which is nearly 10km in diameter. The impact that presumably caused the crater must have come close to shattering the satellite, and a system of striations on its surface are probably another result of the same event.

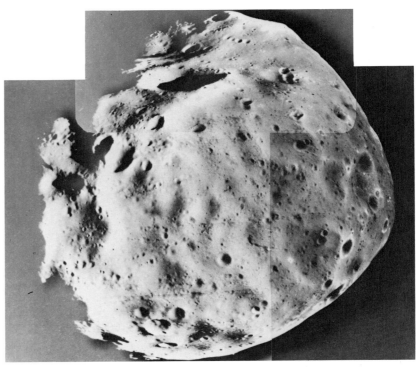

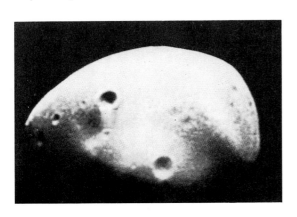

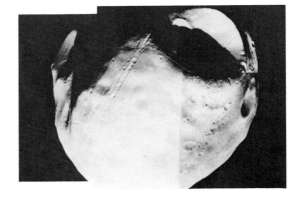

▲ *Viking Orbiter 1 took this composite picture of Phobos, the larger Martian moon, from a distance of only 480km.*

▶ *Phobos was about to enter the shadow of Mars when Viking took this photograph showing the craters Hall and Stickney.*

◀ *Deimos resembles Phobos in many respects. However, it lacks grooves and large craters, and its surface is covered with a thinner layer of dust.*

The first planetary satellites

The first satellites to be discovered (apart from the Moon) were the four "Galileans" orbiting Jupiter – Io, Europa, Ganymede and Callisto. At the same time as they were observed by the famous Italian astronomer Galileo Galilei (1564-1642), they were found independently by a German astronomer, Simon Marius (1573-1624). It was Marius who gave the four satellites their names, although they were not officially used until modern times, the satellites merely being referred to as I, II, III and IV. The fifth Jovian satellite was discovered by American astronomer Edward Barnard (1857-1923) in 1892. This was the last to be found visually – all later satellite discoveries have been photographic. The fifth satellite was named Amalthea, although again the name was not used before the Space Age.

Other Jovian satellites were detected later, but all of them were extremely small and faint. The four outermost satellites have retrograde motion, and may well be captured asteroids. Altogether 16 Jovian satellites are now known.

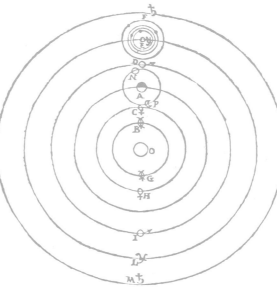

◀ *This diagram of the Copernican system was drawn by Galileo and appeared in his "Dialogo" published in 1632. It shows the four Galilean satellites, which he discovered on 7 January 1610, orbiting around Jupiter.*

▶ *Electrons and ions – such as sodium, potassium and magnesium – expelled from Io's volcanoes spread out along its orbit to form a doughnut-shaped "plasma torus". The tilt of Jupiter's powerful magnetic field causes the torus to be tilted relative to Io's orbit by about 10°. A stream of electrons and ions flows between Jupiter and Io along a "flux tube" which carries over a million megawatts of electrical power.*

Jupiter has 16 satellites, four of which are comparable with, or larger than, the Earth's Moon. These are the "Galilean" satellites: in order of distance from the planet, Io, Europa, Ganymede and Callisto. Apart from Amalthea, an irregularly-shaped body measuring 155km by 270km, and Himalia (170km in diameter), all the other Jovian satellites are considerably less than 100km in diameter.

In terms of their orbits, Jupiter's moons can be divided into three distinct groups. The eight innermost satellites, including the Galileans and Amalthea, lie within 2 million kilometers of the planet's center, and follow near-circular orbits in the plane of Jupiter's equator. The next four, including Himalia, follow more elliptical orbits inclined to the equator by some 26-29°, and at mean distances of between 11 and 12 million kilometers. The outermost four, lying between 20 and 24 million kilometers from the planet, follow highly elliptical retrograde orbits inclined at angles between 147° and 163°. Probably the satellites in the inner group were formed from the same cloud of material as Jupiter itself, while the others are captured asteroids.

Composition of the Galilean satellites

The Galileans differ dramatically from each other. Callisto, the outermost, has a diameter of 4,820km and is similar in size to Mercury. It is much less dense than Mercury, however, suggesting that the satellite contains a substantial proportion of water. It may have a silicate (rocky) core extending to about half its radius, overlain by a mantle of liquid water or soft ice, on top of which lies a rigid crust of rock and ice. Ganymede is about 1·5 times the diameter of the Moon. Slightly larger and a little denser than Callisto, it also probably has a slightly larger silicate core, but is still most likely to contain nearly 50 percent water. An alternative view is that it consists of a fairly uniform mixture of rock and ice throughout. Europa is considerably denser than both Ganymede and Callisto, and probably has a rocky core comprising about 90 percent of its mass.

Finally, Io probably has a crust of sulfur and sulfur dioxide overlying molten silicate and, possibly, a solid core. Its mean density is similar to that of the Moon. Volcanism is evident: it is probably sustained by tidal pumping. Io's orbit is perturbed periodically by Europa and Ganymede, and as a result a tidal bulge rises and falls by as much as 100. The heat released by this motion keeps the volcanoes supplied with molten material. Lying deep within the hostile radiation belts of Jupiter's magnetosphere, Io is bombarded by charged particles and linked to Jupiter by a "flux tube" of electrons. These can carry an electrical current equivalent to about 2·5 million amperes.

Jupiter's influence on Io

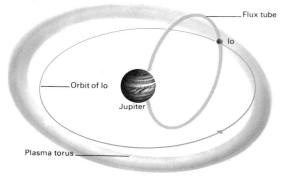

Orbit of Io
Jupiter
Flux tube
Io
Plasma torus

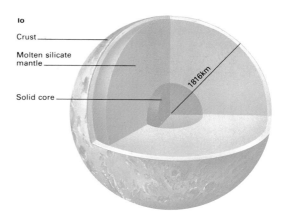

Io
Crust
Molten silicate mantle
Solid core
1816km

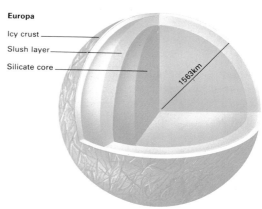

Europa
Icy crust
Slush layer
Silicate core
1563km

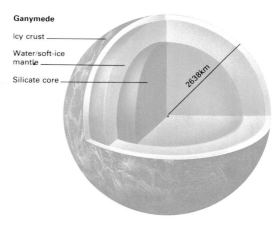

Ganymede
Icy crust
Water/soft-ice mantle
Silicate core
2638km

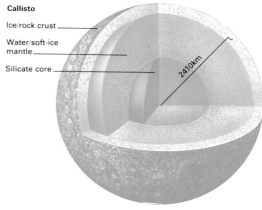

Callisto
Ice/rock crust
Water/soft-ice mantle
Silicate core
2410km

► *Possible structures of the four Galilean satellites are compared on equal-sized images. Io, the innermost, is the densest (mean density 3,530kg/m³); it may have a solid core. Europa (mean density 3,030kg/m³) is an ice-coated rocky world and is the only one of the four which is smaller than Earth's Moon. Ganymede, the largest, and Callisto, the outermost, are less dense (1,930 and 1,790kg/m³ respectively) and probably comprise roughly half rock and half water or ice.*

Impurities in the ice give Callisto's surface quite a low albedo (◀ page 23) of 0·2. It is by far the most heavily cratered body in the Jovian system. The albedo of Ganymede is higher (0·4) and the surface is strikingly different from that of Callisto. Like the Moon, it has two types of terrain, bright and dark, but in Ganymede's case the dark areas are the heavily cratered ancient surfaces, presumably composed of dirty ice, whereas the brighter areas seem to consist of ice which melted later and flowed over the older terrain before freezing again. The differences between Callisto and Ganymede are probably due to greater heating and convection in the latter, resulting partly from the decay of radioactive elements.

Europa is the most reflective of the Galileans (albedo 0·64) and it has such a smooth surface that it has been compared to a billiard ball. There are no craters, but the surface is covered with a pattern of bright and dark stripes and a network of cracks, grooves and short narrow ridges. Vertical relief is generally less than a hundred meters, or at most a few hundred. Any craters that may have existed at one time must have been obliterated by ice flowing over the surface.

By far the most intriguing of the four is the innermost one, Io. Its orange-red surface is pockmarked with volcanic caldera and violently active volcanoes. Voyager 1 recorded eight volcanoes erupting actively, and six of these were still erupting during the later flyby of Voyager 2. Plumes of matter are expelled to heights of 250km or more at speeds of up to 1km/s (3,600km/h) – 20 times faster than ejecta from Earth's Mount Etna. The absence of volcanic craters suggests that the surface is no more than a million years old and that this strange world is resurfaced by volcanism so rapidly that it must have been turned inside out and reprocessed several times since its formation.

▲ The surface of Io is subject to colossal tidal and electrical forces, and is continuously shaken by volcanic activity.

▼ The surface of Europa, the smallest of the Galilean satellites, is remarkably smooth.

► The four Galilean satellites are shown in equal-sized images so that their appearances can be compared. Io (top left) was photographed from 862,000km, Callisto (top right) Ganymede (bottom right) and Europa (bottom left) from 1·2 million km.

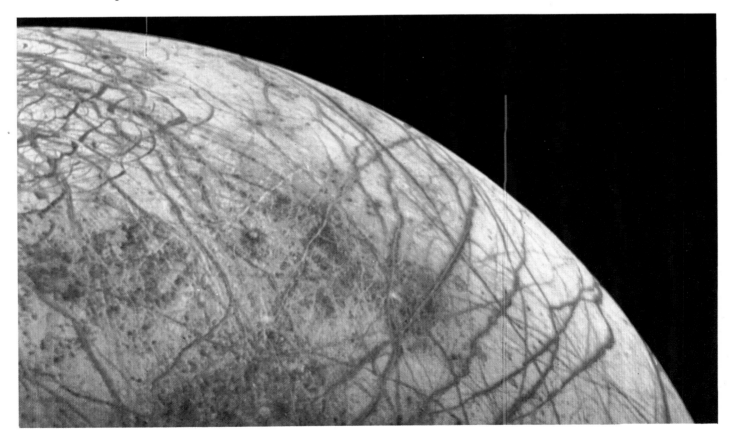

Unlike Jupiter, with its four major satellites, Saturn has one large moon and several of moderate size

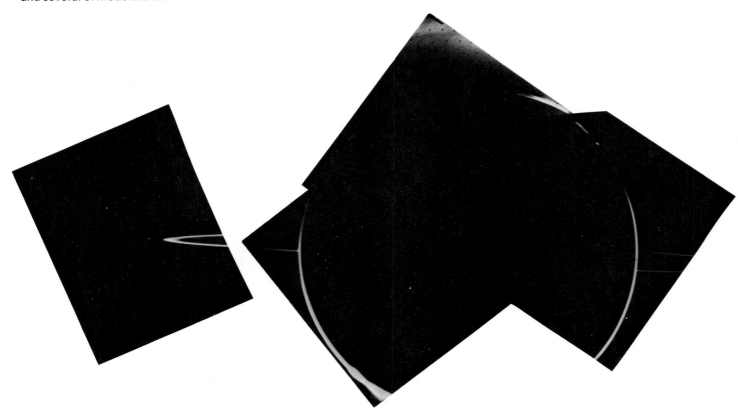

Jupiter's rings

Discovered by Voyager 1 and examined in more detail by Voyager 2, Jupiter's rings are modest by planetary ring system standards. The main ring has quite a sharply-defined outer edge at a radius of some 128,000km, and extends inwards in a rather featureless sheet about 6,000km wide. There is a brighter, narrower zone towards the outer edge of the sheet, and a more tenuous sheet of particles seems to extend inside the main ring down to Jupiter's atmosphere. The particles are tiny, only a few micrometers in diameter; at this size radiation effects will cause them to spiral slowly into the Jovian atmosphere. If the rings are a permanent feature, their material must be continually replenished, possibly by the erosion of material from the surfaces of Jupiter's innermost satellites.

▲ *Following the discovery of Jupiter's rings by Voyager 1, Voyager 2 was programmed to take additional pictures giving better resolution. In this one the ring showed up particularly brightly when Voyager 2 passed behind Jupiter with respect to the Sun. The planet's shadow obscures part of the ring in the direction of the camera. The micrometer-sized particles in Jupiter's ring contrast with the Saturnian ring particles, which are estimated to be several centimeters in size.*

▼ *This composite image of Jupiter's ring was made by Voyager some 26 hours after flying past the planet, at a distance of 1,550,000km. The forward scattering of sunlight reveals a radial distribution of very small particles extending inward from the ring toward Jupiter. There is an indication of structure within the ring, but the spacecraft motion during these long exposures blurred the highest resolution detail. The ring has a characteristically orange color.*

Mimas

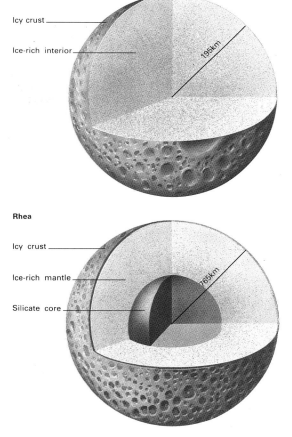

Icy crust

Ice-rich interior

195km

Enceladus

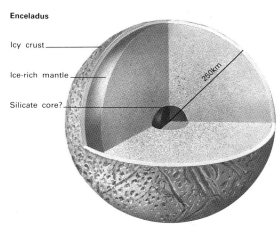

Icy crust

Ice-rich mantle

Silicate core?

250km

► *Possible interiors of some of Saturn's larger satellites are compared on equal-sized images. They are all icy, with differing proportions of rocky material, but their internal structures are very uncertain. Mimas (mean density 1,400kg/m³) is probably composed mainly of water-ice and a proportion (about one-third) of denser materials. It is probably solid throughout, and it has a heavily cratered surface. Enceladus (mean density 1,200kg/m³) is also predominantly icy but may have a small rocky core. Much of its surface is covered by smooth plains and fissures. Rhea, larger and denser (1,300kg/m³) than Enceladus, may have a larger core. Titan is by far the largest and densest (1,900kg/m³) of Saturn's satellites. It probably consists of at least 50 percent rock, most of it in the central core. Iapetus (1,100kg/m³) may be composed of ices of various kinds.*

Rhea

Icy crust

Ice-rich mantle

Silicate core

765km

Titan

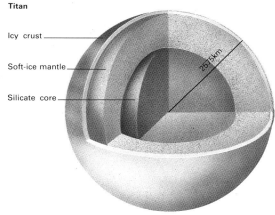

Icy crust

Soft-ice mantle

Silicate core

2575km

Iapetus

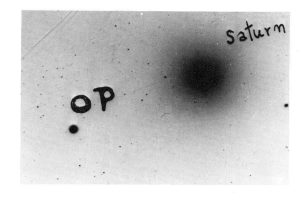

Icy crust

Ice mantle

Core?

720km

Satellites of Saturn

Saturn has a retinue of 21 or 23 satellites. Difficulties of positive identification mean that the exact figure is open to question: in any case, there are doubtless other small satellites yet to be found. Their distances range from 137,760km to 12,950,000km from the planet's center. There is one giant satellite, Titan, 5,120km in diameter – only fractionally smaller than Ganymede. Of the remainder, four (Rhea, Iapetus, Dione and Tethys) are of moderate size, ranging in diameter from 1,050km to 1,530km, seven are small (160-500km), two are about 100km in diameter, and the rest are tiny (less than 35km across). All follow direct orbits apart from Phoebe, the outermost satellite, which pursues a retrograde path inclined at an angle of 150° to Saturn's equatorial plane.

About half of Titan's mass probably consists of a silicate core, most of the rest being a water- and methane-ice envelope. The most intriguing feature of this satellite is its atmosphere, which consists, by volume, of about 85-95 percent nitrogen, 5-10 percent argon and about 1 percent methane, together with minor constituents such as hydrogen cyanide (one of the building blocks of nucleic acids fundamental to the construction of living matter). Titan is the only planetary satellite to have a permanent, substantial atmosphere.

At ground level on Titan the temperature is about 95K and the atmospheric pressure between 1,500 and 1,600mb, about 50 percent greater than atmospheric pressure at the Earth's surface. The temperature declines with height to a minimum of 70K at the tropopause (the top of the lowest atmospheric layer) some 40km above the surface, and thereafter increases to about 160K. The satellite's surface is hidden from view by a deep layer of orange-red smog made up of aerosols (fine particles and droplets), and extending downwards from an altitude of 200km. A layer of methane clouds, from which methane rain probably falls, is thought to lie just below the tropopause (40km altitude).

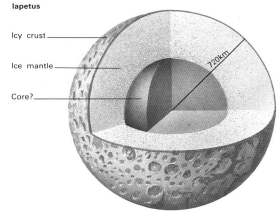

▲ *The discovery photograph of Phoebe. In 1898 W. H. Pickering, a foremost American planetary observer, used photography for the first time in the search for new satellites around Saturn. He exposed four plates for two hours each. Between them they revealed more than 400,000 stars. The plates were compared and an object, clearly not a star, was found to have moved. Saturn's ninth satellite had been found.*

On Titan, there may be cliffs of solid methane and rivers of liquid methane

At the time of the Voyager flybys the northern hemisphere of Titan was darker and redder than the southern hemisphere, and between 1980 and 1981 the dark hood at the north pole developed into a dark collar. These are probably seasonal effects arising from the fact that Titan's orbit lies in Saturn's equatorial plane and is, therefore, inclined to the ecliptic (the plane of the Earth's orbit) by some 27°. Alternate polar regions are thus illuminated by solar radiation.

The nature of Titan's surface remains a matter of speculation. The temperature is close to the triple point of methane, that is, the temperature at which it can exist in solid, liquid or gaseous form. The surface may be completely covered with methane ice or an ocean of liquid methane. Alternatively, there may be methane lakes and methane cliffs, over which a thin drizzle of liquid nitrogen falls.

The moderate-sized satellites in Saturn's system are icy worlds, some of which may have significant rocky cores. Their icy surfaces are peppered with craters, but there are significant differences in the extent to which partial melting and resurfacing has occurred. Iapetus displays a striking contrast of albedo, the trailing hemisphere being about 10 times more reflective than the very dark leading hemisphere. The reflectivity and reddish color of the dark hemisphere is similar to that of carbonaceous chondritic meteorites (◗ pages 72-3). The source of the dark material may be methane-ice that welled up from the interior and then decomposed leaving deposits of carbon "soot".

The small satellites also have interesting features: Mimas boasts a 130km crater, one-third of the satellite's size, and Enceladus is the most reflective body known in the Solar System. Of the multitude of tiny moonlets, three are intimately involved in "marshaling" the planet's ring particles (◗ pages 66-7), two share the same orbit as each other, and several others share orbits with the larger satellites Mimas, Tethys and Dione.

▲ The surface of Mimas is heavily cratered. As well as many small craters as little as 2km across, there is a giant called Herschel, 130km across, with a conspicuous central peak and raised rim. The cratering is evidence of the bombardment that the Solar System underwent four billion years or so ago, shortly after its formation.

▶ Enceladus, although the eighth farthest satellite from the planet, is the most reflective. Some parts of the surface are smooth, whereas other regions show craters up to 35km across. The surface is also crossed by linear grooves several hundred kilometers long, which may be faults resulting from deformation of the crust.

▲ Dione is one of Saturn's larger satellites, with a diameter of 1,120km. The trailing hemisphere ("trailing" in the sense of its motion around Saturn), on the left of this photograph, shows contrasting light and dark areas, the former being probably due to surface water-ice. The leading hemisphere is more uniform.

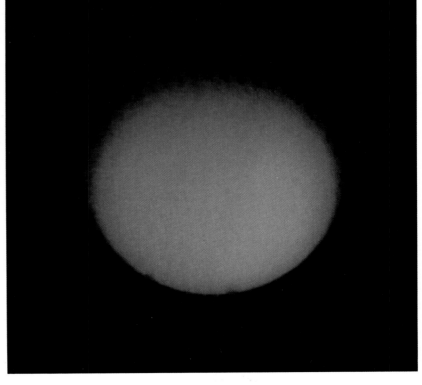

▶ Titan is the second largest satellite in the Solar System (Jupiter's Ganymede being the largest) and the only body apart from the Earth to have a dense, nitrogen-rich atmosphere. Its northern hemisphere is darker and redder than the southern hemisphere, and both Voyagers found that there was darkening at the north pole.

The thickness of Saturn's rings may be as little as one kilometer, and is certainly not much more

▲ *The Dutch astronomer Christiaan Huygens.*

Early ideas about rings

One of the objects observed by Galileo in 1610, with his newly-made telescope, was Saturn. Galileo realized at once that there was something unusual about the planet's shape, but he could not make out exactly what it was. Finally he concluded that "Saturn is not one alone, but is composed of three, which almost touch one another...the middle one is about three times the size of the lateral ones."

Two years later he was surprised by the fact that the two attendant globes had disappeared. In fact, this was because the ring system had become edgewise-on to the Earth, and at such times not even large telescopes will show the rings clearly.

The discovery that the strange appearance of the planet was due to a flat ring – or, more accurately, a system of rings – was made by the Dutch astronomer Christiaan Huygens (1629-1695) in 1655, but it was not for some time that his interpretation was accepted. Sir Christopher Wren (1632-1723) in England worked out a theory involving an elliptical corona around Saturn, but never published his ideas because as soon as he heard Huygens' interpretation he accepted it.

In 1675 the Italian astronomer Giovanni Cassini (1625-1712), working in Paris, found a dark gap in the main ring. This is still known as the Cassini Division. It was, naturally enough, assumed to be empty, and this belief continued until the first probes visited the planet. Pioneer 11, having passed by Jupiter, was rerouted to encounter Saturn in 1979, and the plans included a course straight through the Cassini Division. Fortunately this was not actually attempted. If it had been, Pioneer would have stood little chance of survival, since astronomers now know that there are several ringlets within the Cassini Division.

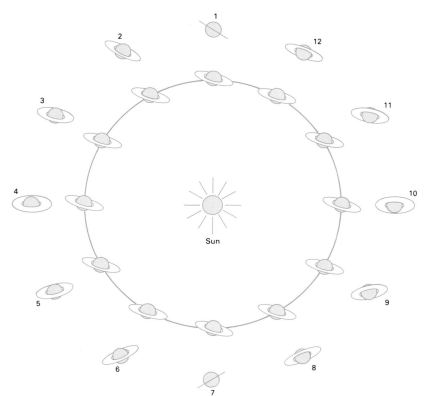

▲ *Due to the tilt of Saturn's axis, the aspect of the rings seen from Earth varies as the planet moves around the Sun. The observed aspect is shown adjacent to the successive numbered positions. At 1 and 7, the rings are edge-on; at 4 and 10 they are seen at their widest angles. The rings were edge-on in 1980 (1), the northern face most fully displayed in 1987 (4) and they will be edge-on again in 1995 (7).*

Saturn's rings

Seen through Earth-based telescopes, Saturn's ring system was for a long time believed to consist of three principal components, rings A, B and C. The outermost of these rings, ring A, had an overall diameter of 272,000km and was separated from ring B, the brightest ring, by a 4,000km gap, the Cassini Division. The innermost of the three, ring C (the Crêpe Ring), was very faint and quite transparent when seen against the disk of the planet. The Voyager spacecraft have revealed that the system is in fact astonishingly complex, each of the main rings being subdivided into thousands of ringlets, some separated by gaps, others being no more than ripples in the main ring structures. There may be over 100,000 such features altogether.

An extremely tenuous D-ring extends in a thin sheet inwards from ring C, possibly down to the cloud-tops of the planet itself. The Cassini Division is not a truly empty gap, but contains at least five bands of ringlets. Farther out, at a distance of 140,000km from the center of the planet, is the peculiar F-ring. Less than 150km wide, and deviating from circularity by up to 400km, it is made up of a number of intertwining strands, each about 10km wide. The particles making up the F-ring are marshaled by gravity into this narrow band by two "shepherd" satellites – 1980 S26 and 1980 S27 – which move, respectively, just outside and just inside the ring. Particles on the outer fringe of the ring are slowed down as they pass S26, and drop inwards, while particles on the inner fringe are accelerated by S27 as it overtakes them, and they move a little way outwards.

◄ *These two photographs, taken 15 minutes apart by Voyager 1, reveal dark spokelike features revolving with the rings themselves. Scientists believe that magnetism is involved in their formation, but the exact mechanism is not understood.*

▼ *Two satellites (S26 and S27) "shepherd" Saturn's thin F-ring. The inner satellite laps the outer one every 25 days. Their combined influence pulls the ring into intertwining strands, as well as keeping it out of circularity by up to 400km.*

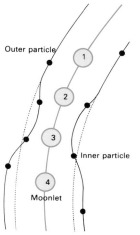

► *The multiple fine ringlets and divisions in the ring system may be produced by small "shepherd" satellites. As a moonlet moves through the ring, the successively numbered positions show how a faster-moving inner particle is slowed down as it overtakes the moonlet and, as a result, drops down into an orbit closer to the planet: a slower-moving outer particle is accelerated as the moonlet passes by and is elevated into a higher orbit farther from the planet. In this way particles could be swept out of certain orbits and concentrated into bands.*

Outer particle

Inner particle

Moonlet

Farther out still from Saturn is an extremely thin G-ring, beyond which a very tenuous sheet of particles, ring E, extends from a distance of 210,000km to nearly 500,000km. The inner rim of this sheet lies beyond Mimas, and Enceladus orbits within it.

The classical theory of the rings suggested that the divisions were due to orbital resonances, rather like vibrations, caused by the gravitational effects of the satellites. For example, a particle at the distance of the Cassini Division would have half the orbital period of Mimas and so at regular and frequent intervals would be perturbed away from that orbit by the gravitational attraction of Mimas. In this way, it was thought, the Cassini Division would be "swept clean" of particles. It now seems unlikely, however, that a resonance theory of this type can account for all the ring features. It may be that density waves spread out, like ripples on a pond, from resonance locations. Another intriguing ring phenomenon is the occurrence of transient dark radial features that form and disperse within ring B, revolving with the ring rather like the spokes of a wheel. These may be due to electrically charged particles elevated away from the ring plane by the planet's magnetic field.

The origins of the ring system remain a matter of debate. It is possible that they represent fragments of a satellite torn apart by gravitational forces exerted by Saturn, but it seems more likely that most of the ring particles are material dating from the formation of the planet that failed to coagulate into a satellite. Certainly Saturn's bright rings are quite different from the darker systems of Jupiter and Uranus.

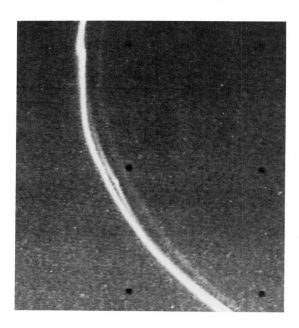

▲ *This detail from the puzzling F-ring shows two distinct bright strands, which appear to be braided. In fact, Voyager pictures have shown that there are at least ten strands in all within this very narrow ring, though it is not clear whether the braiding phenomenon affects them all. The braiding may not be a permanent feature of the F-ring, or it may even be confined to one or more small areas.*

Saturn's rings are so unlike those of Jupiter and Uranus that they may have a completely different origin

▲ *Voyager 2 took this view of Saturn from a range of 3·4 million kilometers. The rings seem to be less than 500m thick; the planet's disk is clearly visible through the ring material.*

▼ *Voyager 2 image of the Uranian ring system taken on 23 January, 1986. From the top: epsilon (bright), 10th ring (extremely faint), delta, gamma, eta, beta, alpha, 4, 5, 6.*

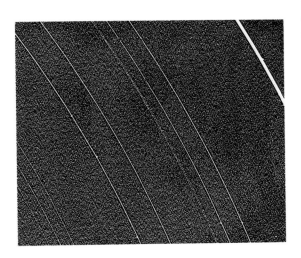

Rings of the outer Solar System

In 1787 the German-born astronomer William Herschel (1738-1822) reported seeing two rings around the planet Uranus. Such rings do in fact exist, but Herschel could not possibly have seen them with the equipment he was using – they were due simply to distortions in his new reflecting telescope. The rings of Uranus were in reality discovered in 1977, while measurements were being made of the occultation of a star by the planet. The star was seen to flicker several times just before the occultation, and again several times after the event, as if it had been temporarily obscured at intervals by concentric rings around the planet. Earth-based observations revealed the presence of nine thin and rather dark rings which are at distances from the center of Uranus of between 42,000km and 52,000km and are all slightly elliptical. They are all extremely narrow, only about 10km wide, apart from the outermost one, the epsilon ring, which varies in width from 20 to 100km. It is the most elliptical of all the rings, its distance from the planet varying by 800km. In 1986, Voyager 2 detected a very faint tenth ring between the epsilon and delta rings. Although some fine dust was detected, the ring system was shown to be made up mainly of large boulders of a metre or more in size. The ring particles may be maintained in their orbits by shepherd satellites.

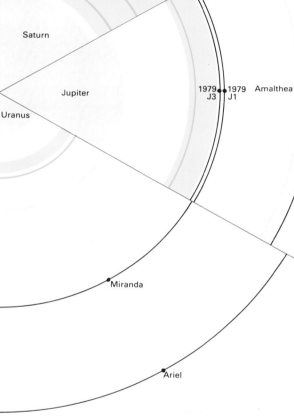

G ring
1980 S1
1980 S3
F ring
1980 S26
Encke division
1980 S27
A ring
1980 S28
Cassini division

B ring

C ring

D ring

Saturn

Jupiter

Uranus

1979 J3   1979 J1   Amalthea

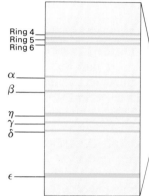

Ring 4
Ring 5
Ring 6

α
β

η
γ
δ

ϵ

▲ This computer-generated image reveals the Encke division in the A-ring; the central ringlet shows clearly in this picture. Called the "Encke Doodle", it is probably one of two.

▼ Saturn's C-ring is the main element of this false-color picture; the B-ring can also be seen at top left. The different colors denote different compositions of the ring particles.

Miranda

Ariel

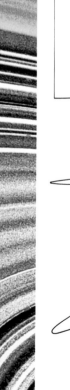

Roche limit

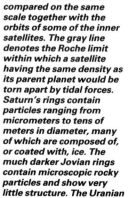

Jupiter

Saturn

Uranus

The ring systems of Jupiter, Saturn and Uranus are compared on the same scale together with the orbits of some of the inner satellites. The gray line denotes the Roche limit within which a satellite having the same density as its parent planet would be torn apart by tidal forces. Saturn's rings contain particles ranging from micrometers to tens of meters in diameter, many of which are composed of, or coated with, ice. The much darker Jovian rings contain microscopic rocky particles and show very little structure. The Uranian system contains ten very narrow dark ringlets made up of large rocky chunks. Due to the different axial inclinations of the planets the rings are tilted relative to the planetary orbits by the angles shown (left).

The satellites of Uranus

Uranus has fifteen satellites, including ten very small and rather dark bodies discovered by the Voyager 2 spacecraft. In order of distance from the planet, the five principal satellites are Miranda, Ariel, Umbriel, Titania and Oberon. These icy worlds range in diameter from about 480km for Miranda to about 1590km for Titania. Miranda has arguably the weirdest surface in the entire Solar System. The ten "new" moons range in size from about 160km to 16km.

The satellites of Neptune

Neptune has two very different satellites, each intriguing in its own way. The inner satellite, Triton, at a mean distance of 353,000km, moves in a circular retrograde orbit inclined at 160° to Neptune's equator. It is a large satellite, possibly comparable in size with Mercury, but there is uncertainty about its exact diameter, estimates ranging from 3,000km to 6,000km. Opinions about the nature of its surface also differ considerably, but one possibility is that there are continents of methane-ice and oceans of liquid nitrogen. Both elements have been detected spectroscopically. There seems to be a methane atmosphere with a pressure of about 0·0001 atmospheres. The satellite's peculiar orbit produces major seasonal changes in the amount of solar radiation reaching different parts of its surface. A cycle of melting and refreezing will result, causing release of gases (mostly methane and nitrogen) which may produce as much as a thousandfold change in the total volume of the atmosphere.

Another odd feature of Triton is that, because it pursues a retrograde path, the tidal interaction with Neptune is causing it to spiral inwards at such a rate that the satellite may break up or collide with the planet within the next 10 to 100 million years. Neptune's other satellite, Nereid, is much smaller (500-800km in diameter) and has the most elliptical orbit of any known satellite. Its distance from the planet ranges between 1,400,000km and 9,700,000km.

Charon – Pluto's satellite

Charon lies at a mean distance of 20,000km from the center of Pluto and revolves around the planet in the same period of time as the planet rotates on its axis. With a diameter of about 800km, Charon is about one-third the size of Pluto, and is the largest of all satellites in relation to the size of its planet (the Moon is about one-quarter of the Earth's diameter, and all other satellites are much smaller in proportion to their primaries). Like Pluto, Charon is probably an icy world, and if so it has about one-tenth of Pluto's mass.

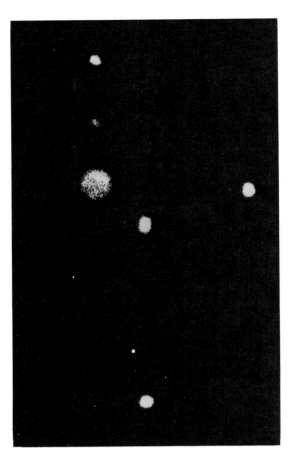

▲ *Uranus and family: from top to bottom, the objects shown here are Umbriel, Miranda (faint), Uranus, Oberon (to the right), Ariel and Titania. Umbriel is unusually dark. Their distances from Uranus range from 583,000km (Oberon) to 129,000km (Miranda). The ten "new" satellites – provisionally designated 1985 U1 and 1986 U1 to 1986 U9 – lie within the orbit of Miranda. Although the axial tilt of the planet is 98°, all the satellites move in the plane of the planet's equator.*

▼ *Neptune is difficult to photograph because of the enormous distances involved, but this picture has succeeded in capturing the planet with both its satellites (arrowed). Almost lost in the contrast glare of Neptune is Triton, the larger of the two moons. Its orbit is retrograde, and some astronomers expect it to spiral into the planet within 10-100 million years. The smaller moon, Nereid, has a highly eccentric orbit. Voyager 2 should make more information available about Neptune in 1989.*

▶ *Pluto and Charon, a picture obtained by a special technique known as speckle interferometry. Pluto is to the left (the apparent bars projecting from it are instrumental). The two bodies are so alike that it may be better to regard them as twin planets – or, more correctly, twin asteroids, since their combined masses are much less than that of our Moon. Although far from being generally accepted, one theory is that they may once have been members of the Neptunian system.*

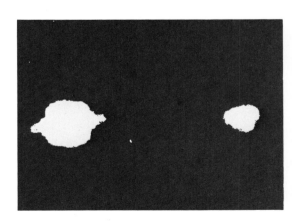

Asteroids and Comets

6

*The Solar System's debris, asteroids and comets...
The asteroid belt and Jupiter's powerful influence...
Meteorites, their devastating impact...Comets, the
spectacular wanderers...The death of comets and
meteoroids...PERSPECTIVE...The "Celestial Police"
and their search for asteroids...Examining stones from
space...How to name an asteroid...Comets, harbingers
of doom...Halley and his comet*

The asteroids, or minor planets, are pieces of rock, most of which pursue orbits lying between those of Mars and Jupiter. The main part of the asteroid belt lies between 2·2 and 3·3AU (astronomical units) from the Sun. Known asteroids range in diameter from 1,000km (for the largest, Ceres) to less than 1km, but only about 200 are known to be larger than 100km in diameter. Just over 2,700 have been named.

Although the larger asteroids are approximately spherical, many smaller ones are elongated or irregular. Some may be double or multiple bodies, loosely held together by gravity, while others may have satellites. Herculina, for example, 220km across, has a suspected satellite with a diameter of 50km at a distance of approximately 1,000km. Deimos and Phobos, the irregularly shaped satellites of Mars, are only 28km and 16·5km respectively at their widest points. It is likely that they formed within the asteroid belt, much nearer to Jupiter, and were captured by Mars during its formation.

▼ *Johann Schröter's observatory at Lilienthal, near Bremen, was the venue for the inaugural meeting of a group of observers who aimed to discover a planet predicted between the orbits of Mars and Jupiter. The largest telescope of continental Europe, built by William Herschel, was housed in Schröter's observatory – destroyed in 1813 when the invading French burned Lilienthal.*

▶ *Johann Elert Bode was one of the first scientists to bring astronomy within the grasp of people who had no training in science. His popular "Introduction to Astronomy" went into nine editions; his other works included a Celestial Atlas. Bode popularized, but did not devise, the law which sometimes bears his name. "Titius-Bode's Law." encouraged observation as a basis of mathematically guided prediction.*

A strange law and the Celestial Police

The story of the minor planets began in the early 1770s with the announcement, by Johann Titius (1729-1796) of Wittenberg, of a strange law linking the distances of the various planets from the Sun. In 1772 this theory was popularized by the German astronomer Johann Bode (1747-1826) and it is known as Titius-Bode's Law. The relationship of the distances can be demonstrated by taking the numbers 0, 3, 6, 12, 24 and 48, each of which, apart from the first, is double its predecessor. Adding 4 to each, and taking the Earth's distance from the Sun as 10 units, the figures give the distances of the planets out to Saturn with reasonable accuracy (Uranus, Neptune and Pluto were then unknown).

Planet	Bode distance	Actual distance
Mercury	4	3·9
Venus	7	7·2
Earth	10	10
Mars	16	15·2
—	28	—
Jupiter	52	52·0
Saturn	100	95·4

Bode did not think this was a coincidence and his conviction was reinforced in 1781, when the German-born English astronomer William Herschel (1738-1822) discovered Uranus. The Bode distance was 196, while the actual distance was 191·8.

The search for a planet to fill the gap

The only gap in the system corresponded to the Bode number 28, and it seemed likely that there should be a planet in that region. Obviously it would be faint, as otherwise it would have been discovered long before. In 1800, a group of observers calling themselves the "Celestial Police" met at Lilienthal, where the German astronomer Johann Schröter (1745-1816) had his observatory, and worked out a plan for a systematic hunt.

In the event, the "Police" were forestalled. At the Sicilian observatory of Palermo, the Italian astronomer Giuseppi Piazzi (1746-1826) came across a star-like object which moved across the sky from night to night. The object was named Ceres, in honor of the patron goddess of Sicily. But the "Police" were not satisfied – Ceres seemed surprisingly small – and so the search continued. Within the next eight years they had detected three more small planets, Pallas, Juno, and Vesta.

In 1832 a new search was begun by a German amateur, Karl Hencke (1793-1866). In 1845 he was rewarded with the discovery of asteroid number 5, Astraea, and a second discovery in 1847. From 1891 onwards, because of the use of photography, asteroids were discovered in large numbers. Their trails have appeared on photographic plates exposed for quite different reasons, and they have even been called the "vermin of the skies".

It was not until the discovery of the planet Neptune in 1846 at an actual distance of 306 on the Bode scale, that the law was shown to be clearly invalid.

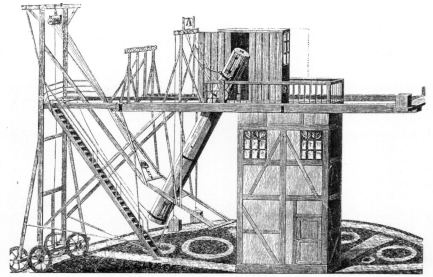

◄ A large meteorite can produce an impact crater such as this one in Arizona. It is over 1,200m in diameter and 175m deep, has a slightly raised rim and a regular bowl shape. Geologists believe that the main mass of the impacting body was totally evaporated, although part may be buried under the south wall. The site bears the name Meteor Crater.

Irons or stones

Traditionally, three types of meteorite have been recognized – stones (aerolites), irons (siderites) and stony-irons (siderolites). The stony meteorites are made up of silicates and contain chondrules, rounded droplets of rocky material often 1-2mm in diameter. Carbonaceous chondrites are an interesting subset of this class. They are rich in carbon compounds and about 5 percent of their mass is in the form of complex organic material. Iron meteorites contain mainly iron with about 5-10 percent nickel. The stony-irons are the least abundant of the main types and contain rock and metal in roughly equal proportions.

The irons, stony-irons and some of the stones show evidence of having been melted in the past, possibly in the interiors of larger bodies, but many of the stones contain material that has not been significantly modified since the formation of the planets. Most meteorites contain mineral crystals of similar age – about 4·6 billion years old – which is taken to be the age of the Solar System.

Tektites

Tektites are curious pebble-sized objects, the nature and origin of which is an intriguing puzzle. Although resembling volcanic glass in some respects, they differ significantly in composition from terrestrial volcanic glasses. Their distribution on Earth is also most peculiar. They are mostly confined to four large fields, in North America, Australasia, the Ivory Coast of Africa and Czechoslovakia (the Moldavite field). They differ considerably from other meteorites and, in particular, the absence of cosmic ray tracks within them suggests that they cannot have spent much time in space. Their origin is a mystery, but the most likely possibilities are either that they originated on Earth – from violent volcanic eruptions, or from impacts that hurled them through the atmosphere and back to Earth – or they were expelled from the Moon by impacts or volcanism in recent geological times.

The perturbing effect of Jupiter's powerful gravitational influence sweeps certain areas of the Solar System clear of any orbiting bodies. As a result there are gaps, named Kirkwood gaps after their discoverer, where no asteroids occur. In addition two families of asteroids, the Trojans, share Jupiter's orbit, lying some 60° ahead of and 60° behind the planet (the angles measured at the Sun).

The albedos of asteroids range from below 0·02 (darker than a blackboard) to about 0·4, and observations of their colors and spectra reveal that there are several distinct types of asteroid. About 75 percent (C-types) are dark, carbon-rich bodies apparenty similar in nature to carbonaceous chondritic meteorites (see below). About 15 percent (S-types) are reddish in color, have moderate albedos, and seem to have a high content of iron and magnesium silicates, while a smaller group (M-types) seem to be composed almost entirely of a mixture of iron and nickel. The S-types are found mainly in the inner part of the asteroid belt, while the C-types dominate the outer part. This distribution probably reflects the conditions prevalent at the time of the formation of the Solar System. The asteroids are probably debris left over from that event, some being planetesimals which never assembled into a single planet, others being fragments of larger asteroids that were broken up by collisions.

Meteorites

Interplanetary space contains a host of meteoroids, debris ranging in size from microscopic particles through sand-grain size to bodies tens or even hundreds of meters in diameter. Small meteoroids, which can enter the Earth's atmosphere at speeds of up to 70 kilometers per second, are destroyed (◗ page 78). Larger bodies, which survive their fiery passage through the atmosphere, are called meteorites. Meteorites of less than 100 tonnes are severely decelerated by the atmosphere and reach the ground – in one piece or in fragments – relatively gently, but more massive meteorites are hardly braked at all and can excavate craters. Meteorites are probably fragments of asteroidal collisions. This view is supported by the similarity between spectra of meteoritic types and those of the different classes of asteroid, and by the fact that the orbits of some meteorites can be traced to the asteroid belt.

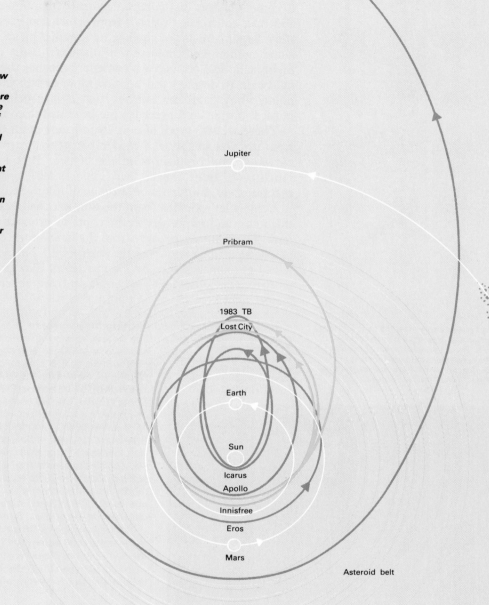

The main asteroid belt is shown as a group of yellow rings separated by the Kirkwood gaps where there are very few asteroids due to the perturbing effect of the giant planet Jupiter. Ceres, the largest asteroid and the first to be discovered, lies near the middle of the main zone, at a mean distance from the Sun of 2·77AU. Although most asteroids lie between Mars and Jupiter, some, such as Hidalgo, pass far beyond the orbit of Jupiter while others, such as Apollo and Icarus, pass inside the Earth's orbit.

Saturn
Hidalgo
Jupiter
Pribram
Trojans
1983 TB
Lost City
Earth
Sun
Icarus
Apollo
Innisfree
Eros
Mars
Trojans
Asteroid belt
Kirkwood gaps

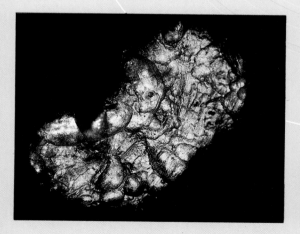

◄ Two types of objects. The iron meteorite (left) is comparatively common because of its durability. The rarer tektite (right) is quite different, and may not be of meteoritic origin.

Asteroid 1983 TB, discovered by the IRAS satellite, passes closer to the Sun than any other known asteroid. Its distance from the Sun ranges between 0·1AU and 2·5AU so that it travels from inside the orbit of Icarus to beyond that of Mars. Also shown are the pre-impact orbits of three meteorites (Pribram, Lost City and Innisfree) which indicate that these meteorites came from the asteroid belt.

On several occasions the Earth has passed through a comet's tail without suffering the slightest damage

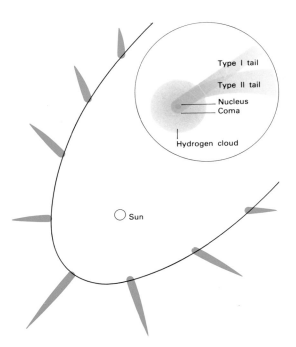

Comets

A comet consists of a compact nucleus surrounded by a cloud of gas and dust called the "coma", from which emerges a tail, or tails. In some larger comets the coma is surrounded by an extensive hydrogen cloud, millions of kilometers in diameter. Most comets follow long, highly elliptical orbits. As a comet approaches the Sun, the coma and tail begin to develop and become more conspicuous. The tail always points away from the Sun, so that it lags behind the head on the inward journey and precedes the head as the comet recedes.

There are two types of tail. Type I tails point almost directly away from the Sun and show considerable structure, whereas Type II tails curve gracefully but show little structure. Type I tails are typically as much as 10 times longer than Type II tails, and extend to tens or, exceptionally, hundreds of millions of kilometers in length.

Ultraviolet radiation from the Sun knocks electrons out of some of the atoms and molecules in the coma to produce electrically charged ions. These are swept away from the head of the comet by a stream of charged particles known as the solar wind. This gives rise to a Type I tail of gas which shines by the process of fluorescence, whereby ions absorb solar ultraviolet radiation and are thereby excited to emit visible light.

▲ *A comet's tail always points away from the Sun, following the head as it approaches and preceding it as the comet departs after perihelion. The icy nucleus is surrounded by the coma, a cloud of gas and dust, and some comets are enveloped in a huge hydrogen cloud. Type I plasma tails are fairly straight while Type II (dust) tails are curved.*

▼ *Austin's Comet of 1982, photographed by R. Arbour. The comet, a bright telescopic object, has a period so long that it is classed as non-periodic.*

Naming the asteroids

The discoverer of a minor planet has the right to choose a name for it – and some recent names are not too serious. R. S. Dugan, discoverer of minor planet 518, named it Halawe, after an Arabian sweet of which he was particularly fond. No. 694 is Ekard, "Drake" spelled backwards – the orbit was computed by students at Drake University. No. 1625 is The NORC, in honour of the Naval Ordnance Research Calculator at Dahlgren, Virginia. No. 1581 is Abanderada ("one who carries a banner") and No. 724 is Hapag, after the Hamburg-Amerika shipping line. The 250th asteroid was discovered by the Italian astronomer Palisa, who sold his right of naming for £50 to Baron Albert von Rothschild, who named the asteroid Bettina after his wife.

There are also the Trojan asteroids, which move in the same orbit as Jupiter. They were named after the heroes of the Trojan War, in Greek mythology, a conflict between the Greeks and Trojans culminating in a ten-year siege of Troy.

Chiron – the odd one out

One of the most unexpected discoveries was that of Chiron, by Charles Kowal from Palomar, in 1977. (Chiron should not be confused with Charon, the satellite of Pluto.) Chiron is large by asteroidal standards, with a diameter of several hundred kilometers, but it is far beyond the main swarm or even the Trojans, and its orbit lies mainly between those of Saturn and Uranus. Its revolution period is 50 years. Calculations show that in 1664 BC it approached Saturn to within 16,000,000km, which is not so very much greater than the distance between Saturn and its outermost satellite, Phoebe. Phoebe has a retrograde orbit, and may be a captured asteroid, in which case it and Chiron might be of the same nature. It has also been suggested that Chiron is in an unstable orbit, so that eventually it may be thrown out of the Solar System altogether.

Type II tails are made up of micrometer-sized dust particles driven from the cometary head by the pressure of light itself. These particles move away from the head at slower speeds than the ions and so get "left behind" as the head moves along its orbit, forming a curved tail which shines by reflecting sunlight.

According to the widely-accepted icy conglomerate or "dirty ice" model, the nucleus of a comet is a lump of ice, no more than a few kilometers in diameter, within which are embedded particles of silicate dust and larger rocky fragments. As the icy nucleus approaches to within about 3AU from the Sun, solar heating begins to vaporize its skin, releasing gases and dusty particles into the developing coma which can extend its diameter to between 100,000 and 1,000,000km.

Each time a comet passes the Sun it loses some of its mass. Some calculations indicate that a layer 1-3 meters thick may be lost from the nucleus each time, so that a comet cannot survive more than a few thousand perihelion passages before being completely disrupted. Many astronomers believe that fresh comets are perturbed from time to time into the inner Solar System from a vast reservoir of icy conglomerates – known as the Oort cloud – which extends some 40,000-50,000AU from the Sun and contains some hundreds of billions of potential comets.

▲ "The figure of a fearful comet", from Dr Ambroise Paré's "Surgery", gives a subjective impression of the comet of 1664-5. Swords, daggers, coffins and men's heads were supposed to be omens of plague, and plague did indeed break out in London in June of 1665, within 3 months of the comet's visit.

Blaming the comets
Occasionally cometary nuclei must collide with the Earth, and it has been suggested that a great explosion in Siberia in 1908 – the Tunguska event – was due to part of the icy nucleus of a comet which exploded in the atmosphere and did not produce a crater as a meteorite might have done.

An intriguing and controversial suggestion has been made by British astronomers Sir Fred Hoyle (b. 1915) and Chandra Wickramasinghe that comets contain bacteria and viruses and that the incidence of epidemic diseases on Earth may be related to close encounters with comets. This view is hotly disputed, however, by most astronomers and biologists.

Malice in the skies
A famous description of one non-periodic comet was given in 1528 by a French doctor, Ambroise Paré: "This comet was so frightful, and it produced such great terror that some died of fear and others fell sick. It appeared to be of extreme length, and was the colour of blood. At the summit of it was seen the figure of a bent arm, holding in its hand a great sword as if about to strike. At the end of this point there were three stars. On both sides of the rays of this comet were seen a great number of axes, knives, and blood-colored swords, among which were a large number of hideous human faces, with beards and bristling hair."

No doubt the good doctor's description is wildly exaggerated, and he may even have been describing an aurora rather than a comet, but it illustrates the alarm with which comets were regarded in those days.

▲ At the Tunguska event in Siberia in 1908, trees were blown down and animals killed. Possibly a fragment from a cometary nucleus caused the explosion.

▶ Periodic comets – those for which reasonably accurate orbits have been computed and which have been seen at more than one return – are divided into "short-period" (period of up to 20 years), "medium-period" and "long-period" (over 60 years). Many short-period comets have aphelion points close to the orbit of Jupiter; long-period comets travel beyond the orbit of Neptune. Comets of very long period are called "non-periodic" because it is impossible to compute their orbits accurately.

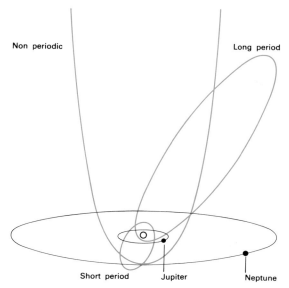

Non periodic

Long period

Short period   Jupiter   Neptune

Halley's Comet

▲ Edmond Halley examined the records of comets that had appeared in 1531, 1607 and 1682, and deduced from his study of their orbits that it had been the same comet on each occasion. He predicted that it would return again in 1758, but regrettably did not live to see his prediction fulfilled. The comet now bears his name. Halley also showed that comets followed solar orbits that were consistent with Newton's theory of universal gravitation.

An unusually bright comet

Practically all spectacular comets have very long orbital periods (and are known as non-periodics), far too long to be calculated with any precision. Those with periods of less than a few hundred years (periodics) tend to be faint objects without conspicuous tails. The one exception is Halley's Comet, which returns to perihelion at intervals of 75-76 years and is usually a conspicuous object on these occasions. Its most recent perihelion return was in February 1986 when viewing conditions were very poor. Its next return is due in 2061.

Comets have always been regarded as unlucky, and the great fear of them had not even been dissipated by the 1910 return of Halley's Comet, when an enterprising salesman made a large sum of money by selling anti-comet pills, though he did not explain just what they were meant to do.

History and Halley's Comet

Halley's Comet has made an impact throughout history. It appeared in AD 79, when the Roman emperor Vespasian commented that the comet "menaced rather the king of the Parthians; for he is hairy, while I am bald". (Comets had often been referred to as "hairy stars".) It is perhaps worth mentioning that Vespasian died in the same year.

The return of 1066 took place as the Normans were preparing to invade England, and a scene in the Bayeux Tapestry, said by some to have been designed by the Conqueror's wife, shows King Harold tottering on his throne, while his courtiers look on aghast as the comet blazes overhead. In 1546 the current pope Calixtus III publicly preached against the comet as an agent of the Devil.

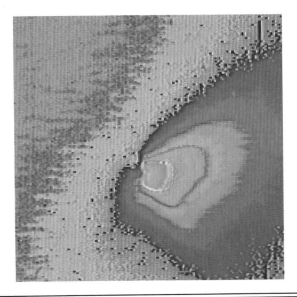

▲ Halley's Comet was first recorded in the year 240 BC, since when it has been observed returning to the inner Solar System at intervals of 76 years. This photograph was taken at its 1910 return, on 25 May from Helwan, Egypt.

◄ False color image of Halley's Comet taken at a range of 24,400km from the nucleus on 13 March 1986 by the Giotto spacecraft. The central object in the frame is a bright jet emerging from the nucleus which lies to the upper left of this object.

Spacecraft to Halley's Comet

In March 1986 Halley's Comet was explored by a flotilla of five spacecraft, which returned a wealth of data. Two small Japanese craft – Suisei and Sakigake – took a long-range view, particularly of the coma and hydrogen cloud; two Soviet probes, Vega 1 and Vega 2, passed the nucleus at ranges of 8900km and 8000km, and the European Space Agency's Giotto spacecraft – with the benefit of positional data gained by the Vegas – was able to pass the nucleus at a distance of only 600km.

Water ice was confirmed as the major constituent, and the nucleus was revealed to be an elongated structure measuring about 15km by 8km by 8km and spinning on its axis once every 53 hours. Most of the nucleus was covered by a thin, very dark crust, with a reflectivity of only about 2 percent. Jets of dust and gas erupted from craters, cracks and fissures in this crust. The bow wave where the comet plowed through the solar wind was detected about a million kilometres from the nucleus, and the surrounding hydrogen cloud was found to extend to beyond 30 million kilometres.

▲ *This episode from the famous Bayeux Tapestry depicts King Harold quaking on his throne while his courtiers tremble at the sight of Halley's Comet.*

▶ *Halley's Comet follows an elliptical orbit ranging from within the orbit of Venus to out beyond that of Neptune. Its motion is retrograde.*

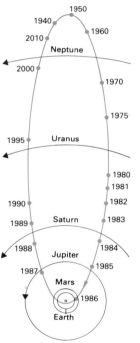

▲ *The European spacecraft Giotto passed the nucleus of Halley's Comet in 1986. It is named after the Italian artist Giotto di Bondoni (1267-1337) whose "Adoration of the Magi" (left) was probably inspired by the apparition of Halley's Comet in 1301.*

The death of comets

An orbiting satellite has photographed a comet disintegrating on impact with the Sun, but such a violent end must be rare. What happens to a comet when it has lost all its gases? Possibly the nucleus remains in orbit round the Sun in the guise of an asteroid. This theory could account for the so-called "Earth-grazers", such as Hermes, which are fundamentally different from the larger asteroids that are farther away from the Sun, and keep strictly to the zone between the orbits of Mars and Jupiter.

Two British astronomers, Victor Clube and Bill Napier, share this view. They believe that comets are formed from interstellar material, and that every time the Sun passes through one of the spiral arms of the Galaxy it collects a new swarm of comets. Inevitably some of these collide with the Earth and, according to Clube and Napier, one such collision occurred 65,000,000 years ago, causing so great a climatic change that the dinosaurs were unable to adapt to the new conditions, and became extinct.

Meteors and meteor showers

When a tiny meteoroid enters the atmosphere at high speed, its destruction is marked by a brief streak of light which lasts for at most a few seconds. These phenomena are called meteors. Most of the millions of meteors daily entering the atmosphere are too faint to be seen, but radar beams pick up their trails of ionized gas by day or night.

Sporadic meteors can appear at any time from random directions, while shower meteors appear fairly regularly at particular times of the year. Meteor showers occur when the Earth crosses the path of a stream of meteoroids strung out along a particular orbit round the Sun. Since the meteoroids are following parallel tracks, they seem to radiate from a particular point in the sky, known as the radiant. Each shower has its own particular radiant point.

Shower meteors are thought to consist of cometary debris – dusty particles spread out along the orbits of dead, or dim, elderly comets. A significant number of correlations between the orbits of meteor streams and of known comets have been established.

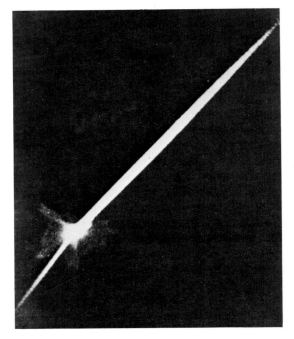

▲ The Bielid meteor shower is now very feeble, but in 1895 it produced this meteor which exploded in the Earth's atmosphere.

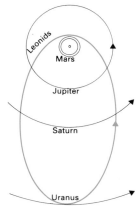

◄ The Leonid meteor shower occurs when the Earth crosses the orbit of a stream of meteoroids associated with the comet Tempel-Tuttle (left). Seen from Arizona, the Leonids produced a spectacular shower in 1966 (below); as indicated, all the individual meteors appear to radiate from one particular position in the sky because they are moving in parallel paths.

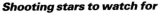

Shooting stars to watch for

Meteors, or shooting stars, are associated with certain comets. The Perseids in August are the most reliable shower, and occasionally the November Leonids are brilliant. They are associated with the periodic comet Tempel-Tuttle, which has a period of about 33 years. There were magnificent displays in 1799, 1833, 1866 and again in 1966 (the displays of 1899 and 1933 failed to materialize because the orbit of the main swarm had been perturbed by the giant planets and the Earth did not pass through it).

Comets lose material each time they pass the Sun, and by cosmic standards comets are short-lived. They have been observed in their death-throes. Biela's periodic comet broke in two during its return of 1845. At the comet's next appearance, in 1852, the pair had separated, and they were never seen again, although the debris of the defunct comet was seen in 1872 as a meteor shower coming from the direction in which the comet should have appeared. A few Bielid meteors are still seen every year, although the shower has now become very feeble.

Overview of the Universe

7

Astronomical distances...The light year...Our Sun compared with other stars...Stars, nebulae and galaxies introduced...Grasping the vastness of the universe... PERSPECTIVE...Early speculations on the scale of the universe...The first attempts at measuring stellar distances...The true status of our Solar System

Like the Sun, the stars are self-luminous gaseous bodies generating energy in nuclear reactions. Their distances from the Earth and from each other are vast. The star nearest to the Solar System, Proxima Centauri (a dim red star in the constellation of Centaurus), lies at a distance of over 40 million million kilometers, some 270,000 times greater than the distance between the Earth and the Sun.

When considering astronomical distances it is convenient to think not in conventional units like meters or kilometers, but in terms of how long it takes a ray of light to travel across these distances. Moving at about 300,000 kilometers per second, light takes 1·3 seconds to travel from the Moon to the Earth, 8·3 minutes to reach the Earth from the Sun and about 5·4 hours to cross the distance between the Sun and the planet Pluto. However, a ray of light takes 4·3 *years* to reach us from Proxima Centauri. This, more graphically than huge numbers, sets the scale of stellar distances.

The distance that light travels in one year – 9·46 million million kilometers – is called a "light year", and this provides a convenient unit for describing distances in the universe. Proxima Centauri lies at a distance of 4·3 light years, and in our locality the average distance between stars is from three to four light years.

The Earth and the center of the universe
Civilizations such as China and Egypt carried out useful observations, notably of comets and eclipses, but had no idea of the real nature of the universe. To the Egyptians, the universe was shaped like a rectangular box, with a flat ceiling supported by pillars at the four cardinal points; these pillars were connected by a ledge along which ran the celestial river Ur-nes, in which the boats carrying the Sun, Moon and other gods sailed. The Egyptian Pharaoh Akhenaton (reigned c. 1379-1362 BC) even founded a new cult of Sun-worship, which was soon rejected after his death.

Astronomy as a true science began with the Greeks; up until the first of the great Greek philosophers, Thales (c. 636-546 BC), mythology had been used to explain the nature of the physical world. With the realization that the Earth is indeed a globe and not flat, one or two of the Greeks – notably Aristarchus of Samos (c. 320-250 BC) – even relegated it to the status of a planet moving round the Sun. Unfortunately Aristarchus found few supporters, and the later Greeks reverted to the idea of a central, motionless Earth. Ptolemy of Alexandra (fl. AD 2nd century), last of the major figures of the Greek school of astronomy, maintained that the Earth could not be spinning, as in this case there would be a constant gale as the world rotated beneath its atmosphere. On the other hand Ptolemy was an excellent observer and mathematician and his theory of the universe persisted until the 16th century. In it the Solar System was thought to be the entire universe with the Earth as its center and the distant stars located just beyond the farthest planet. It was not until 1530 that it was first suggested that the stars are at very great distances compared to the planets.

◄ An astonished observer, having poked his head through the sphere of stars, looks out towards the driving mechanism of the cosmos. This medieval representation of the universe illustrates the long-held view that the stars were fixed to a sphere which rotated round the Earth once a day, driven by a prime mover.

The Scale of the Universe

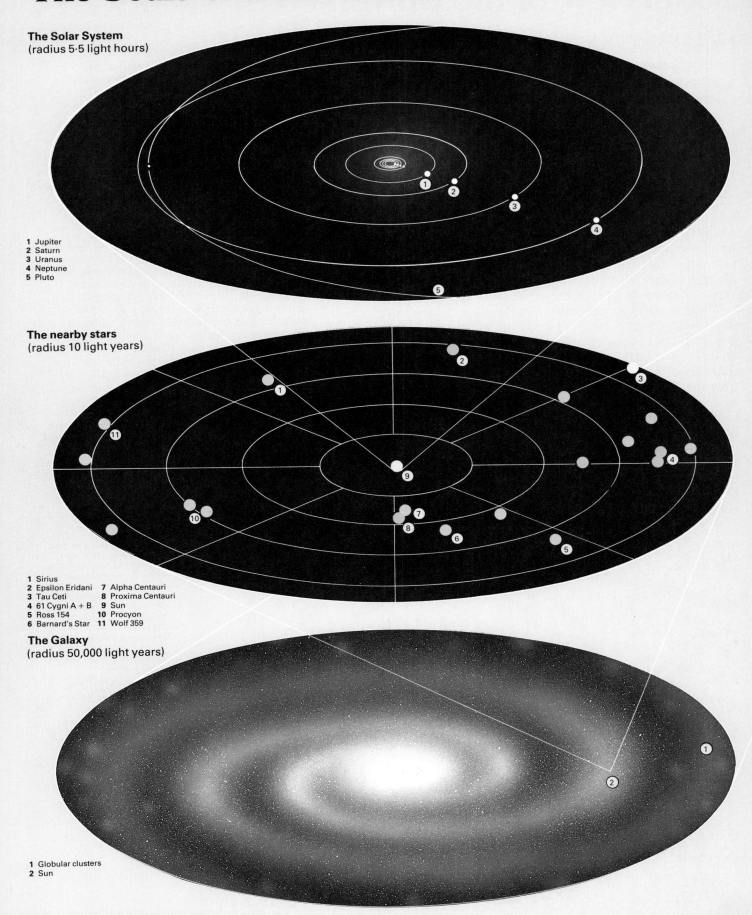

The Solar System
(radius 5·5 light hours)

1 Jupiter
2 Saturn
3 Uranus
4 Neptune
5 Pluto

The nearby stars
(radius 10 light years)

1 Sirius	**7** Alpha Centauri
2 Epsilon Eridani	**8** Proxima Centauri
3 Tau Ceti	**9** Sun
4 61 Cygni A + B	**10** Procyon
5 Ross 154	**11** Wolf 359
6 Barnard's Star	

The Galaxy
(radius 50,000 light years)

1 Globular clusters
2 Sun

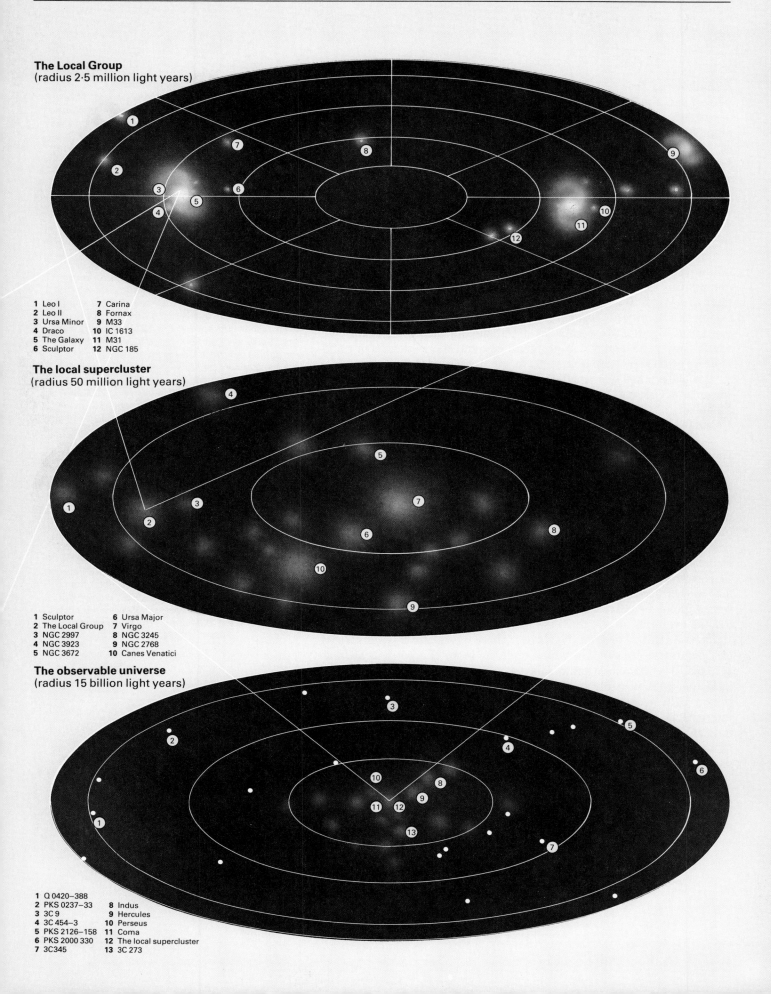

The Local Group
(radius 2·5 million light years)

1	Leo I	7	Carina
2	Leo II	8	Fornax
3	Ursa Minor	9	M33
4	Draco	10	IC 1613
5	The Galaxy	11	M31
6	Sculptor	12	NGC 185

The local supercluster
(radius 50 million light years)

1	Sculptor	6	Ursa Major
2	The Local Group	7	Virgo
3	NGC 2997	8	NGC 3245
4	NGC 3923	9	NGC 2768
5	NGC 3672	10	Canes Venatici

The observable universe
(radius 15 billion light years)

1	Q 0420−388	8	Indus
2	PKS 0237−33	9	Hercules
3	3C 9	10	Perseus
4	3C 454−3	11	Coma
5	PKS 2126−158	12	The local supercluster
6	PKS 2000 330	13	3C 273
7	3C345		

Although the space between the stars (interstellar space) is a near-perfect vacuum by terrestrial standards, it contains a certain amount of matter in the form of thinly spread gases and tiny particles of dust. Some of the gas clouds are visible directly as luminous patches in the sky. Known as "nebulae", from the Latin word for "clouds", most are revealed by their emission of radio or infrared radiation. New stars are being born continuously within clouds such as these.

Galactic neighbors

The Sun is a member of a system of stars, gases and dust known as the Galaxy, or as the "Milky Way" galaxy. The diameter of the Galaxy is about 100,000 light years ($\blacklozenge$ page 116), and it contains about 100 billion (10^{11}) stars. Beyond the edges of our own star system astronomers can see billions of other galaxies. Many of these are smaller than the Milky Way system, but some are significantly larger. Our Galaxy is a member of a small group of about thirty galaxies known as the Local Group. Most galaxies are members of clusters, some of which contain several thousand members, and there even seem to be clusters of clusters (superclusters) in the hierarchy of the universe.

The Galaxy has two smaller satellite galaxies, the Large and Small Magellanic Clouds – named after the Portuguese navigator Ferdinand Magellan (*c.* 1480-1521) – which lie at distances of 160,000 and 190,000 light years respectively.

Looking back in time

The nearest large galaxy comparable with our own is the Andromeda spiral, or M31. At a distance of 2,200,000 light years, it is just visible without telescopic aid on a good, clear, dark night, and it is by far the most distant object visible to the naked eye. The light which is now arriving from M31 was emitted 2,200,000 years ago, and depicts that galaxy not as it is now, but as it used to be all that time ago. The farther astronomers probe into deep space, the more "out of date" their new information becomes, but there is a compensating advantage in that they are able to study distant parts of the universe as they were billions of years ago, and in this way they can attempt to trace out the evolution of the universe itself.

In addition to "ordinary" galaxies, there exists also a wide variety of violently active galaxies which emit far more energy than normal systems. These include radio galaxies and quasars which are so brilliant that it is possible to detect them at distances of well over 10 billion light years. The universe also contains exceedingly tenuous intergalactic matter and radiation, and recent observations seem to indicate that the visible matter in galaxies may be considerably outweighed by non-luminous forms of matter. The entire universe seems to be expanding and evolving.

Astronomers can look out to distances greater than 10 billion light years and can probe back through aeons of time to an era when the universe was much younger than it now is. Compared to this broad panorama, interplanetary distances within the Solar System seem microscopic indeed.

The true vastness of the universe

It was almost impossible for early peoples to form any real idea of the distance-scale of the universe, but at least it was known that the Sun is a long way away; Ptolemy gave its distance as 8,000,000km. Obviously the stars were more remote still, but it was not then known that they were suns in their own right; it was widely believed that they were lamps attached to an invisible crystal vault.

With the revelation that the Earth is a planet moving round the Sun – a change in outlook which was complete by 1687, with the publication of Newton's great work – the status of the Sun among the stars became questioned. Thomas Wright (1711-1786) suggested that the universe might extend to infinity. The great Danish astronomer Tycho Brahe (1546-1601) had already shown that the stars must be much more remote than the Sun. But actual distance-measures were very difficult; even William Herschel (1738-1822) arguably the greatest of all observers, failed in his efforts – though he did make the discovery that many double stars are binary systems instead of being mere line-of-sight effects.

Success was finally achieved by F.W. Bessel (1784-1846) in 1838, when he measured the distance of the faint star 61 Cygni as around 11 light years. He used the parallax method ($\blacklozenge$ page 83). Other measures followed; the parallax method worked well enough for relatively close stars, but not for those which were beyond a few hundred light years, and less direct methods were found.

The next step was to decide upon the status of our star-system or Galaxy. Did it comprise the entire universe, or was it a mere unit? This fundamental problem was not cleared up until 1923, when Edwin Hubble (1889-1953) observed short-period variable stars in "spiral nebulae" and proved that these objects are independent galaxies. Today we know that the universe is vaster than ancient peoples could have credited; we see the most remote known objects not as they are now, but as they used to be before the Earth existed.

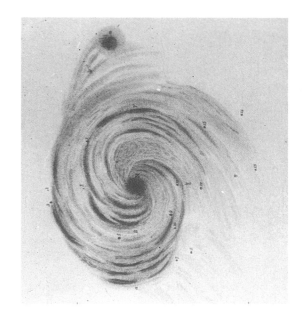

▶ *When the third Earl of Rosse (1800-1867) drew this spiral galaxy in 1845, his was the only telescope of the time powerful enough to show the spiral forms of the objects we now know to be galaxies. Their nature was then a mystery, and it was not until 1923 that it was finally shown that the spirals and other so called "starry nebulae" are external to our Galaxy; most of them many millions of light years away.*

Brightness...Distance measurements...Apparent magnitude, absolute magnitude and luminosity...Color, temperature and the spectrum...Dividing stars into spectral classes...Weighing and sizing stars...The "Hertzsprung-Russell" diagram – its significance... PERSPECTIVE...The mystery of the "wobbling" dog star...Stellar record breakers

Even in the largest Earth-based telescopes stars appear as mere points of light. Nevertheless, by applying their knowledge of physics and chemistry to the analysis of such facts as observation does reveal, astronomers have been able to achieve a detailed understanding of the nature of the stars.

Brightness

The brightness of a star as an Earth-based observer sees it is given by a quaint system of stellar "magnitudes", according to which the faintest stars have the highest values and the brightest stars the lowest. A conspicuous star such as Spica has a magnitude of 1 as seen from Earth, and is described as a "first magnitude" star. Polaris, the Pole Star, is of magnitude 2, while the faintest star visible to the naked eye under good conditions is of magnitude 6. There are 15 stars brighter than magnitude 1. Vega, for example, is of magnitude 0. Stars brighter than this have negative magnitudes. Sirius, the brightest star in the sky, is of magnitude −1·45, while the Full Moon and the Sun have magnitudes of −12·6 and −26·7 respectively.

Measuring stellar distances

It is possible to measure the distances of relatively nearby stars by the parallax method. This consists of making observations of a star's position relative to the more distant background stars at intervals of six months – that is, when the Earth is at opposite sides of its orbit. The two observing sites are thus 300 million kilometers apart, and for a nearby star this baseline is long enough to reveal a small shift in its position. The maximum shift of the star from its mean position in the sky is known as the annual parallax, and it is possible to calculate the star's distance by applying simple trigonometry to the triangle made up of Earth, Sun and star. The angles are always very small, and the angle of parallax grows even smaller with increasing distance.

The annual parallax of a star at a distance of 3·26 light years would be precisely one arcsec (one second of angular measurement). This distance is known as the "parsec" (for a *par*allax of one arc*sec*). In fact, no known star apart from the Sun is as near as that.

Parallax provides the first step in measuring distances in the universe, but because it is difficult to measure such small angles, errors begin to become significant at a range of only 20 parsecs, and the method is not effective at distances greater than 100 parsecs (326 light years). Less direct methods are available for measuring greater distances, but these depend on the accuracy with which the distances of nearby stars have been measured by parallax. Astronomers expect the Hipparchus satellite, due to be launched in the late 1980s, to produce parallaxes at least ten times more accurate than ground-based telescopes can achieve.

The parallax method

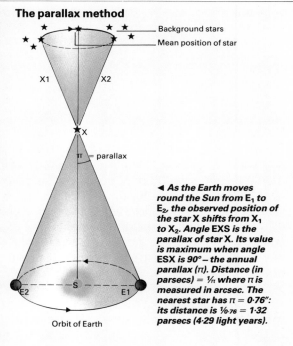

◄ As the Earth moves round the Sun from E_1 to E_2, the observed position of the star X shifts from X_1 to X_2. Angle EXS is the parallax of star X. Its value is maximum when angle ESX is 90° – the annual parallax (π). Distance (in parsecs) = $1/\pi$ where π is measured in arcsec. The nearest star has π = 0·76": its distance is $1/0·76$ = 1·32 parsecs (4·29 light years).

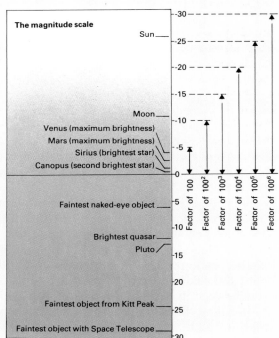

The magnitude scale

Explaining the scale of stellar magnitudes

The magnitude scale (above) is logarithmic: it is based on the fact that a difference of 5 magnitudes corresponds to a factor of 100 in brightness. A difference of 1 magnitude corresponds to a factor of 2·512. Thus a first magnitude star is 2·512 times brighter than a second magnitude star, and 2·512 × 2·512 = 6·310 times brighter than a third magnitude star, and $(2·512)^5$ = 100 times brighter than a sixth magnitude star. Although this scale appears strange, it does in fact reflect the way in which the human eye responds to different levels of brightness.

Astronomers use a star's color and brightness to unlock the secrets of its age, its chemical and physical composition, and its life story

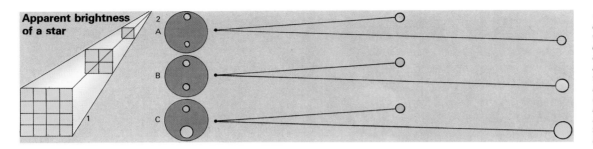

◄ *The apparent brightness of a light source decreases with the square of its distance as light is spread over progressively larger areas (1). If two stars have the same luminosity (2) the more distant looks fainter (A). Two stars seem equally bright if the farther is the more luminous (B). If the farther star is very luminous it appears the brighter (C).*

Apparent magnitude, absolute magnitude and luminosity

The apparent magnitude of a star is a measure of the amount of its light that reaches the Earth. This depends on a number of factors such as the star's distance, whether or not any of its light is absorbed in space, and its luminosity. The luminosity of a star is the amount of energy which its entire surface radiates in one second. This output is measured in watts, just like the power output of an electric light or heater. The Sun radiates a little under 4×10^{26} watts, and is a fairly average star in this respect.

If all the stars were at the same distance, their apparent magnitudes would be a true guide to their real luminosities; it is thus helpful to consider the apparent magnitudes that they would have if they all lay at a distance of ten parsecs. The *apparent* magnitude that any given star would have at this distance is known as its *absolute* magnitude. For example, the Sun has an absolute magnitude of 4·8, so that if it were moved to a distance of ten parsecs, its apparent magnitude would be 4·8 – and it would barely be visible on an average night. Comparing a star's absolute magnitude (the quantity of light it emits) with the apparent magnitude (the quantity which reaches Earth) makes it possible to calculate its distance.

Color, temperature and the spectrum

The color of a star is a guide to its temperature. There is a relationship, known as the Wein law, according to which the higher the temperature of a star, the shorter the wavelength at which it shines most brightly. A star such as the Sun, with a temperature of just under 6,000K, emits most strongly at the middle of the visible spectrum and so appears yellowish. Cooler stars appear red, and hotter stars appear white or blue. The coolest stars of all emit mainly at infrared wavelengths, while the hottest stars peak in the ultraviolet. Astronomers define the color of a star by reference to its color index – the difference between its magnitudes measured at two different wavelengths.

Spreading starlight out into its constituent wavelengths produces a spectrum consisting of a continuous rainbow band of color, together with a pattern of dark absorption lines appearing at a number of particular wavelengths. Sometimes, as with very hot stars, bright (emission) lines are superimposed on the spectrum.

Atoms in the outer layers of a star absorb light coming from the hotter, denser interior at wavelengths which depend upon the chemical elements present. Each element produces its own characteristic "fingerprint" pattern of lines at a number of known wavelengths, so that identification of the lines gives a clue to the chemical composition of the outer layers of a star. The spectrum requires careful interpretation, but can yield a great deal of information about such factors as temperature, chemical composition, density, rotation rate, and the presence of magnetic fields.

Stellar luminosity – the technical details

Astrophysicists define the luminosity of a star as the amount of energy emitted by one square meter of surface, multiplied by the total surface area (in square meters) of the star. The value given for the luminosity of a star depends on two factors, its radius and its temperature, and is expressed as watts.

The energy output per square meter depends on the fourth power of a star's surface temperature, and the surface area depends on the square of its radius. For example, a star with a temperature of 6,000K emits 16 times more energy from each square meter of its surface than a star with a temperature of 3,000K. If two stars have the same radius, the hotter one will be the more luminous of the two. On the other hand, if two stars of different sizes have the same temperature, the larger of the two will be the brighter.

Stellar luminosity

► ▼ *Two stars of the same temperature emit equal amounts of energy from equal areas. The larger is the more luminous (L). The Stefan-Boltzmann law (1): the amount of energy emitted from equal areas depends on the 4th power of their temperatures. The Wein law (2): the higher the temperature, the shorter the wavelength of the peak emission of radiation.*

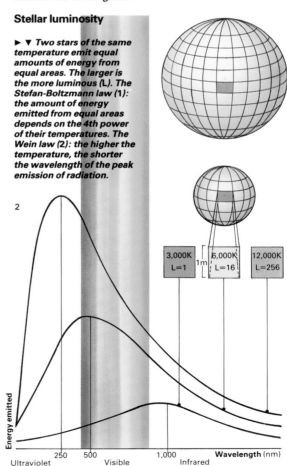

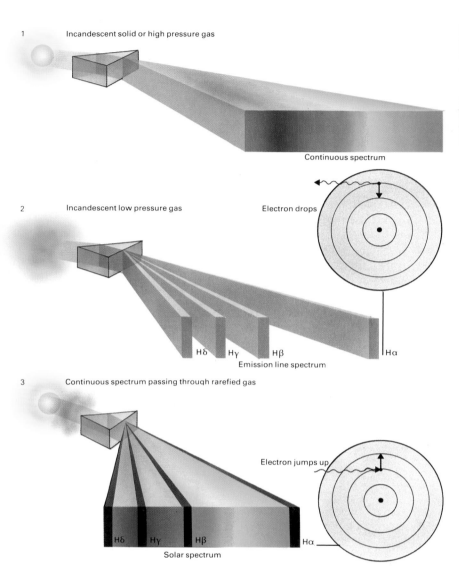

1 Incandescent solid or high pressure gas

Continuous spectrum

2 Incandescent low pressure gas

Electron drops

Hδ   Hγ   Hβ   Hα
Emission line spectrum

3 Continuous spectrum passing through rarefied gas

Electron jumps up

Hδ   Hγ   Hβ   Hα
Solar spectrum

◄ The English astronomer William Huggins (1824-1910) was one of the pioneers of stellar spectroscopy. He analyzed the spectra of 50 bright stars, and concluded that some of the same elements were present in the Sun. His work led directly to the first measurements of a star's radial velocity.

Spectral class

Stars are classified according to the appearance of their spectra. In the Harvard Classification they are graded in order of decreasing temperature into the following principal classes: O, B, A, F, G, K, M, with subsidiary classes R, N, S for cool stars and the class W for very high-temperature "Wolf-Rayet" stars. This curious sequence of letters can be recalled with the aid of a dreadful mnemonic, which runs: (Wow), Oh Be A Fine Girl, Kiss Me Right Now, Sweetie. The sequence is alphabetically chaotic because there were several major revisions during the research period.

Each class is divided into ten subsections denoted by one of the numbers between 0 and 9, again in order of decreasing temperature. The Sun, for example, is a type G2 star.

O- and B-types are bluish in color, the O-types having temperatures in the range 35,000K to 40,000K. A-types are white, F-types creamy, G-types yellow, K-types orange and M-types red, with temperatures around 3,000K.

Additional letters are used to denote special peculiarities – for example, "e" denotes the presence of emission lines in the spectrum. Within a given class, a highly luminous star will be larger than a less luminous one, and its outer layers will be more rarefied. The lower pressures in the more tenuous atmospheres of the larger stars produce narrower, sharper lines than those produced in more compact stars.

▲ A hot dense body emits a mixture of all wavelengths of light which is spread out by a prism into a band of colors – a continuous spectrum (1). In a hot, low density gas, many atoms have electrons in high energy levels. When an electron drops to a lower level it emits light of a characteristic wavelength – an emission line spectrum – (2). When a continuous spectrum passes through a low density gas, electrons in low energy levels absorb light at certain wavelengths and superimpose dark lines on the spectrum – a solar spectrum (3).

► Examples of the principal spectral classes arranged in order of decreasing temperature – a major factor in determining which lines are prominent.

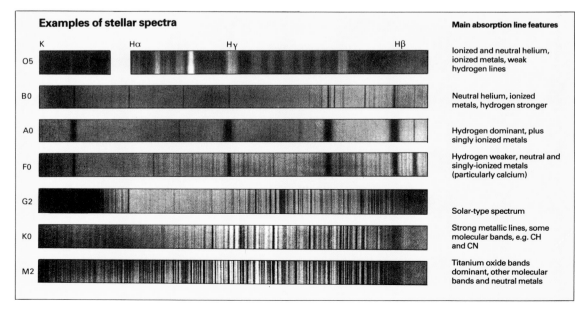

Examples of stellar spectra

Main absorption line features

Class		
O5	K Hα Hγ Hβ	Ionized and neutral helium, ionized metals, weak hydrogen lines
B0		Neutral helium, ionized metals, hydrogen stronger
A0		Hydrogen dominant, plus singly ionized metals
F0		Hydrogen weaker, neutral and singly-ionized metals (particularly calcium)
G2		Solar-type spectrum
K0		Strong metallic lines, some molecular bands, e.g. CH and CN
M2		Titanium oxide bands dominant, other molecular bands and neutral metals

The vital statistics of stellar bodies show that many of them have remarkably little in common – except that they are all called stars

Stellar masses

It is possible in principle to "weigh" a star by observing the effect of its gravity on neighboring bodies. Thus, working out the force necessary to keep the planets in their orbits at their known distances and speeds makes it possible to calculate the mass of the Sun. Planets of other stars, even the closest, are too faint to see, and it is only possible to measure the mass of a star if it is a member of a binary system (a binary is a pair of stars which revolve round each other). Analyzing measurements of the orbital period of a binary, and of the separations between the stars, can give the masses of the stars (◆ page 99).

The majority of stars are less massive than the Sun, but astronomers think that the lowest possible mass for a fully fledged star is about 0·08 solar masses. Few stars have more than ten times the Sun's mass, but the most massive stars may be more than 100 solar masses.

Stellar diameters

Although scientists can deduce the diameter of a star from measurements of its luminosity and temperature, direct measurements of stellar diameters are very hard to achieve. In theory the largest telescopes should be able to resolve some of the nearest large stars into visible disks, but in practice atmospheric turbulence rules this out.

Stellar record breakers

The most massive star known at present is probably Plaskett's Star, HD 47129, in the constellation of Monoceros (the Unicorn). It is a binary system; each component is about 55 times as massive as the Sun, while the primary has a radius of 25 times that of the Sun and at least 50,000 times the Sun's luminosity.

The most powerful star known is the unique Eta Carinae, which is about 6,500 light years away and perhaps 4,000,000 times as luminous as the Sun; even this may be something of an underestimate. In the Large Magellanic Cloud, immersed in the nebula 30 Doradus, is the extraordinary HD 38268. If it is a single star, it could be ten times as powerful as Eta Carinae and far more massive, but it is quite likely that it is made up of a compact group of highly luminous objects.

Of the largest stars, the system of Alpha Herculis, made up of a red supergiant with a double companion is enveloped in a huge cloud of gas of perhaps 250,000 million kilometers while other red supergiants have immense diameters – at least 400,000,000km in the case of Betelgeux in Orion.

Among stellar glow-worms, pride of place must go to the red dwarf RG 0050-2722 in Sculptor, with an absolute magnitude of 19. Some "brown dwarfs", such as the recently-discovered companion of Van Biesbroeck 8 (21 light years away) may be even feebler; their cores have never become hot enough for nuclear reactions to be triggered off.

▼ *Edward Pickering (1846-1919) and his "harem" at Harvard College Observatory developed the system of spectral classification at the beginning of this century.*

The first attempts to measure stellar diameters were made with the Michelson stellar interferometer, which used two mirrors attached to a long beam mounted at the front of a telescope. The idea was to examine a star and to produce at the focus an interference pattern, which, when analyzed, would give the diameter of the star. A more advanced instrument, the intensity interferometer set up at Narrabri, Australia, has used two 6·5m movable segmented mirrors to focus light onto photomultipliers. Correlating the intensities of the signals produced by the two mirrors has enabled observers to obtain stellar diameters as small as 0·0004 arcsec.

Very short photographic exposures of star images show that the blurred image produced by atmospheric turbulence consists of a large number of little blobs, or "speckles", formed by individual cells of air in the atmosphere. Careful analysis of a large number of short exposures can yield information on the diameter and surface structure of a star down to the theoretical resolving power of the telescope. This technique is known as "speckle interferometry".

The way in which a star's light fades away if the Moon passes in front of it can also provide information on stellar diameters.

Stellar diameters range from thousands of millions of kilometers down to about ten kilometers – a truly enormous spread.

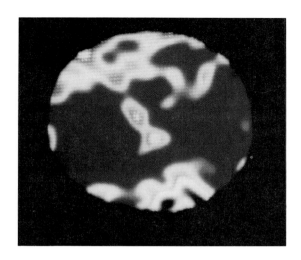

▲ The disk of the star Betelgeux, a red supergiant in Orion, was the first (other than the Sun) to be resolved. Astronomers at Kitt Peak National Observatory produced this picture in 1974 using the newly developed speckle interferometry technique. Some surface structure is clearly discernible; earlier photographs had shown only a featureless blur.

▲ The stellar intensity interferometer at Narrabri Observatory, Australia, has two 6·7m reflectors mounted on circular tracks. It is sensitive enough to measure the diameters of many main-sequence stars.

◀ In this photograph of Sirius and its white dwarf companion, the bright star is highly over-exposed – the spikes are photographic effects. Its dim companion is barely visible, yet the mass ratio is only 2·5 to 1.

The mystery of the wobbling Dog Star...
The brightest star in the sky is Sirius, in Canis Major (the Great Dog). It is not highly luminous – only 26 times more powerful than the Sun – but it is a mere 8·6 light years away, which is closer than any other bright star except Alpha Centauri. Its spectrum is of type A, and it is pure white.

Friedrich Wilhelm Bessel (1784-1846), a German astronomer, had found that Sirius was not moving steadily against the background of more remote stars. He observed a very slight, very slow "wobbling", and attributed this to the gravitational effect of a companion star, too faint to be seen in the telescopes of the time. In 1862 Alvan Clark (1832-1897), a famous American telescope-maker, was testing a large new refractor when he saw a faint speck of light close to Sirius. This proved to be the companion, almost exactly where Bessel had predicted. Since Sirius is often known as the Dog Star, it was natural that the companion should be nicknamed the Pup.

...and the dense white Pup
The Pup has only one ten-thousandth of the luminosity of Sirius itself, and astronomers assumed that it would be dim and red. It came as a major shock when in 1915 Walter Sidney Adams (1876-1956), an American astronomer at Mount Wilson, obtained a spectrum which showed that the Pup was in fact white, and had a surface temperature much higher than that of the Sun.

If the Pup were both hot and faint, it would have to be very small, and in this case its known mass could be explained only if it was also extremely dense. In fact Sirius B, the Pup, is smaller than Uranus or Neptune but has a density some 60,000 times that of water: it is a white dwarf, an aging star which has used up its main sources of energy and now shines feebly as it loses heat to its outer layers. Today many white dwarfs are known, some of them even smaller and denser than the Pup.

▶ *The Hertsprung-Russell diagram compares the surface temperatures or spectral classes of stars with their luminosities or absolute magnitudes. It revolutionized the study of stellar evolution.*

The Hertzsprung-Russell diagram

This diagram, which is of crucial importance to an understanding of stellar evolution, shows the relationship between luminosity and temperature for the stars. The vertical scale shows luminosity (or an equivalent quantity such as absolute magnitude), and the horizontal scale gives temperature (or an equivalent quantity such as spectral class or color index). Scientists use the luminosity of the Sun as a unit of luminosity, so that the Sun belongs on the diagram as a point of luminosity 1 and temperature 5,800K. If a large number of stars are plotted according to their luminosities and temperatures, it becomes clear that most stars lie within a band which slopes from upper left (high temperature, high luminosity) to lower right (low temperature, low luminosity). This band is known as the "main sequence".

Stars off the main sequence – stellar outsiders

Not all stars lie on the main sequence. For example, some stars of low temperature but high luminosity lie above it and to the right. These stars are known as red giants because they are cool red stars of enormous diameter (stars of the same temperature emit the same amount of energy per square meter of surface, so if one outshines another it must be bigger). A typical red giant has a radius about one hundred times larger than the Sun's, a luminosity one thousand times greater and a surface temperature of about 3,000K.

White dwarfs are stars which lie below and to the left of the main sequence. Despite their high temperatures – 10,000K or more – they have less than one thousandth of the Sun's luminosity. A typical white dwarf has about one hundredth of the Sun's diameter and is comparable in size with the Earth. White dwarfs contain as much material as the Sun within about one millionth of the volume, and therefore are about a million times denser than the Sun.

Neutron stars are a great deal smaller than white dwarfs. The diameter of a typical neutron star is only 10-20km, and stars of this type are so dense that a teaspoonful of their material would weigh between one hundred million and one billion tonnes. By contrast, the mean density of matter in the outer layers of a red supergiant is about one ten-thousandth of the density of air at sea-level.

Type of star	Diameter (Sun = 1)	Luminosity (Sun = 1)	Surface temperature (K)
Red Supergiant (MOI)	500	30,000	3,000
Red giant (K5III)	25	200	3,000
Main sequence stars:			
05	18	500,000	40,000
B0	7	20,000	28,000
A0	2.5	80	9,000
F0	1.35	6.3	7,400
G0	1.05	1.5	6,000
G2 (Sun)	1	1	5,800
K0	0.85	0.4	4,900
M0	0.63	0.06	3,500
M5	0.32	0,008	2,800
White dwarf	0,01	0,001	10,000
Neutron star	10^{-5}	–	10^6

▲ *E. Hertzsprung 1873-1967*

▶ *Relative sizes of stars of various types are compared with the size which a black hole would have if it had a mass equal to that of the Sun (◆ page 107).*

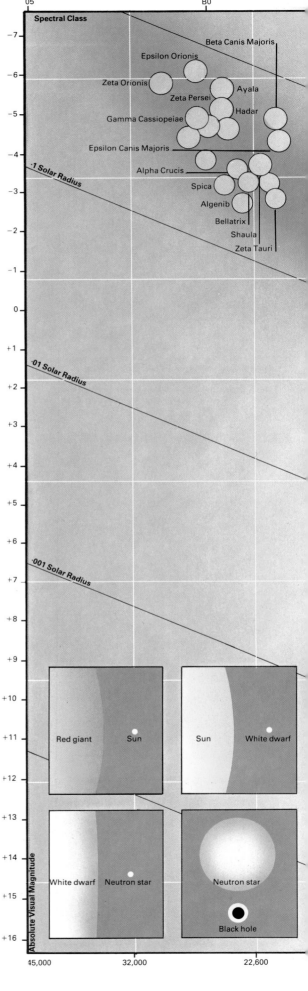

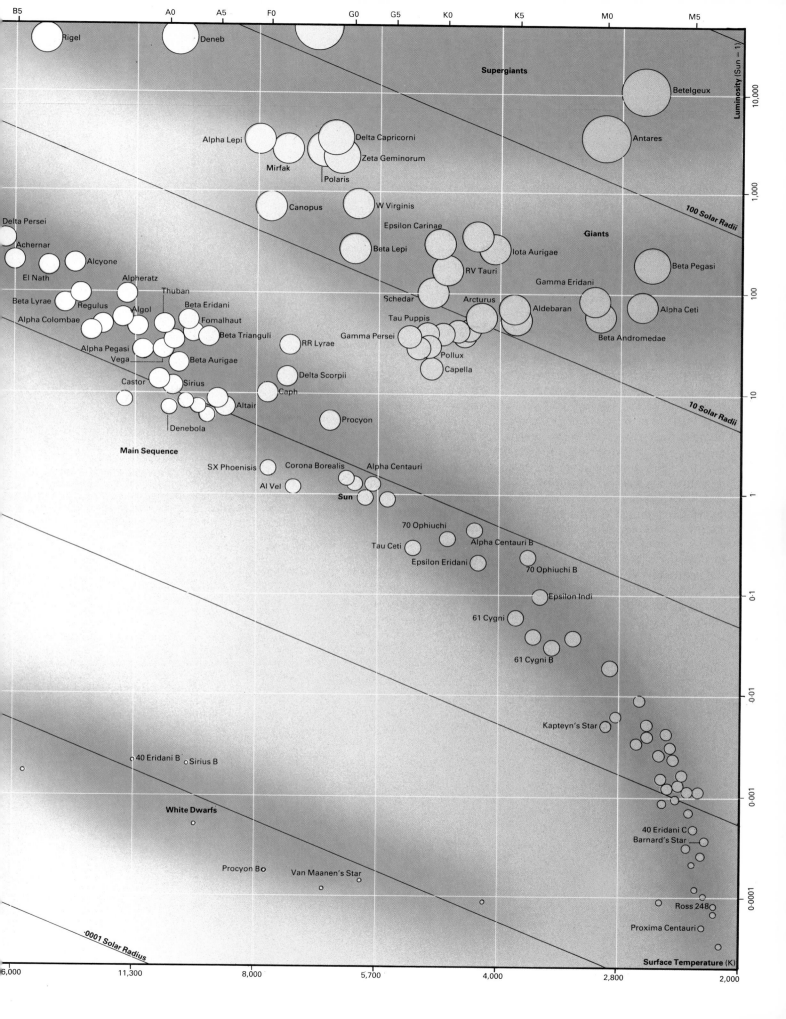

The motion of stars in space

The stars are all moving through space, although their distances are so great that their motions are imperceptible to the human eye even over centuries and millenia. Relative to the Earth, their velocity consists of two components – "proper motion" across the line of sight, and "radial motion", directly towards or away from the Solar System.

In referring to proper motion, astronomers give the angle through which a star travels across the sky in a year (after allowing for effects such as parallax). The angle is always very small. Barnard's Star, six light years away, has the largest known proper motion (10·31 arcsec per year) and crosses an angle equal to the apparent diameter of the Moon in 180 years. Most proper motions are far smaller than this. If they know the distance of a star, astronomers can convert proper motion into speed across the line of sight (transverse velocity). In the case of Barnard's star this is 88km per second.

Radial motion and the Doppler effect

The Doppler effect makes it possible to measure a star's radial velocity. If a source of light is moving away from an observer, the light waves are "stretched out" and the wavelength reaching the observer is longer than the wavelength emitted by the source. This happens because each successive wavecrest is emitted from a slightly greater distance away, and so takes longer than its predecessor to reach the observer. Fewer wavecrests per second arrive at the observer's position than the source is emitting. Conversely, if a source is approaching the observer, the waves are "squeezed up", and the observer perceives shorter wavelengths. A similar effect occurs in the pitch of sound when a source is approaching or receding.

The spectral lines that occur due to the different chemical elements in a star have precisely known wavelengths. If a star is receding from the Earth, all the lines in its spectrum will occur at longer than normal wavelengths (they will be red-shifted), while if it is approaching, the wavelengths of its spectral lines will be shorter than normal (blue-shifted). Astronomers can measure the velocity of approach or recession by analyzing the blue shift or red shift in a star's spectrum.

The radial velocity of Barnard's Star is −108km per second, which implies that it is approaching the Solar System at this speed (a "+" sign denotes recession). Combining radial and transverse velocities shows that Barnard's Star is moving relative to the Solar System at about 140km per second and will make its closest approach, at a distance of 3·85 light years, in just under 10,000 years' time.

Stellar motions

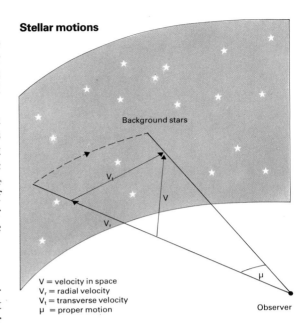

Background stars

V = velocity in space
V_r = radial velocity
V_t = transverse velocity
μ = proper motion
Observer

Spotting stellar movement
The stars were once called "fixed stars", because they seemed to remain stationary with respect to each other; to the naked-eye observer the constellation patterns remain unaltered for many lifetimes. Proper or individual motions of the stars were only first appreciated in 1710, by Edmond Halley. He was able to show that the stars Sirius, Procyon and Arcturus had moved perceptibly against their background since the time of Ptolemy.

All proper motions are small; however, modern techniques provide very accurate measures. Photographic atlases, such as that compiled at Palomar Observatory, provide the basic data here; comparison with atlases compiled years later show up the proper motions clearly. The artificial satellite Hipparcos, devoted entirely to this problem, will provide data in 2½ years which would take 50 years by Earth-based equipment. It is, of course, true that it is only relatively near stars which show detectable proper motions. On the other hand radial or toward-or-away measures can be made spectroscopically even for remote galaxies, where the velocities are tremendous – in some cases appreciable fractions of the velocity of light.

The Doppler effect

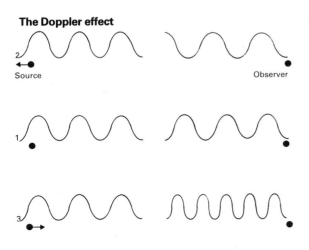

2
Source
Observer

1

3

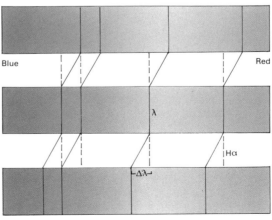

Blue
Red

λ

$H\alpha$

$\Delta\lambda$

◄ *Light reaching an observer from a stationary source has the same wavelength (1) as the light emitted from that source, and the lines in its spectrum have normal "rest wavelengths". Light arriving from a receding source is stretched in wavelength and the spectral lines appear at longer wavelengths – nearer to the red end of the spectrum by an amount proportional to the radial velocity (2). If the source is approaching, its light waves are compressed and the spectral lines appear at shorter wavelengths (3).*

*Stellar evolution – piecing together the whole story...
What powers the nuclear furnace?...Ending with a
bang...Why stars may occur in clusters...A special
class of stars...PERSPECTIVE...Early attempts to discover
stellar fuels...Investigating the new stars in Orion*

Astronomers have never been able to witness the life of a single star from beginning to end, because the time scale is too great. Instead they have analyzed a broad cross-section of stars, some young, some middle-aged and some very old, and have combined their data to compile a reasonably complete evolutionary sequence for most stars.

A star begins life as a cloud of dust and gas which, triggered by some mechanism which scientists have not fully understood, begins to collapse under its own gravitational attraction. Once started, the process continues very rapidly, exerting pressure on the material at the center of the cloud, where the temperature rises. The collapsing cloud, or "protostar", becomes extremely brilliant for a while, but then begins to fade as collapse continues still farther – but more slowly – and the central region becomes hotter and hotter. At a temperature of about 10 million K, nuclear fusion begins to take place within the core, providing the energy which will keep the star shining for many millions of years – although not to the end of its life.

Everyday life on the stellar main sequence
When nuclear reactions are well under way in its interior, a star ceases to collapse because the explosion outwards of hot gases counteracts the inward force of gravity. A star in this state of balance is said to be on the "main sequence", because this is how the majority of stars spend most of their visible lives. A one solar-mass star (one which has the same mass as the Sun) takes about 50 million years to reach the main sequence, and remains there until the hydrogen in its core is spent. More massive stars arrive on the main sequence much sooner and less massive stars much later. Those of less than 0·08 solar masses never reach this stage at all, but merely go on shrinking to become first brown and then black dwarfs.

The declining years of a typical star
When all the hydrogen in a star's core has been used, nuclear fusion reactions cease to counteract the force of gravity and the star begins to contract under its own weight, increasing in temperature as it does so. This process transfers enough heat to the shell of material around the core – which does still contain hydrogen – to start a new series of fusion reactions. This hydrogen "burning" zone spreads outwards from the original core, depositing the helium created by fusion as a kind of "ash" in the center of the star.

The energy output from the expanding hydrogen zone increases, so that the star becomes brighter and perceptibly larger, even though its core continues to shrink. Eventually the core temperature will reach about 100 million K, and at this stage a new fusion process begins, in which the nuclei of helium atoms fuse to form carbon nuclei. This process, the "triple-alpha" reaction, sustains the star as a red giant.

The cornerstone of modern astrophysics
In 1914 a Danish astronomer, Ejnar Hertzsprung (1873-1967), and an American, Henry Russell (1877-1957), published the first of a series of diagrams that was to revolutionize the study of stellar evolution. Working independently, the two astronomers had discovered that there was a correlation between the brightness (absolute luminosity) and the color (spectral class) – and hence surface temperature – of stars. Plotting these two values on a graph gives the diagram known as the Hertzsprung-Russell (or H-R) diagram. Drawing such a diagram for a large number of stars shows that most lie within a broad band of decreasing brightness and surface temperature. This band is now known as the "main sequence". Most stars move across the main sequence, or on to it and back again the same way; once on, they tend to stay there for a long time.

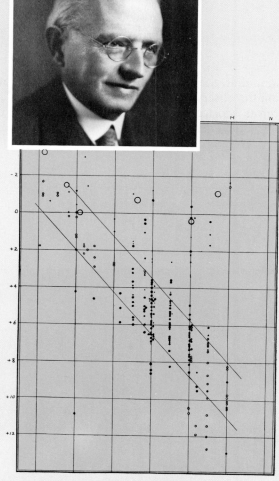

▲ *Henry Russell, one of the co-originators of the graph known as the Hertzsprung-Russell diagram, is seen here with the first one. On it he has plotted absolute luminosity on the vertical axis and color on the horizontal axis, and has highlighted with diagonal lines the tight grouping now known as the main sequence. Similar diagrams can be drawn for specific groups or types of stars, and offer astronomers valuable insights into their nature.*

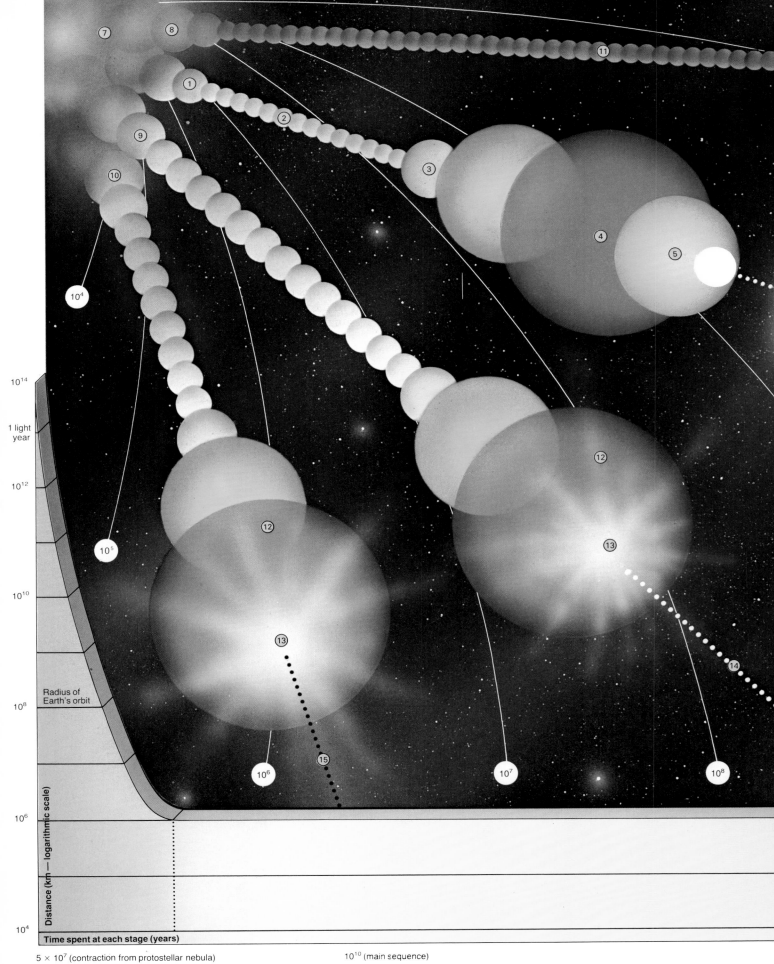

10¹⁴

1 light
year

10¹²

10¹⁰

Radius of
Earth's orbit

10⁸

10⁶

Distance (km — logarithmic scale)

10⁴

Time spent at each stage (years)

5 × 10⁷ (contraction from protostellar nebula)   10¹⁰ (main sequence)

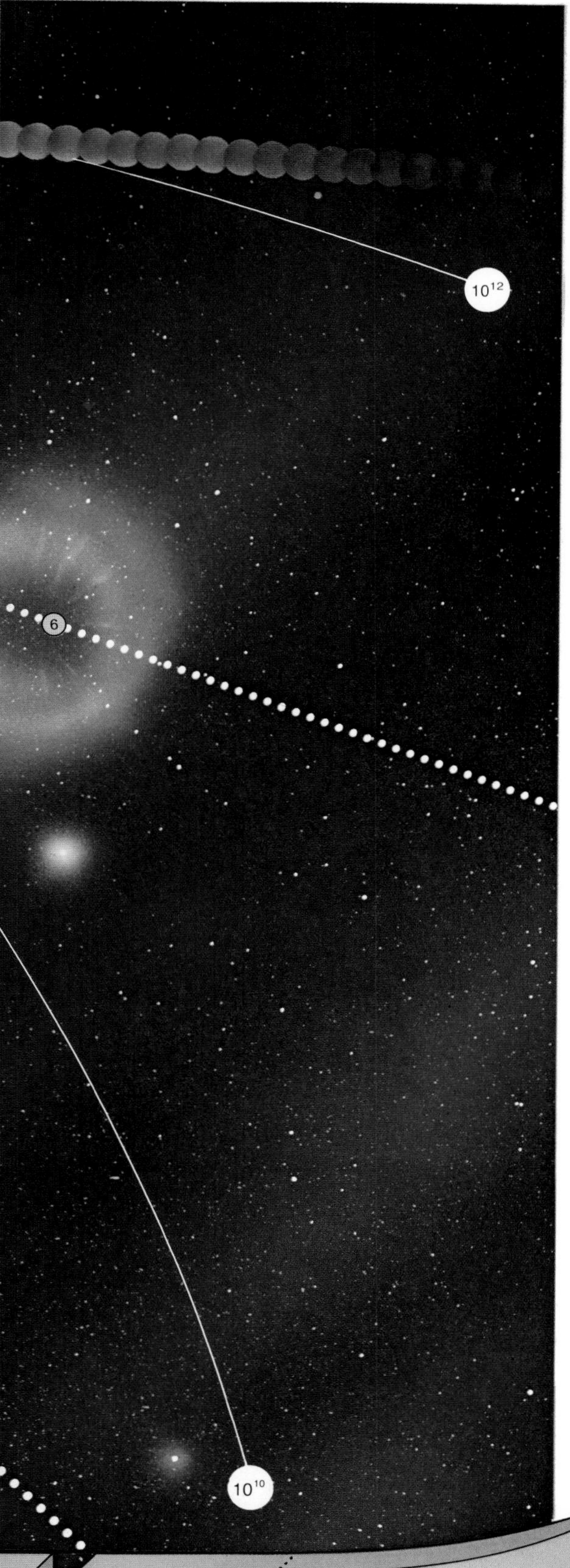

◄ *How four stars of different mass evolve. The evolutionary paths are plotted against an approximate timescale in years and on the H-R diagram below. The lifespan of our Sun (one solar mass) lies between the long-lived low mass star (0·05 solar mass) and the massive stars (10 and 30 solar masses).*

A star the size of the Sun contains enough hydrogen "fuel" to keep it going on the main sequence for about 10 billion years, whereas more massive stars have shorter main-sequence lifetimes because they use up their fuel very much faster. For example, a star ten times more massive than the Sun consumes fuel not ten, but 5,000 times faster, and burns itself out within about 20 million years (naturally it is also 5,000 times more luminous than the Sun). The most massive stars of all evolve to red giants within a million years; at the other end of the scale the low-mass stars, if they evolve to the main sequence at all, will outlive the Sun many times over.

The end-product of the triple-alpha reaction (◗ page 103), which sustains red giant stars, is carbon. Eventually this carbon begins to clog the core of the star, so that it ceases to generate energy. The core shrinks once again and this time may trigger helium-"burning" in the surrounding shell. In the most massive stars further reactions can take place leading, eventually, to the formation of iron in the core. This is the last in the series of possible energy-releasing fusion reactions, and is very uncommon. In stars having the same mass as the Sun or less, fusion probably ceases with the production of carbon.

When all its fuel is spent, gravity crushes a solar-mass star until it is a "white dwarf" – a hot body comparable in size with the Earth, and with a mean density as high as one billion kilograms per cubic meter. Astronomers expect most stars, including the Sun, to become white dwarfs which in time will fade and cool to become black dwarfs.

Stellar life paths

1 1 solar mass star – luminous phase
2 Main sequence phase
3 Expansion phase
4 Red giant phase
5 Conracting phase
6 White dwarf phase
7 Protostellar nebula
8 0·05 solar mass star
9 10 solar mass star
10 30 solar mass star
11 Brown dwarf
12 Supergiant
13 Supernova
14 Neutron star
15 Black hole

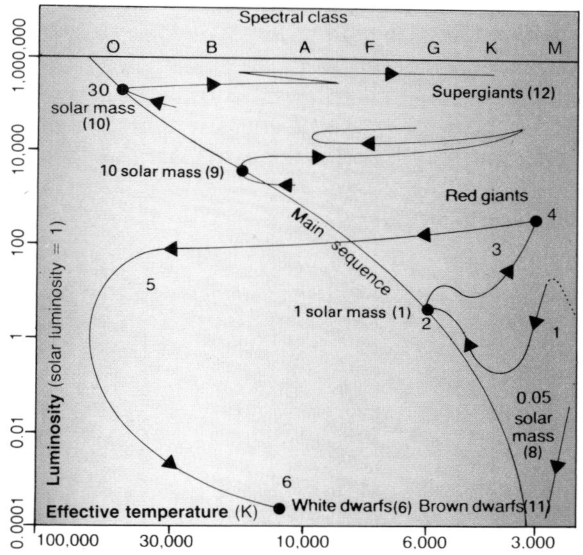

▲ *This version of the Hertzsprung-Russell diagram shows the evolution of the same four star types as the illustration on the left, divided into the same numbered stages. The diagram demonstrates the relationship between the luminosities and temperatures of the stars and defines their spectral class.*

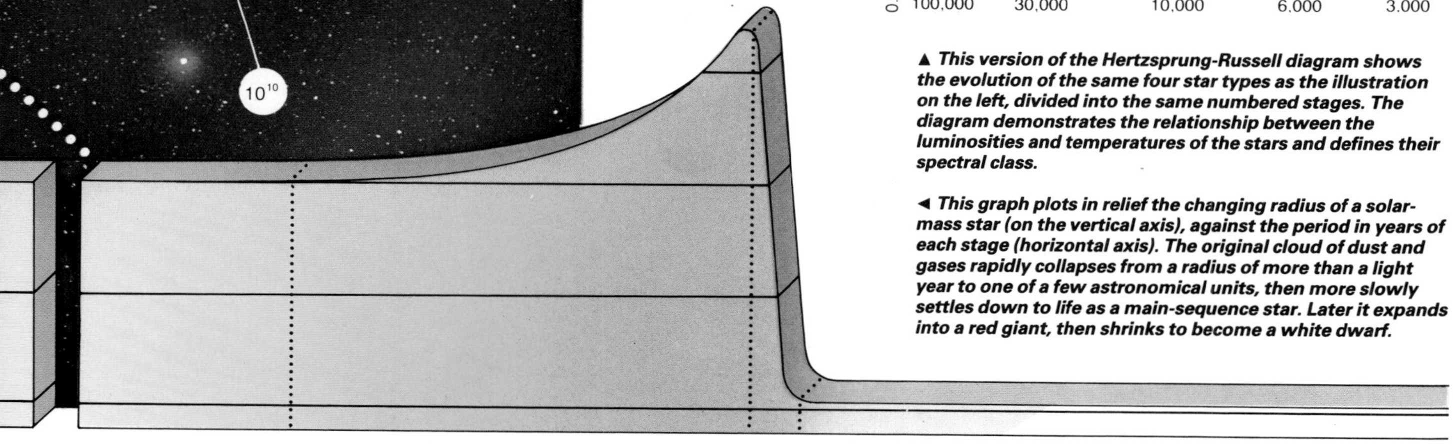

◄ *This graph plots in relief the changing radius of a solar-mass star (on the vertical axis), against the period in years of each stage (horizontal axis). The original cloud of dust and gases rapidly collapses from a radius of more than a light year to one of a few astronomical units, then more slowly settles down to life as a main-sequence star. Later it expands into a red giant, then shrinks to become a white dwarf.*

10^9 (red-giant stage) 10^8 (collapse to white dwarf)

The eventual fate of stars

A star of up to about 1·4 solar masses is likely to end its days as a white dwarf, and there is evidence that stars considerably more massive than this can shed enough matter late in life (by blowing off planetary nebulae, for example) to come within the limit. If a star is above this mass limit when it runs out of fuel, the most probable outcome is that it will suffer a violent supernova explosion which blasts its outer layers of material into space, and compresses its core to form a body even denser than a white dwarf – a "neutron star".

There is also a mass limit for a neutron star, although physicists are not sure exactly where this limit lies – probably somewhere between 2 and 5 solar masses. Once a more massive stellar remnant begins to collapse, nothing can halt the process: it continues to collapse in on itself until it becomes a point of infinite density. Before it reaches this stage, the force of gravity at the surface of the collapsing star becomes so great that it prevents light itself from escaping. Thus the star becomes literally invisible and forms – if current widely accepted views are correct – a black hole.

A closer look at the birth of stars

Scientists do not know why interstellar gas and dust clouds should start to collapse and form stars in the first place. These clouds are cool and of low density – typically one atom per cubic centimeter – but still have enough internal pressure to resist collapsing under their own gravity. Rotation of clouds and the presence of magnetic fields within them would also tend to forestall collapse. Nevertheless, collapse does occur, and there must be an explanation. One suggestion is that such clouds become compressed during an encounter with the spiral arm of a galaxy, or by collision with another cloud, and that an event of this kind may be all it takes to start the process of collapse.

Inside an evolving star

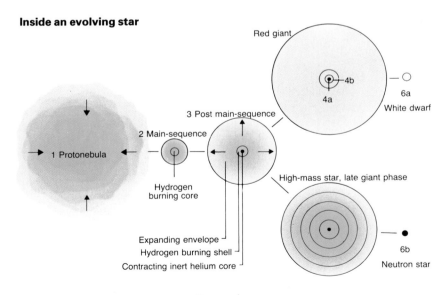

▲ *This diagrammatic sequence shows the nuclear reactions inside typical stars, numbered as in the "evolutionary tracks" of pages 154-5. In the protonebula (1) energy is released by contraction. On the main sequence (2) a star generates energy in its core by nuclear fusion – "burning" hydrogen as fuel; once this is exhausted the core shrinks (3). In its red giant stage, helium is converted to carbon in the star's core (4a), which is surrounded by a hydrogen-burning shell (4b). Thereafter collapse produces a white dwarf (6a) or a neutron star (6b).*

▲ *Sir Arthur Eddington, seen here talking to Albert Einstein, was one of the greatest of pioneer astrophysicists. He was the first to suggest that the transmutation of elements might be the process by which the stars kept shining for thousands of millions of years. Einstein once said it was worth learning English simply in order to talk to Eddington.*

Stellar fuel...hydrogen and oxygen?

Around the turn of the century there were many theories concerning the fuel that kept the stars shining. In 1908 Hermann Helmholtz calculated that if the Sun were burning and were made of oxygen and hydrogen, combustion would keep it shining for 3021 years. Even if this seems rather over-precise, Helmholtz was right in saying that "known chemical forces are so completely inadequate... that we must quite drop this hypothesis."

...or cold meteorite swarms?

An altogether different theory had been summed up by Sir Norman Lockyer in 1888: namely, that the stars were connected with nebulae consisting of swarms of cold meteorites. The energy output of the stars would be maintained by constant meteoritic bombardment. The great British physicist Lord Kelvin even calculated how long the infalling of the planets could keep the Sun burning (if the planets are being steadily "braked" by friction against the tenuous interplanetary medium, then they will eventually spiral into the Sun). Kelvin found that the impact of all the planets combined would keep the Sun shining for no more than 46,000 years, which meant that again the timescale disproved the theory.

...or the mutual annihilation of particles?

Astronomers had identified two definite types of red and orange stars – giants and dwarfs – and the earliest Hertzsprung-Russell diagrams seemed to indicate that red giants were very young stars that had not yet joined the main sequence, while red dwarfs were very old. Russell himself believed that the source of stellar energy was the mutual annihilation of protons with electrons – an idea that was consistent with this view of stellar evolution. But calculation showed that the mutual annihilation process would sustain the stars for millions of millions of years, which was far too long – and yet another theory failed to survive the timescale test.

...or the transmutation of elements?

The British physicist Sir Arthur Eddington realized that the mutual annihilation of electrons and protons cannot occur in the way envisaged by Henry Russell. In 1927 he pointed out that there was another possible process – the transmutation of elements. He calculated that one helium nucleus could be formed from four hydrogen nuclei, that energy would be released in the process, and that this could provide enough energy to keep the Sun burning for about 10,000 million years.

...and, at last, the complete explanation

The problem was finally solved in 1939 by Hans Bethe, a German astronomer working in America, who realized that a straightforward transformation process was inadequate. Bethe was returning home to Washington by train after a conference at Cornell University, when he started to jot down some thoughts. Before he reached Washington he had solved the main problem. In the more massive stars, hydrogen is indeed converted into helium, but by the use of one other element – carbon – as a catalyst in a carbon cycle.

This new theory made it possible to take a fresh look at the H-R diagram. Scientists could now see that a star condenses out of nebular material, and is at first unstable, but eventually settles down to join the main sequence at a point determined by its initial mass. After it has used up all its available hydrogen "fuel", it develops into a giant located at the upper right of the H-R diagram before embarking on its final decline. Thus Betelgeux and other red giants, instead of being the stellar infants that they were once considered to be, are now regarded as cosmic geriatrics.

The carbon cycle

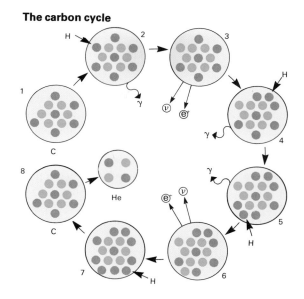

◄ *Energy in the more massive stars is generated by the "carbon cycle", in which carbon is a catalyst. The carbon nucleus (1) changes its identity before emerging at the end. An extra proton is captured producing a lightweight nucleus of nitrogen (atomic mass 13) and a photon (a "particle" of radiation) is expelled (2). Next a positron and a neutrino are expelled, making carbon-13 (3). The capture of another proton produces a normal nitrogen-14 nucleus and more radiation is released (4). Next oxygen-15 (5) and nitrogen-15 (6) are produced. Finally a proton is added to the nitrogen-15 (7) which splits the nucleus to form a helium nucleus and a carbon nucleus that is recycled (8).*

Neutron
Proton
Positron e⁺
Electron e⁻
Neutrino ν
Photon γ

The triple-alpha reaction

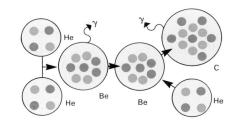

◄ *Energy in red giants is created by the "triple-alpha" reaction. In the first step 2 helium nuclei combine to form a nucleus of beryllium, and radiation is released. Next another helium nucleus is added and a carbon nucleus is produced.*

► *The Lagoon Nebula in Sagittarius is a complex cloud lit up by highly luminous young stars, part of a cluster which is probably less than two million years old. The numerous dark blobs, some only a fraction of a light year in diameter, are known as Bok globules, after Bart J. Bok. They are dense dusty clouds which will probably collapse to form stars.*

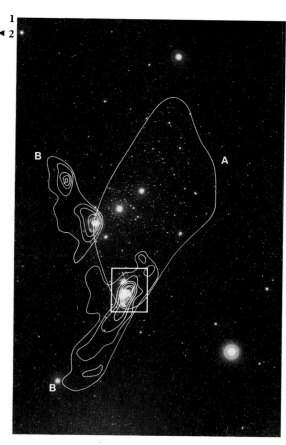

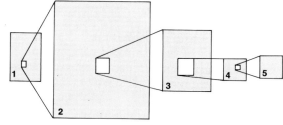

► *This scale drawing shows how the white rectangle on each of the numbered images relates to the next in the sequence. It starts with Orion as viewed with the naked-eye and ends with an infrared detail.*

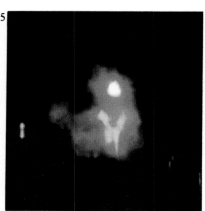

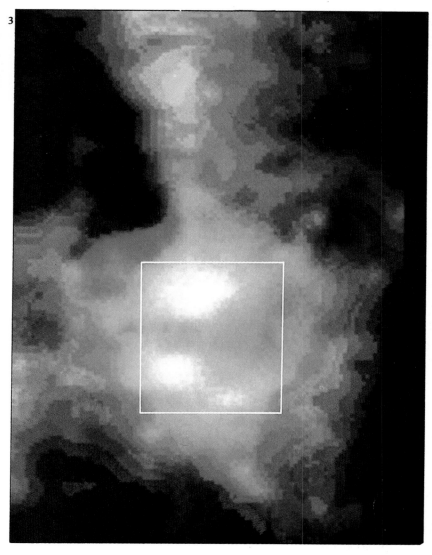

Orion — birthplace of new stars

Within the constellation of Orion (1) there is an expanding batch of O and B-type stars less than 10 million years old and known as the Orion 1 Association (1A). The complex includes two giant molecular clouds (B) each of which measures over 150 light years in diameter and contains more than 100,000 solar masses of material. Most of this is molecular hydrogen which is too cool to emit detectable radiation (the cloud contours have been drawn following the microwave emission from carbon monoxide mixed in with the hydrogen).

The Orion Nebula or M42 (2), the best known of the many emission nebulae, lies at a distance of about 1,600 light years. The concentration of gas which coincides with the nebula in the line of sight, but which actually lies behind it, is the Orion Molecular Cloud 1 (OMC1) of around 1,000 solar masses. The false-color radio map (3) shows the most intense area of carbon monoxide emission from OMC1; blue represents the most intense emission and green the least.

The visually brightest region of OMC1 (4) also coincides with the most intense infrared emission. It is illuminated by a group of four O-type stars, the Trapezium, probably formed within the last 100,000 years. Within this area the strongest emissions arise from a few compact sources. The false-color infra-red view (5) shows one of these sources known as the Becklin-Neugebauer object (colored white), believed to be a single star in the process of formation. The more complex source is the Kleinmann-Low nebula, a region of protostars.

See also
The Basic Properties of Stars 83-90
Black Holes 107-110

The formation of star clusters

Once a cloud of thousands of solar masses has started to collapse, it will break up into fragments, the subsequent collapse of the fragments yielding individual stars or clusters of stars. The more massive fragments evolve rapidly into brilliant O and B-type stars, many of which will later become supernovae. These stars heat the surrounding gases, causing them to expand. This expansion, together with the strong stellar winds which blow from these stars in their youth and with blasts from supernovae, send shock waves through surrounding clouds and can cause new bursts of star formation.

As a protostar collapses, the inner part shrinks more rapidly than the outer part and a cocoon of dust particles forms round the emerging star, hiding it from view. (However, the young star heats the dust cocoon sufficiently for it to emit infrared radiation, and this may be detectable.) Most stars emerge from their cocoons in the pre-main-sequence phase, when the dust is either vaporized, blown away, or coagulates into larger lumps – and perhaps planets.

A class of young stars

Astrophysicists have identified a particular type of star that is cool, varies erratically, and is found in the neighborhood of dense, dusty molecular clouds. Stars of this class (named "T Tauri" stars after a famous one in Taurus ◗ page 106) produce strong stellar winds and rotate rapidly – both characteristics of very young stars – and most have ages between a few tens of thousands and a few million years. Their infrared variation indicates the presence of surrounding dust, and supports the view that these are stars emerging from their cocoons but which have not yet reached their stable main-sequence phases.

Stars appear to form in batches within molecular clouds, perhaps in a repeating series of events which continues until the cloud is dissipated. The remnants of batches formed only tens of millions of years ago are seen today as youthful star clusters. Such clusters will disperse with time in the same way as the Sun's original cluster has dispersed – so that it is no longer possible to identify any cluster within which the Sun may have formed when it first came into existence nearly five billion years ago.

The Infrared Astronomical Satellite

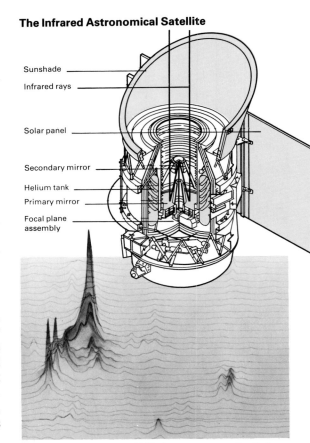

Sunshade

Infrared rays

Solar panel

Secondary mirror

Helium tank

Primary mirror

Focal plane assembly

▲ *This contour map from IRAS shows the strength of infrared emission at a wavelength of 100 micrometers in the Large Magellanic Cloud, our nearest neighbor galaxy. The high peak corresponds to the Tarantula nebula – a massive cloud that contains many large stars in the process of formation. Other discoveries by IRAS included the planetary system round Vega.*

Infrared radiation – the key to stellar births

Newly born stars, cocooned in dense clouds of dust, reveal their presence by the emission of infrared radiation from these clouds. This radiation is invisible to the human eye, and to make matters worse, most of what there is becomes absorbed by water vapor in the atmosphere. One of the best ground-based telescopes, the United Kingdom Infrared Telescope (UKIRT), is sited 4,300m up on the top of Mauna Kea in Hawaii, where it is above 90 percent of the atmospheric water vapor.

However, the Infrared Astronomical Satellite (IRAS), launched on 26 January 1983, has attained sensitivities almost 1,000 times better than UKIRT. To minimize the infrared radiation emitted by the telescope itself, the system was cooled to 2K by liquid helium; the usable lifetime of the satellite was limited by the time taken for the helium to boil off. The satellite weighed 1,076kg and surveyed the sky at wavelengths from 8 to 119 micrometers.

◄ *The Pleiades are a cluster of young stars. Although with the naked eye only six can be seen easily, there are several hundred stars in the cluster. Less than 50 million years old, they lie within a volume of space some 30 light years in diameter, about 400 light years distant. The brighter stars are surrounded by hazy nebulosity due to their light reflecting off dust particles.*

Binary and Variable Stars

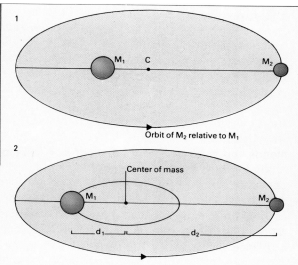

10

Describing double stars – astrometric, spectroscopic and eclipsing...Origins and behavior of double stars... Describing stars which vary in brightness – regularly or erratically...Stars that suddenly flare up or completely explode...PERSPECTIVE...Where mythology and astronomy coincide...Variable stars – the "standard candles" that determine intergalactic distances...The next candidate for a cataclysmic stellar outburst?

A binary consists of two stars which revolve round each other under their mutual gravitational attraction. More than half of all the stars exist as binaries or in multiple systems of up to six members. The orbital periods of binaries range from less than a day to hundreds of years, depending on the masses and separations of the stars.

In a "visual binary" the two stars are far enough apart to be seen telescopically as separate stars. Astronomers have identified about 70,000 visual binaries to date, most of them having separations of 10-100 astronomical units and orbital periods of decades or centuries. (An "optical double" consists of two stars which appear close together in the sky, but which actually lie at very different distances and are not physically connected.)

Astrometric binaries

The center of mass of a binary moves through space in a straight line, while the stars themselves revolve round the center of mass. Even if one member of a binary is too faint to be seen, the wobbling motion of the brighter companion gives its presence away: as it weaves to and fro, its position relative to the center of mass varies by an amount which depends on the relative masses of the two stars. A star which reveals the existence of an invisible companion in this way is known as an "astrometric binary". The faint white dwarf companion of Sirius was discovered in this way (◀ page 87), and several nearby stars, notably Barnard's star, wobble by such small amounts that their companions must be planets rather than stars.

Astrometric binaries

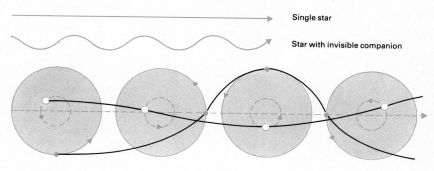

▲ *Of the two stars making up an astrometric binary, one is too faint to be seen. Both revolve around the center of mass of the system, the brighter and more massive lying closer to the center of mass. The combination of this motion with the straight-line motion of the center of mass, results in the visible star following a wobbly track across the sky.*

▲ *In a typical binary (1) the fainter companion (having mass M_2) seems to orbit round the more massive primary (M_1). In fact (2) both stars follow elliptical paths round the center of mass (C). The ratio of the two masses $M_1/M_2 = d_2/d_1$.*

Binary stars: scientific fact...
If the mean separation (a) of two members of a binary is given in astronomical units, and their orbital period (P) in years, it is possible to find the combined mass of the pair by applying Newton's law of gravitation to their motions. The combined mass is given by the simple relationship
$$M1+M2 = a^3/P^2$$
where M1 and M2 are the masses of the stars in solar masses. For example, if a binary has a period of 20 years and a mean separation of 10 astronomical units, the combined mass is $10^3/20^2 = {}^{1000}/_{400} = 2.5$ solar masses.

In fact, each star moves round the center of mass of the binary – a point which lies between the stars. If the two stars are of equal mass, the center of mass will be midway between them. However, if the masses are unequal, then just as a weightlifter's bar carrying unequal weights must be balanced at a point closer to the heavier weight, so the center of mass of the binary will lie closer to the more massive star.

...and ancient mythology
Some stars which appear to alter in brightness are not true variables, as was first thought: they are eclipsing binaries, of which the most famous example is Algol, in Perseus (◀ page 101). In mythology, Perseus was the hero who rescued the Princess Andromeda from the sea-monster Cetus. The monster was about to gobble her up when Perseus appeared, riding on his winged sandals, and turned it to stone by showing it the head of the Gorgon, Medusa, whom he had killed. Algol's position in the sky lies in Medusa's head, and the star "winks" in a sinister fashion every 2·87 days when the darker component of the binary pair blots out most of the light from the brighter one. Algol is known, naturally enough, as the Demon Star. Yet the "winking" of Algol was unknown before 1669, so that its position in Medusa's head is purely fortuitous.

In the image 1 labels: M_1, C, M_2 — Orbit of M_2 relative to M_1

Image 2 labels: Center of mass, M_1, M_2, d_1, d_2

Astrometric binaries diagram labels: Single star, Star with invisible companion

Binary stars are particularly rewarding subjects for the watcher with a small telescope

Spectroscopic binaries

In most binaries the stars are so close together that an Earth-based observer cannot see them as individuals. A "spectroscopic binary" is one which looks like a single star, but its spectrum consists of the combined spectra of two stars. As the stars revolve round each other, star A may be approaching the Earth while star B is receding. Due to the Doppler effect, the spectral lines of star A are blue-shifted, while those of star B are red-shifted. As the stars continue in their orbits they cross the line of sight, after which star A begins to recede while star B begins to approach. The spectral lines of A then become red-shifted and those of B become blue-shifted. The spectral lines from each star will thus oscillate to and fro in wavelength, so that the combined spectrum betrays the presence of two stars.

If one star is too faint for its light to register in the combined spectrum, the orbital motion of the visible star will nevertheless cause periodic variations in the wavelength of its spectral lines, and these variations reveal the presence of a binary companion. Stars of this type are known as "single-line binaries".

Spectroscopic binaries

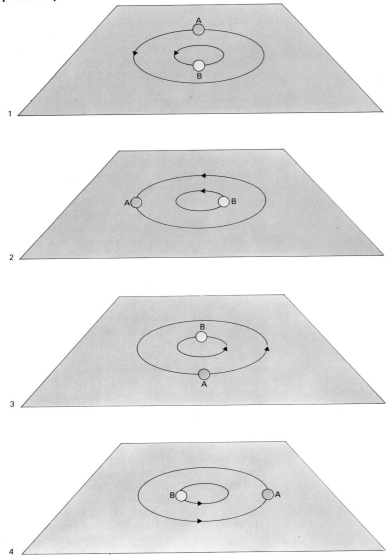

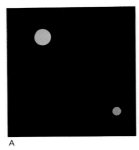

A

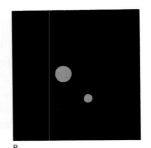

B

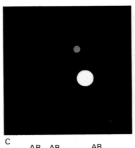

C

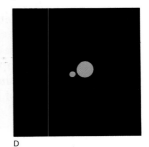

D

▲ *These visual binaries can be resolved by small telescopes (south is at top as seen in an astronomical telescope).*
(A) β Cygni – stars of magnitudes 3·2 and 5·5 separated by 34 arcsec (").
(B) γ Andromedae – magnitudes 2·2 and 5·5; separation 10".
(C) β Orionis (Rigel) – magnitudes 0·1 and 7·0; separation 9".
(D) α Scorpii (Antares) – magnitudes 1·0 and 6·5; separation 2·9".

◄ *Spectroscopic binaries. At stages (1) and (3) the stars are moving across the line of sight. There is no Doppler shift of their lines and the two sets merge at the same wavelengths. At (2) and (4) one star is approaching while the other is receding. One set of lines is blue-shifted and the other is red-shifted, so that the two sets are seen in the combined spectrum.*

▶ *Eclipsing binaries. (1) If two identical stars totally eclipse each other the minima in the light-curve are equally deep, but (2) if the orbital plane is tilted to the line of sight, the eclipses are partial and the minima shallower. (3) If the stars are unequal in size or luminosity the depths of the successive minima are different. The flat bottom of the minima shows the duration of the total (or annular) phase. (4) Unequal stars with partial eclipses: A is hotter and brighter than B. The primary minimum occurs when the dull star (B) eclipses the bright star (A).*

Eclipsing binaries

If the orbital plane of a binary is edge-on to the line of sight (or very nearly so), each star will pass in front of the other alternately, causing eclipses, so that what appears to be a single star shows regular changes in brightness. Such a star is called an "eclipsing binary". Usually an eclipsing binary is also a spectroscopic binary, and astronomers can obtain a great deal of information about the components. For example, plotting brightness against time gives a curve known as the "light-curve", and the shape of this reveals whether the eclipses are partial or total. Also, since measurements of the Doppler effect in the stars' spectra yield their orbital speeds, it is possible to calculate the size of each star from the duration of the eclipses and the time taken to fade from maximum to minimum brightness. If one star is more luminous than the other, the drop in brightness will usually be greater when the dimmer star eclipses the brighter. The dips in the light-curve will be unequal, the deeper of the two being known as the primary eclipse.

The best-known eclipsing binary is Algol, in Perseus. The primary eclipse is easy to see, as the brightness drops by about one magnitude.

Three types of close binary

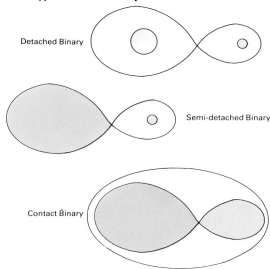

Detached Binary

Semi-detached Binary

Contact Binary

Eclipsing binaries

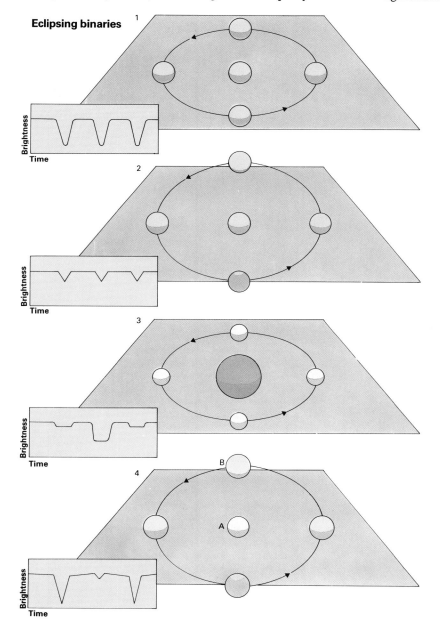

Brightness / Time (1)

Brightness / Time (2)

Brightness / Time (3)

Brightness / Time (4)

Life histories of binary stars

If the stars making up a binary are far apart, they were probably born as two separate protostars, but were sufficiently close together for gravity to keep them in orbit round each other. But many of the short-period, close binaries may have resulted from the splitting apart of a single protostar which, as it collapsed, spun too fast to hold itself together.

There is a three-dimensional figure-of-eight shape, known as an equipotential surface, around the two stars in a binary, and the force of gravity is equal at all points on this imaginary surface. The two parts of the curve, each containing one star, are called "Roche lobes" after Edouard Roche (1820-1883). Matter which lies inside a lobe remains under the influence of the star in that lobe. The nearer a star comes to filling its Roche lobe, the more distorted its shape becomes due to the gravitational attraction of its companion.

Some possible variations

When both components of a binary are on the main sequence they lie well inside their lobes, but if one star is more massive than the other it will evolve more rapidly towards the red giant stage. As it expands it may grow to fill, or even to exceed, its Roche lobe, and matter will flow from its surface through the crossover point of the figure-of-eight (the "inner Lagrangian point") towards the secondary. Although some material from the red giant may escape altogether from the system, substantial amounts of matter can be dumped on the secondary – enough to make a significant difference to its mass and to speed up its evolution. A system in which one star fills its lobe is called a "semi-detached binary." If both stars fill their lobes they form a "contact binary"; in addition to the eclipses, both of the stars show continuous brightness variations due to their changing apparent shapes as they revolve round each other.

Evolution may continue to a stage where the original primary becomes a collapsed star and the secondary becomes a red giant, filling its Roche lobe and dumping material onto its companion.

The identification of one type of variable star led, eventually, to the realization that our Galaxy is just one among many millions

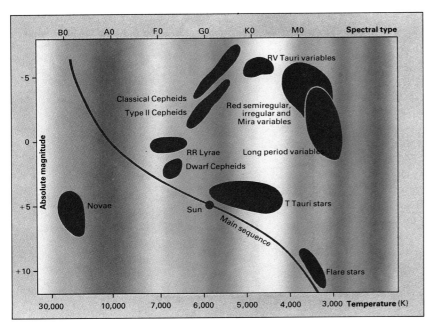

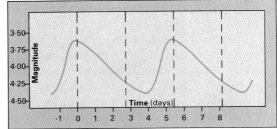

◀ *Variables have specific locations on the H-R diagram. Thus T Tauri stars are young pre-main sequence, and pulsating variables are old, becoming unstable late in their lives.*

▼ *The graphs show how the luminosity, temperature and radius of a Cepheid fluctuate throughout its cycle. The doppler effect in its spectrum reveals the expansion and contraction.*

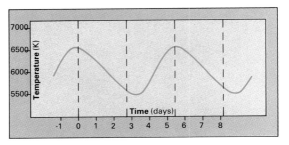

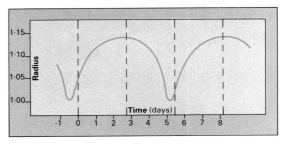

Variable stars

Variable stars are stars which vary in brightness. If such variations are due to some external influence – eclipsing binaries being the most obvious example – they are called "extrinsic variables"; if they vary because of genuine fluctuations in light output they are known as "intrinsic variables".

Astronomers classify variable stars according to how they vary. One group consists of stars that vary in a regular periodic manner, and these are subdivided into short-period variables and long-period variables according to whether their periods are shorter or longer than about 80 days. Semi-regular variables show variations of both period and amplitude, while irregular variables fluctuate in an erratic and unpredictable way. Most variables are pulsating or eruptive in nature.

Pulsating variables

These are stars which expand and contract as their brightness varies. The best-known examples are the Cepheid variables, named after δ Cephei, the first star of this type to be recognized. They vary in a regular and characteristic way, increasing in brightness rather more rapidly than they decrease, and having periods of between 1 and 60 days. The radius of a typical Cepheid varies by 10-20 percent, its light output fluctuates by about one magnitude, and there are also variations in its temperature and spectral class.

Pulsating variables "vibrate" at their natural frequency rather as a bell rings when struck. It is the periodic storage and release of energy in a layer some way below the star's surface that sustains these vibrations. The layer consists of partly ionized helium (some of the helium atoms have lost electrons) and electrons. As the star contracts the ionization increases (more electrons are stripped off) and the layer becomes more effective at trapping outgoing radiation. Eventually the stored radiation builds up enough pressure to push out the outer layers of the star, which then cool down and become less opaque, so allowing the stored radiation to escape. The star then shrinks and initiates another cycle of expansion and contraction. The pulsation cycle continues for as long as the right conditions exist inside the star.

Two types of Cepheid variables

Type I Cepheids are very bright F and G-type giants and supergiants with absolute magnitudes of −2 to −6. They are relatively young massive stars which have evolved away from the main sequence. Their period of variation is related to their brilliance by a "period-luminosity law": the longer the period the greater the luminosity. Cepheids are so bright that they are visible at very great distances, and observers can pick them out in other galaxies by their variability. Measuring their periods enables scientists to work out their luminosities or absolute magnitudes using the period-luminosity law, and comparing their apparent and absolute magnitudes can then reveal their distances.

Type II Cepheids, also known as W Virginis stars, show a similar pattern of behavior but are about two magnitudes fainter. They are older low-mass stars which have evolved away from the main sequence and have reached the stage where they are "burning" helium in their cores. RR Lyrae stars are a closely related type, commonly occurring in globular star clusters. Their mean absolute magnitudes are about 0·5 and their periods range from 0·3 to 1 day.

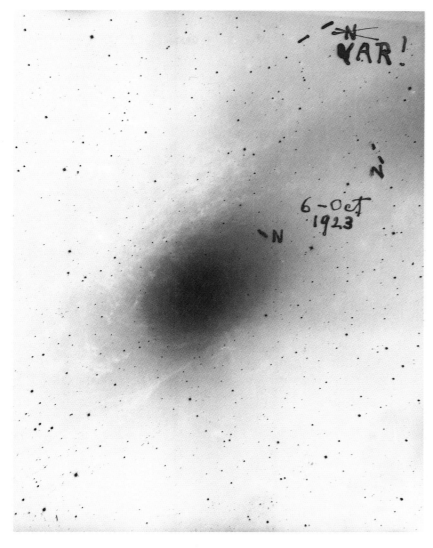

Cepheid variables and intergalactic distances

The parallax method of distance determination (◀ page 83) works well for distances up to about 300 light years, but breaks down after that because the shifts become too small to be measurable. It is then necessary to use less direct methods, most of which involve using spectroscopes to work out the real light output of a star: from this, it is possible to work out its distance.

However, there are some short-period variable stars, known as Cepheids after δ Cephei, the brightest member of the class, which reveal their luminosity by the manner in which they brighten and fade. The longer the period, the more powerful the star. Cepheids thus act as "standard candles", and because they are so luminous they are visible over great distances.

A crucial discovery

In 1912 an American astronomer at Harvard, Henrietta Leavitt (1868-1921), was studying some photographs of the Small Magellanic Cloud. This looks rather like a detached part of the Milky Way, and although it was known to be a distinct system, astronomers still believed that it was contained within our Galaxy. Miss Leavitt found Cepheid variables in the Cloud, and realized that the brighter Cepheids were those with the longest periods. For practical purposes it was reasonable to regard all the stars in the Cloud as lying at the same distance from Earth, and therefore the longer-period stars really were the more powerful.

The discovery was even more important than Miss Leavitt appreciated, because it led on to final proof that the so-called spiral nebulae are external systems, millions of light years away. In 1923 the American astronomer Edwin Hubble (1889-1953) detected Cepheids in some of the spirals. He determined their distances and found that they were much too remote to belong to our Galaxy. This could only mean that the systems in which they lay were also external. Hubble estimated the distance of the Andromeda spiral as 900,000 light years, which he later amended to 750,000 light years. Herschel, long before, had suggested that the spirals might be "island universes", but had been unable to obtain any proof.

▲ Edwin Hubble found the first Cepheid variable in a spiral galaxy while studying this historic plate. His triumphant "VAR!" marks the event.

◀ Miss Henrietta Swan Leavitt, who discovered Cepheid variables in the Small Magellanic Cloud.

▶ The best-known example of a long-period variable is Mira Ceti, in the constellation of Cetus, which varies in brightness between magnitudes 3 and 9 over a period of about 332 days as shown by its light-curve. On each cycle it disappears from naked-eye view for more than 200 days; its temperature varies between about 2,600K and 1,700K. Long-period variables such as Mira Ceti are red M-type giants, so cool that they emit most strongly in the infrared.

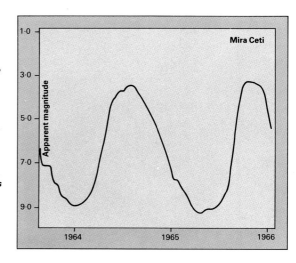

The next cataclysmic outburst?

Eta Carinae is a very peculiar star which lies at a distance of some 6,500 light years from Earth, within the spectacular η Carinae nebula. Despite its great distance, during the 1840s η Carinae became for a time the second brightest star in the sky, reaching an apparent magnitude of about −1. Thereafter it faded to about magnitude 7. The star itself is no longer visible, but lies within a compact cloud of gas and dust, known as the Homunculus nebula, which is expanding at a rate of about 500km per second. Physicists believe that the star is at least a hundred times more massive than the Sun, and several million times more luminous. Dust grains heated by the star make η Carinae the brightest star in the sky at infrared wavelengths of around 10 micrometers.

Astronomers are not certain whether η Carinae is a massive young star which has not yet reached the main sequence, or a highly evolved star approaching the end of its life. However, recent observations of nitrogen-rich blobs of matter which may have been expelled from the star support the view that it has evolved sufficiently far to produce nitrogen by nuclear reactions and that it cannot, therefore, be a protostar. If η Carinae is well advanced in its evolution, then, because it is so massive, it is likely to end in a cataclysmic outburst – a supernova. When this happens, it will probably outshine Venus in our skies.

Four views of η Carinae. In true color (left) the Carina nebula is a staggering 300 light years across. The two X-ray views (above and below) are approximately in the same scale as the optical view and show η Carinae in the center. In the color-coded version blue is the least intense, white the most. The nebula around η Carinae, called the "Homunculus" – the "little man" (right) – contains as much matter as ten Suns.

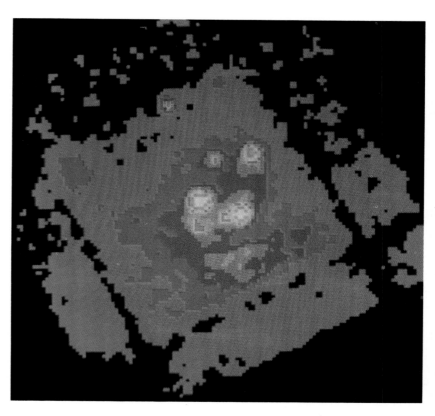

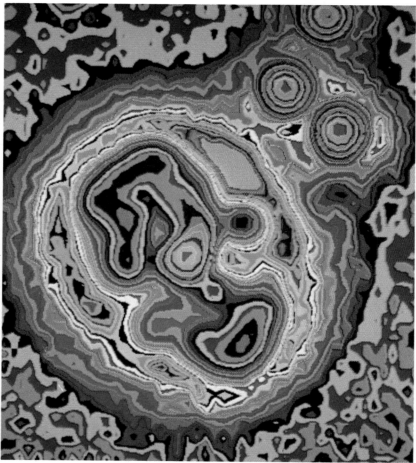

See also
The Basic Properties of Stars 83-90
Birth, Life and Death of Stars 91-98
Black Holes 107-110

Irregular and eruptive variables

Among the different kinds of irregular variables the group known as T Tauri stars is particularly interesting. Their spectra show that these are young, rapidly rotating stars which are blowing into space as much as 10^{-7} solar masses of material per year. They are enveloped in clouds of gas and dust, and their variability may be due to a combination of intrinsic and extrinsic factors, such as flares in their atmospheres and fluctuations in the density of the swirling clouds of enveloping dust.

Flare stars, otherwise known as UV Ceti stars, are cool dim M-type stars on the lower end of the main sequence which flare up suddenly once or twice a day. Typically they increase in brightness by one or two magnitudes in seconds, then fade back to normal in a few minutes. Astronomers think that the flares are similar to, but more spectacular than, flares which occur on the Sun due to the sudden release of energy stored by localized powerful magnetic fields.

Novae

A nova ("novae" is the plural) is a star which flares up within a matter of hours, or at most a few days, increasing in brightness by a factor of between ten thousand and one million. The nova then declines back to its previous luminosity, over a couple of months, in the case of Nova Cygni, or a number of years. A typical nova expels a shell of matter containing up to one hundred-thousandth of the star's mass.

Novae occur in close binary systems in which one member is a hot compact body such as a white dwarf. The larger component dumps material onto the compact star, or into a disk of matter around it, and this material undergoes violent explosive burning to result in the flare up. Recurrent novae repeat this pattern at intervals of a few decades, while so-called dwarf novae show repeated nova-like outbursts, brightening by two to five magnitudes, at intervals of tens or hundreds of days.

Supernovae

Supernovae are exploding stars which can become ten billion times more luminous than the Sun and, for a short time, can outshine entire galaxies. The explosion completely disrupts the star, throwing most of its material into space and leaving at most a tiny collapsed remnant (◀ page 92).

Type I supernovae occur among older stars and Type II supernovae among younger stars. The light-curves of Type I supernovae show a steep rise in brightness to an absolute magnitude of about −19 followed by a fairly slow decline of about 0·5 magnitudes per month. Type II supernovae show a similarly sharp rise, but are about two magnitudes fainter at maximum, and go through a period of faster, more irregular fading, before settling to a long, slow decline.

R Coronae Borealis stars

Among the most peculiar of variables, stars like R Coronae Borealis have been described as being rather like "novae in reverse" because they suffer sudden and irregular drops in brightness, declining by as much as ten magnitudes (a factor of 10,000) and then returning to normal between the events. They are supergiants with carbon-rich atmospheres and it is possible that the sudden minima result from the accumulation of clouds of carbon dust which are eventually blown away, allowing the star to revert to its normal brightness.

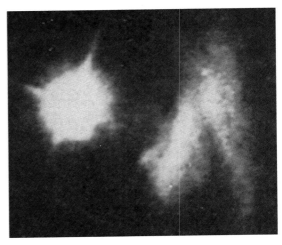

▲ *T Tauri seen with neighboring nebulosity (right).*

▼ *Typical light curves and periods are shown for a T Tauri star (1), a nova (2), a Type 1 supernova (3) and R Coronae Borealis (4).*

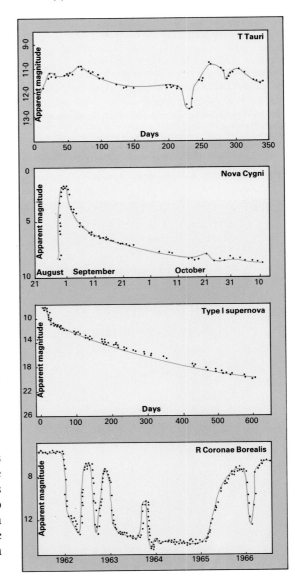

Black Holes

11

Describing a black hole...Black holes as cosmic energy generators...Black holes and X-ray emissions – the evidence so far...Supermassive or mini black holes?... Can black holes evaporate?...PERSPECTIVE...The "effect" of a black hole on a passing astronaut... Black holes and fringe ideas

A black hole is a region of space into which matter has fallen and from which nothing, not even light itself, can escape. If a lump of matter is compressed, the force of gravity and the value of escape velocity at its surface increase. If it is squeezed within a radius known as the Schwarzschild radius, escape velocity exceeds the speed of light and gravity prevents light from escaping into space. Thereafter gravity overwhelms all other forces and the body collapses to a point of infinite density known as a "singularity". A black hole is the region of space around the singularity, with a radius equal to the Schwarzschild radius, within which gravity is so powerful that nothing can move outwards. Matter or radiation can fall in and be sucked down to the central singularity, but nothing can get out. The term "black hole" is entirely appropriate, as it is a "hole" in the sense that matter can fall in, and "black" in the sense that no light, radiation or matter can get out. The boundary of a black hole is called the "event horizon", because no means exists by which information about events occurring within it could be communicated to the universe outside.

The Schwarzschild radius R_s (in kilometers) for a mass M can be calculated from the simple formula $R_s = 3M/M_\odot$, where $M_\odot$ denotes the mass of the Sun. The Schwarzschild radius for the Sun is about 3km, while that of the Earth is about 1cm, and there is no natural process in the present-day universe which can compress either of these bodies sufficiently to form a black hole. However, one way in which a black hole can be formed is by the collapse of a massive star which has run out of nuclear fuel, and which is too massive to become either a white dwarf or a neutron star. Such a star will collapse without limit, for there is no known force capable of halting the process, but before collapsing to infinite density it will pass inside its Schwarzschild radius and disappear from view. A black hole formed from the collapse of a 10 solar-mass star would have a radius of some 30km.

A black hole

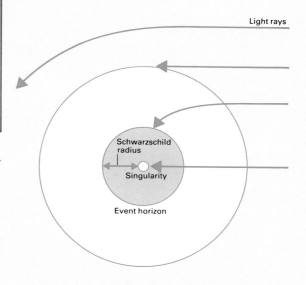

▲ The boundary, or event horizon, of a non-rotating black hole has a radius equal to the Schwarzschild radius (R_s). Not even light can escape from within this region. A passing ray of light will be deflected by the gravitational field of the black hole. If it approaches to 1·5 R_s it may be bent into a circular orbit (orbiting light rays form the "photon sphere") while if it comes still closer it will fall into the event horizon.

Object	Mass	Schwarzschild Radius (R_s)	Density when object reaches R_s (kg/m²)
Small mountain	10^{12}kg	$1\cdot5\times10^{-15}$m	10^{56}
The Earth	6×10^{24}kg	9mm	10^{30}
The Sun	2×10^{30}kg (=1$M_\odot$)	3km	10^{19}
100 million Suns	$10^{8}M_\odot$	3×10^{8}km (=2 astronomical units	10^{-3} (= water density)
Entire Galaxy	$10^{11}M_\odot$	0·03 light years	10^{-3}

NB density figures are rounded to the nearest power of 10

The making of a black hole

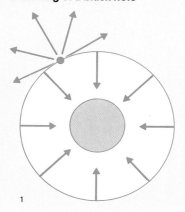
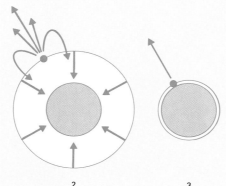

1   2   3   4   5

◄ As a star begins to collapse (1) light can escape from its surface at any angle, but as the collapse accelerates (2) the surface gravity increases rapidly and rays of light emitted at shallow angles are bent back. Just before it reaches its Schwarzschild radius (3) only vertical rays can escape. As soon as the star collapses inside that radius gravity prevents any light from escaping and the star immediately vanishes from view (4). An event horizon is formed and the entire mass of the star then falls into a singularity (5).

Down into a black hole – a one-way voyage to the most exotic regions known to physics

Black holes as cosmic energy generators

Since stars rotate, it is reasonable to expect black holes formed from collapsing stars to be rotating rapidly. Outside the event horizon of a spinning black hole there is a region, called the "ergosphere", within which nothing can avoid being dragged round in the direction of the black hole's rotation – it is as if space itself were spinning round with the black hole. In principle it is possible for particles to enter the ergosphere and, if they are moving fast enough, escape again with more energy than they had originally. It has been speculated that the ergosphere of a black hole could be used as an energy source.

Black holes and X-ray emissions

Matter falling in towards the event horizon of a black hole is accelerated until it approaches the speed of light, releasing copious quantities of energy before vanishing across the event horizon. If a black hole is a member of a close binary system, matter dragged in from the companion star falls into a circulating accretion disk. Friction in the disk causes matter to spiral in towards the event horizon, and the high temperatures generated by the infalling matter result in the emission of X-rays from the inner part of the disk.

Most astronomers agree that some cosmic X-ray sources are of this type. The best evidence for this view comes from Cygnus X-1, a powerful, rapidly fluctuating X-ray source in the constellation of Cygnus. Cygnus X-1 coincides in position with a hot blue supergiant of 20-30 solar masses, which has an invisible companion of some 9-11 solar masses – far in excess of the maximum possible mass for a neutron star. The X-ray emission seems to come from an accretion disk of material swirling round the invisible companion drawn from the visible star. Although there is no conclusive proof, the evidence is strong that Cygnus X-1, at a distance of some 8,000 light years, contains a black hole.

Similar cases include the binary X-ray nova AO620-00 in Monoceros and LMC X-3, in the Large Magellanic Cloud. LMC X-3 may be a member of a binary system comprising a B-type main sequence star and a dark object of between 6 and 14 solar masses.

A rotating black hole

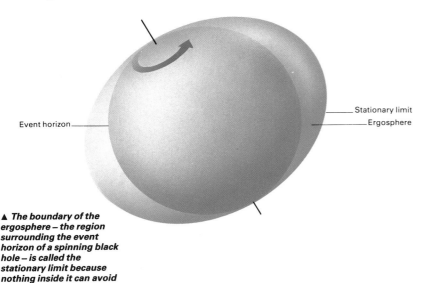

Event horizon

Stationary limit
Ergosphere

▲ *The boundary of the ergosphere – the region surrounding the event horizon of a spinning black hole – is called the stationary limit because nothing inside it can avoid being dragged round.*

An astronaut stretched on the cosmic rack

Although the star itself has vanished from view, the resultant black hole still exerts a powerful gravitational influence on its surroundings, and one way in which this would make itself felt is in strong tidal effects on neighboring matter.

For example, if an astronaut were falling feet first towards the hole, his feet, being closer to the black hole than his head, would be subject to stronger gravitational force, and this difference in attraction would stretch him apart on a cosmic "rack" of ever-increasing severity. Close to the event horizon of a 10 solar-mass black hole the tidal force would be equivalent to that which a person would experience swinging from a bridge with the entire population of London or New York dangling from his ankles. Any material body approaching the event horizon of such a black hole would be torn to shreds by "tidal forces".

In the illustration (below) the arrows indicate schematically the gravitational forces acting on the astronaut's head and feet. The larger the black hole the weaker are the tidal forces near its event horizon. Strong tidal forces would not occur until well inside a supermassive black hole.

The cosmic space rack

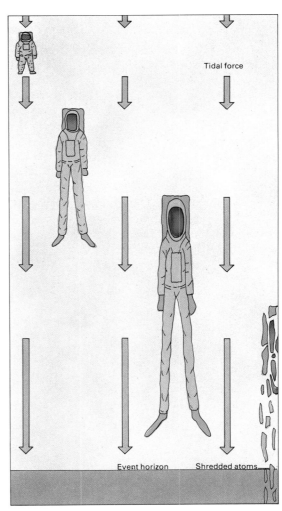

Tidal force

Event horizon   Shredded atoms

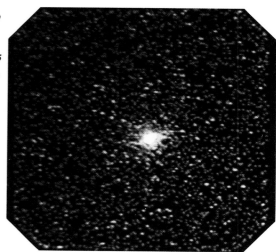

Cygnus X-1

1 Center of supergiant primary
2 Center of mass
3 Hot spot
4 Black hole
5 Accretion disk
6 Orbit of supergiant
7 Orbit of black hole

▲ *Cygnus X-1 is thought to be a binary – of 5·6 day period – comprising an O or B supergiant and an invisible companion of 9-15 solar masses – believed to be a black hole. Because of the rotation of the binary, matter torn from the star does not fall directly into the hole but instead joins a fast-spinning disk of matter around the hole. The temperature of this "accretion disk" is so high that X-rays are emitted. Matter on the inside of the disk eventually spirals in through the event horizon.*

◄ ▶ *Cygnus X-1 – an optical view (left) and an X-ray view (right).*

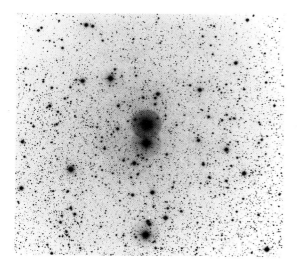

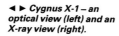

See also
Birth Life and Death of Stars 91-98

At the frontiers of knowledge

In principle a black hole could be made from any mass of material provided it can be compressed within its Schwarzschild radius. It is perfectly possible for black holes of millions or even billions of solar masses to exist, and many scientists believe that objects of this kind exist in the cores of violently active galaxies and quasars, and even in the core of our own Galaxy. It has also been suggested that if the universe began in a hot dense state, mini or "primordial" black holes with masses of only a few billion tonnes might have been formed in the extreme conditions which existed in those early instants.

An intriguing suggestion, made by Professor Stephen Hawking, is that black holes may not be as black as they were thought to be, but that particles may be able to leak out of them at a very slow rate. For a stellar-mass black hole the leakage would be utterly negligible, but, since the suggestion is that the leakage rate is inversely proportional to mass, a mini black hole would radiate particles at a significant rate. The more mass it lost, the greater the evaporation rate would become, until, finally, the mini black hole would explode in a blast of gamma rays and exotic nuclear particles. Nobody has ever observed an event of this kind, and mini black holes remain strictly a theoretical concept; but if such an event is ever seen to occur, it will be a most dramatic demonstration of the link between gravity, the universe and the exotic world of particle physics.

Black holes probably exist in a wide variety of forms throughout the universe; the evidence in favor of both stellar-mass and super-massive black holes, although not indisputable, is quite convincing.

◀ *Professor Stephen Hawking of the University of Cambridge has made fundamental advances in our understanding of gravity and black holes. In 1971 he proposed the possible existence of mini-black holes and in 1974 suggested that particles might be able to leak out of black holes.*

▼ *When a particle and antiparticle pair is formed in the gravitational field of a black hole one member of the pair may fall in while the other escapes and appears to an outside observer as a particle emitted by the hole.*

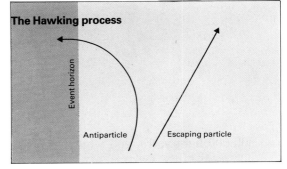

The Hawking process

Event horizon

Antiparticle

Escaping particle

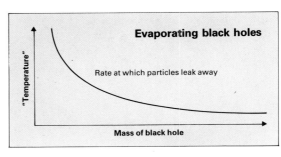

Evaporating black holes

"Temperature"

Rate at which particles leak away

Mass of black hole

An exploding mini-black hole

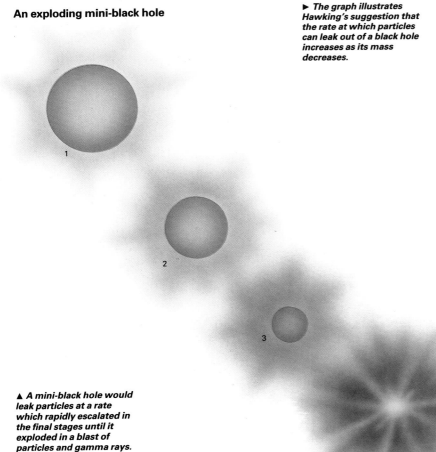

1

2

3

▲ *A mini-black hole would leak particles at a rate which rapidly escalated in the final stages until it exploded in a blast of particles and gamma rays.*

▶ *The graph illustrates Hawking's suggestion that the rate at which particles can leak out of a black hole increases as its mass decreases.*

Can particles leak out of black holes?

The "uncertainty principle", proposed in 1927 by Werner Heisenberg, implies that on a subatomic scale we cannot simultaneously measure both energy and time precisely. The more accurately one is known the more uncertain the other becomes. In 1974 Stephen Hawking applied this concept to black holes. Over a fleetingly short instant of time the uncertainty principle allows enough energy to appear in a tiny volume of space to create a particle and its antiparticle. These almost immediately collide and annihilate so that their brief existence cannot be observed and there is no net creation of particles in the universe. However, this process is enhanced in the powerful gravitational field of a black hole, and the strong tidal forces can sometimes cause one member of a pair to fall into the black hole and the other to escape, as if, to a distant observer, it had emerged out of the event horizon. This process takes energy from the gravitational field of the hole and so reduces the black hole's mass to a point where, given sufficient time, it could evaporate completely.

The size and structure of our Galaxy...Globular star clusters...The Sun's orbit in the Galaxy...The galactic corona...The spiral arms fully revealed...The galactic center – an intriguing puzzle...The evolution of the Galaxy...PERSPECTIVE...The first observations...The Milky Way seen in five wavelengths...Estimating the age and size of the Galaxy..."The great debate" – were the spiral nebulae within our Galaxy?

Our Galaxy contains more than 100 billion stars, most of which are concentrated, together with clouds of gas and dust, into a flattened system 80,000 to 100,000 light years in diameter.

The greatest concentration of stars is in the nuclear bulge, a flattened sphere some 15,000 light years in radius. Surrounding this bulge is a disk 40,000 to 50,000 light years in radius but less than 3,000 light years thick, which, in addition to stars, contains most of the gas and dust in the Galaxy. Outside this is a nearly spherical distribution of widely separated stars and massive globular star clusters extending to a radius of some 75,000 light years. This is known as the "halo". Recent observations have produced evidence to suggest that the halo is itself surrounded by a tenuous but much more extensive "corona" of invisible matter which extends to a distance of between 200,000 and 300,000 light years, and which may contain up to 90 percent of the total mass of the Galaxy.

It is difficult to determine the size and structure of the Galaxy because the Solar System lies inside the galactic disk, and clouds of dust obscure the view towards the center. That the basic shape is a flattened disk is obvious from the appearance of the Milky Way – the faint band of starlight which encircles the celestial sphere and is readily seen on a clear moonless night. A telescope reveals the Milky Way to be composed of millions of individual stars spread out in a thin but extensive disk. In recent years, observers have studied the Milky Way at wavelengths ranging from gamma rays to radio waves, infrared and radio waves being particularly valuable in the study of galactic structure since they are unaffected by the dust.

The Galaxy's basic structure

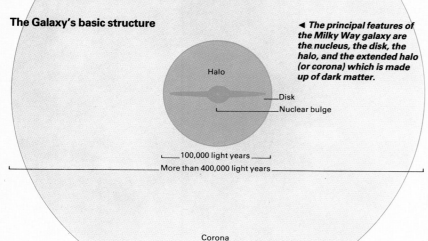

◀ *The principal features of the Milky Way galaxy are the nucleus, the disk, the halo, and the extended halo (or corona) which is made up of dark matter.*

Halo

Disk
Nuclear bulge

100,000 light years
More than 400,000 light years

Corona

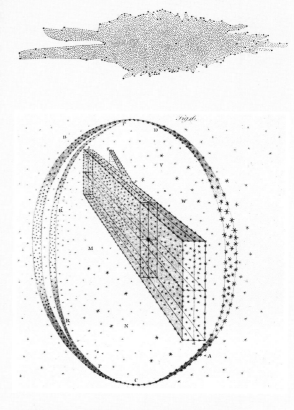

▲ *William Herschel's diagrams of the Milky Way.*

Exploring the stars of the Milky Way

On a clear dark night when the sky is studded with stars it is easy for a person without prior knowledge to think that they number in their millions. Yet appearances are deceptive: in all, naked-eye observers will be lucky to see as many as 2,500 stars at any one time.

Using binoculars or a telescope changes the situation. The total rises to millions, and to count them is a physical impossibility. Therefore, in order to estimate the number of stars in the Galaxy, at the end of the 18th century the German-English astronomer William Herschel (1738-1822) decided to count the stars in selected areas and average out the results. While making his survey, he confirmed that stars were concentrated into the band of the Milky Way and tended to be increasingly sparse in other directions. On this evidence he envisaged a star system shaped like "cloven grindstone", which is a reasonably accurate description of the shape of the Galaxy.

Other important observations that Herschel made in the course of his survey concerned the nebulae. Noticing that the "starry nebulae" tended to avoid the region of the Milky Way, while the "irresolvable nebulae" (which he correctly took to be gas clouds) were common there, he suggested that the former might be external star systems. But the idea met with only a lukewarm reception and Herschel himself later expressed grave doubts about this crucially important observation.

Astronomers are now looking into what was, until quite recently, one of the obscurest regions in space – the center of our own Galaxy

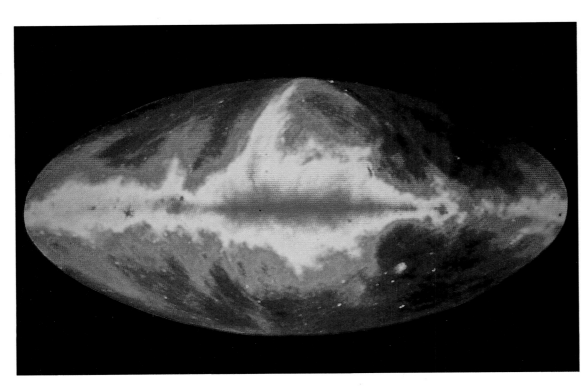

◄ *This map of the radio sky is the result of 15 years' work with three radio telescopes. Emissions are strongest in the plane of the Milky Way: the black regions are dark at radio wavelengths. Since these wavelengths can penetrate the interstellar dust, this map gives an accurate, hitherto unobtainable portrait of our Galaxy.*

► *The X-ray sky is shown here in the same projection as the Lund Observatory map. Two X-ray bursters are shown, that at top left as seen by three detectors, the one at lower right (in the Small Magellanic Cloud) by a single one. The map was made by the Vela 5B satellite in 1972, and the positions of the X-ray bursters added later.*

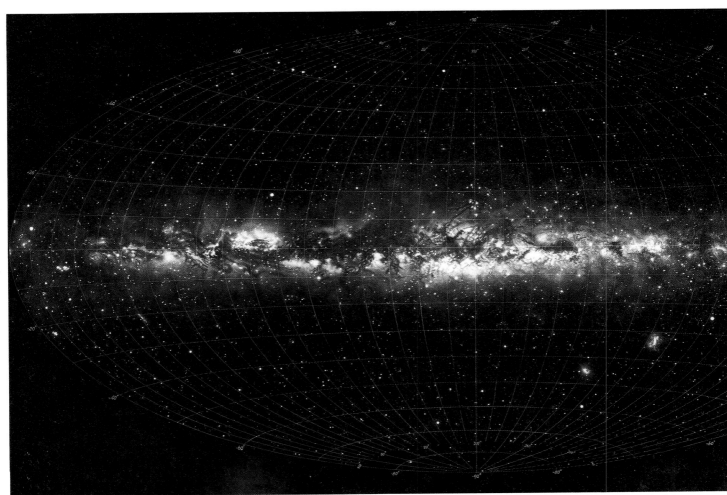

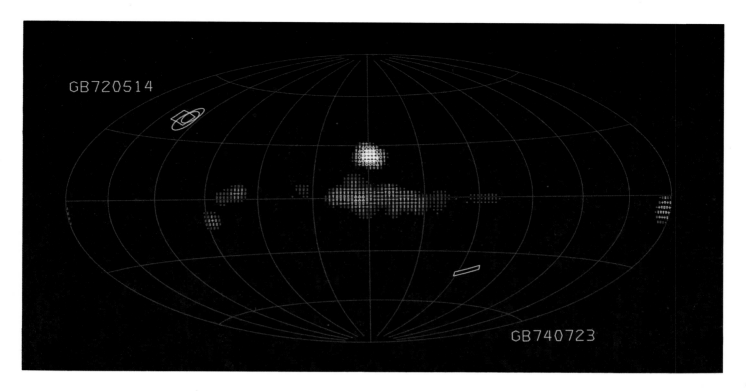

GB720514

GB740723

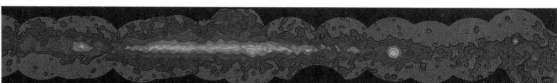

▲ In this gamma-ray map of the Milky Way, made by the European satellite COS-B, the colors show the intensity of the radiation, yellow being the areas of strongest emission.

◄ This composite map of the whole sky was compiled from photographs by a team of astronomers at the Lund Observatory in Sweden. The constellation of Auriga is at the extreme left and right, while Sagittarius is in the center. The extreme 360° "fish eye" view causes distortions, but each rectangle covers an equivalent area.

► This false-color infrared image obtained by the IRAS satellite shows the distribution of dust along the plane of the Milky Way and across the galactic center. The temperature of the dust ranges from about 30K (red) to about 250K (blue).

Recent studies suggest there may be ten times more material in the Milky Way than anybody has so far been able to observe

Globular star clusters and the scale of the Galaxy

The galactic halo contains about 200 globular star clusters, and these are distributed fairly uniformly round the galactic center. A typical globular cluster contains hundreds of thousands of stars and, because many of them lie above or below the plane of the Milky Way, they are not heavily obscured by dust. Some of the stars are of the RR Lyrae type – variable stars of known luminosity (◀ page 102). Comparing the apparent brightness of an RR Lyrae star with its known luminosity can reveal its distance – and hence the distance of the cluster in which it lies. Studies of the distance and distribution of globular clusters show that the Sun is about 28,000 light years away from the center of the Galaxy, which lies in the direction of Sagittarius.

Almost all the young O and B-type stars, the dense clouds in which stars are forming, the illuminated HII regions and the young open star clusters lie in the galactic disk. Rather confusingly, the younger stars, which contain higher proportions of heavy elements and which lie close to the galactic plane, are called "Population I" stars, while the older stars of the halo and bulge are known as "Population II."

The rotating Galaxy

The Galaxy is rotating, with the Sun moving at about 230km per second in a near-circular orbit round the galactic center and taking about 220 million years to complete each orbit. Most Population I stars in the disk move in the same direction as the Sun, also in near-circular orbits, but many of the Population II stars follow elliptical orbits at quite steep angles to the galactic plane.

Shapley's determination of distance

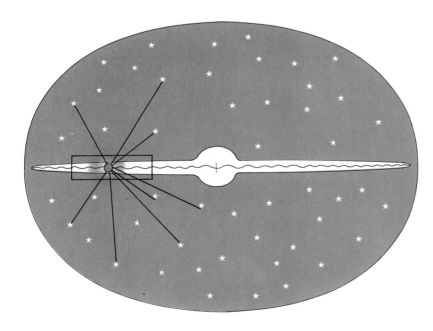

▲ *Interstellar dust is concentrated in the plane of the Galaxy and restricts optical astronomers to observing a limited part (boxed). Most globular clusters lie above and below the galactic plane and thus are not heavily obscured by dust. Shapley assumed that the center of the system of globular clusters coincided with the center of the Galaxy. He then estimated the Galaxy's size by measuring their distances.*

◀ *Dr Harlow Shapley, the first astronomer to work out accurately the size of the Milky Way, was Director of the Harvard College Observatory for over thirty years.*

▼ *M13, the brilliant globular cluster in the constellation of Hercules, was discovered by Edmond Halley in 1714. The most prominent globular cluster in the northern hemisphere, it is 22,500 light years away.*

Harlow Shapley and the size of the Galaxy

Most of the credit for accurately measuring the size of the Galaxy must go to the American astronomer Harlow Shapley (1885-1972), who joined the staff of Mount Wilson Observatory in 1914. Shapley was aware of the relationship between the period of a Cepheid variable and its real luminosity: this had been established by observations of the short-period variables in the Small Magellanic Cloud made by Henrietta Leavitt (◀ page 95). Studying the Cepheid variables in the globular clusters, Shapley found that they lay round the boundary of the main Galaxy. He also deduced from their uneven distribution (most of the globular clusters lie in the southern hemisphere) that instead of being centrally placed in the Galaxy, the Sun was about 50,000 light years out towards the edge.

The Great Debate of 1920

Shapley's determination of the size of the Galaxy was of the correct order. However, at that time he still believed the spiral nebulae to be contained in the Galaxy. This view was challenged by another American astronomer, Heber Doust Curtis (1872-1942), then of the Lick Observatory. Curtis believed that the spirals were extragalactic, and that the Galaxy itself was very much smaller than Shapley had estimated. The whole problem was made the subject of a "great debate" between Shapley and Curtis, held at a meeting of the National Academy of Sciences in 1920. The debate itself was inconclusive, but history has shown that Shapley was closer in his estimate of the size of the Galaxy, and wrong in believing the spirals were members of it, so the final verdict can be seen as a draw.

Estimating the age of the Galaxy

Globular clusters, in common with the halo and the nuclear bulge, contain old, metal-deficient stars that were born early in the history of the Galaxy, when it was composed almost entirely of hydrogen and helium, and before the heavier elements generated inside stars were blown into space in supernova explosions. The ages of the clusters are revealed in their H-R diagrams, which show that the only main-sequence stars they contain are old, low-mass stars. All others have evolved to the red giant stage and beyond. Studies of this kind show that the Galaxy must be at least 12 billion years old.

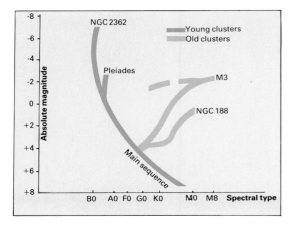

Stars closer to the galactic center have shorter orbital periods than those which are farther away, but they do not behave like planets traveling round the Sun. The mass of the Galaxy is spread out over a vast volume and the speed of a star is determined not only by its distance, but also by the mass which lies between it and the center. The greater the distance of the star, the greater the mass acting upon it.

Close to the galactic center, velocities are quite high. They decrease towards the outer fringe of the nucleus, and then farther out they increase to about 230km per second at the Sun's distance, and to some 300km per second at a radius of 60,000 light years.

The galactic corona

The high speeds of stars in the outermost parts of the galactic disk imply that a large fraction of the Galaxy's mass lies in the fringes of the system. If this were not so, the speeds of stars would begin to decrease at distances beyond that of the Sun. One high-speed RR Lyrae star, nine globular clusters, 3 dwarf elliptical galaxies and the two Magellanic Clouds are known to lie at distances between 65,000 and 200,000 light years from the galactic center. If, as appears to be the case, they are all part of the halo, then it is possible to calculate from their speeds how massive the Galaxy must be in order to prevent these objects from escaping into intergalactic space. This mass turns out to be between 1,000 billion and 2,000 billion solar masses.

This mass consists of neither luminous stars nor neutral hydrogen, or it would be visible. Possibly it consists of cool planet-sized lumps of matter, old dead stars, or very low-mass stars too faint to be seen.

▲ *H-R diagram showing that faint stars in galactic clusters are on the main sequence.*

▶ *All the stars within our Galaxy are following orbits centered on the galactic nucleus. Stars closer to the center overtake the Sun because they are moving in smaller orbits. Stars farther out lag progressively farther behind. The spiral pattern is a "density wave" rotating independently at about half the Sun's rate. Stars and gas clouds pass periodically into and out of the spiral arms.*

▼ *The rotation curve shows how the speeds of stars and gas clouds, orbiting the galactic center, vary with distance from the center.*

Galactic rotation

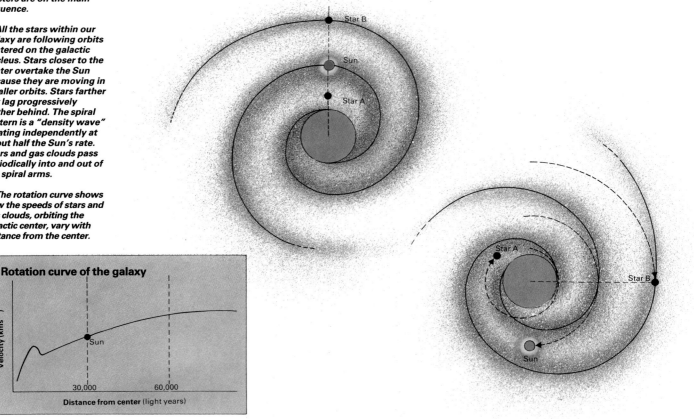

100,000 light years

10,000 light years

1,000 light years

100 light years

◄ *The structure of our Galaxy. The spiral structure in the Sun's locality is deduced from optical observations; the large-scale distribution of gas is revealed by radio observations. The true core of the Galaxy coincides with a compact radio source which may contain a black hole.*

The spiral structure of the galactic disk

Like many other galaxies, the disk of the Milky Way has a lumpy, coiled structure as if the stars and gas clouds were arranged along the arms of a spiral spreading out from the nuclear bulge. The basic scheme has two arms extending from opposite sides of the nucleus, and wound round quite tightly into a Catherine-wheel shape. An alternative view suggests a four-arm spiral, although in practice observations do not show a simple, clear-cut pattern.

The positions of the spiral arms in the Sun's locality can be picked out optically by studies of the distribution of bright O and B-type stars, HII regions and galactic clusters. The Sun is near the inside edge of a spiral arm, known as the Orion arm. The Perseus arm lies about 6,000 light years farther out from the center and the Sagittarius arm some 6,000 light years farther in. The Carina arm meets the Sagittarius arm at the Carina nebula and there is evidence for another – the Centaurus arm – closer again to the galactic center.

Neutral hydrogen extends in a thin disk to about twice the Sun's distance from the galactic center, but most of the molecular hydrogen and the dense molecular clouds are concentrated into a broad ring with its inner and outer edges at 12,000 and 25,000 light years respectively from the center. This is where most of the current bout of star-formation is taking place.

The nuclear bulge

Very little hydrogen is present within a radius of about 12,000 light years of the galactic center, but there are many old red stars, increasing in concentration towards the center. There is an expanding ring of gas – known as the "3 kiloparsec arm" – lying at a distance of just under 10,000 light years from the center, and containing some 30 million solar masses of gas. This may have been expelled from the nucleus some 30 million years ago, and was possibly responsible for sweeping much of the gas and dust out of the central regions. Closer in, there is an expanding disk of atomic and molecular hydrogen apparently tilted at an angle of nearly 20° to the galactic plane, and at a radius of about 100 light years there is a ring of massive molecular clouds and ionized clouds heated to some 10,000K by hot young stars. There is another, slightly cooler ring about 30 light years from the center, while inside a radius of 10 light years there are vast numbers of stars and fast-moving ionized clouds.

The structure of the Galaxy	
A	The Galaxy and corona
B	The galactic disk
C	The local spiral arms
D	Nuclear HI disk
E	Expanding molecular ring

Details of the local spiral arms	
1	Centaurus arm
2	Sagittarius arm
3	Orion arm
4	Perseus arm
5	NGC 6231
6	Triffid nebula
7	Eagle nebula
8	Wild Duck nebula
9	Omega nebula
10	Lagoon nebula
11	Eta Carinae nebula
12	Gum nebula
13	Ring nebula
14	North America nebula
15	The Sun
16	M35
17	Orion nebula (M42)
18	California nebula
19	Rosette nebula
20	Crab nebula

● Bright nebula (HII)
■ Neutral hydrogen (HI)
○ Open star clusters
▲ Associations (young stars)

300 light years

▼ *The center of the Milky Way: this radio photograph shows a region measuring ten light years across.*

► *The optical photograph shows lanes of dust hiding the Galaxy's center at visible wavelengths.*

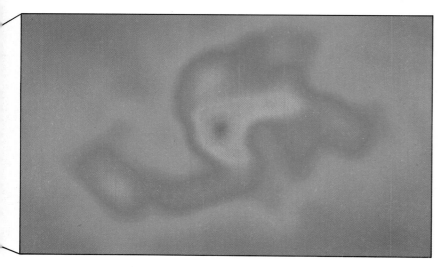

See also
Overview of the Universe 79-82
Galaxies 119-126

The galactic center

The nature of the galactic center presents an intriguing puzzle. It is marked by a powerful radio source, known as Sagittarius A. Much of the radio emission comes from a region of space less than 10 astronomical units across – that is, a region considerably smaller than the Solar System. This central region also includes an X-ray source and a collection of infrared sources, many of which are cool giant stars.

In order to explain the very high speeds of orbiting gas clouds close to it, the center must contain about 5 million solar masses of material within a radius of one light year. This suggests that the center of the Galaxy may contain a black hole of several million solar masses into which gas and stars may fall. If such a black hole does exist, it could be the underlying energy source responsible for some of the emission from the galactic core.

The evolution of the Galaxy

Since the older Population II stars have a near-spherical distribution around the galactic center, the conventional view is that the Galaxy originated as a near-spherical, slowly rotating cloud of hydrogen and helium, and that the first objects to form were the massive globular clusters. As time went by the rest of the gas settled into a spinning disk within which newer generations of stars have been born, and continue to be born, while the old stars still trace out orbits through the halo in which they were formed.

However, astronomers do not really understand the evolution of galaxies, and there are many alternative theories. One suggestion is that supermassive stars formed first in the nucleus of the Galaxy, then exploded, scattering forth the material to make the disk and halo. The various clouds which seem to be moving out through the nuclear bulge do seem to hint at a succession of (modestly) violent events in the Galaxy's history.

Star formation

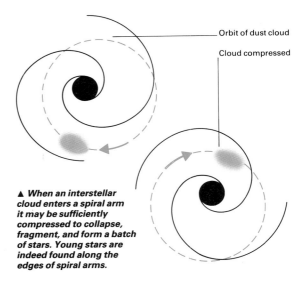

▲ *When an interstellar cloud enters a spiral arm it may be sufficiently compressed to collapse, fragment, and form a batch of stars. Young stars are indeed found along the edges of spiral arms.*

Locating the gas clouds

Unlike optical astronomers, whose view is blocked by dust, radio and millimeter-wave astronomers can plot the distribution of gas clouds throughout the Galaxy. Clouds closer to the galactic center have shorter orbital periods than the Sun, while those farther out have longer periods. The radial velocity of a cloud relative to the Sun depends on its distance from the galactic center, and on the angle between Sun, cloud and galactic center. This velocity can be measured from the Doppler shift (◀ page 90) in the cloud's radiation, and it is then possible to determine the location of the cloud.

Analyzing the spiral structure

▶ ▼ *Radio emissions from three hydrogen clouds: the cloud in ring B is stationary relative to the Sun and the received radiation has a wavelength of 21cm. The cloud in ring A is pulling ahead and receding; its radiation is red-shifted. The cloud in ring C is approaching; its radiation is blue-shifted. The relative speeds of clouds show the distribution of hydrogen in the Galaxy.*

▲ *Computer-processed view of the Galactic core.*

Signal strength

C

B

A

Sun

C

B

A

Line of sight

21 −Δλ 21cm 21 +Δλ

Galaxies

13

Measuring the distances of the galaxies...Our nearest galactic neighbors...Classifying the types of galaxy... Calculating their masses...The evolution of galaxies... PERSPECTIVE..."The great debate" continued...The pioneers of galaxy classification

Within range of present-day telescopes there are billions of galaxies. Some are swirling spiral systems like the Milky Way, but others are very different, and there is a wide variety of types. Our nearest neighbors are a motley collection of some thirty galaxies comprising the "Local Group." Its senior members apart from our Galaxy are the massive Andromeda spiral, the smaller spiral in the constellation Triangulum and the two Magellanic Clouds, which lie within 200,000 light years and may be regarded as companions of our Galaxy.

Measuring galactic distances

It is possible to determine the distance of galaxies by identifying within them conspicuous objects, such as highly luminous stars, star clusters or HII regions, which are similar to well-known objects in the Milky Way system, and by then computing either a "luminosity distance" or a "diameter distance."

To obtain a luminosity distance, astronomers must estimate the absolute magnitude or brightness of an identifiable object, and compare this with its apparent brightness. Cepheid variables (◀ page 102) provide a basic yardstick out to about 12-15 million light years. Luminous supergiants and novae extend the range to some 30 million light years, while observations of rare supernovae extend the range of distance measurement to billions of light years.

Diameter distance relies on the measurement of the apparent diameters of objects such as globular clusters and HII regions, and comparison of these with the known size of similar objects in the Milky Way. Needless to say, accuracy diminishes with increasing distance.

There is a relationship between the distance of a galaxy and the redshift in its spectrum. This is known as the Hubble Law, and astronomers can use it to assign distances to the remotest galaxies; but the uncertainty in this method may be as much as 100 percent.

▲ ▶ With this plate giving details of stellar motions, Adriaan van Maanen hoped to prove that M101 and similar spirals were not distant enough to be separate star systems.

Arguments about the spirals
One of the quarrels that punctuate the history of astronomy arose between the Dutch astronomer Adriaan van Maanen (1884-1946) and his great American colleague Edwin Hubble (1889-1953), concerning the nature and distance of the spiral nebulae. Hubble believed that they were "island universes" as originally suggested by William Herschel, but van Maanen, who had taken photographs of some of the spirals, claimed to have detected slight movements in some of the stars they contained. If this were correct, the spirals could not possibly be outside our Galaxy; however, van Maanen later conceded that his measurements had been incorrect.

Astronomers have now probed much farther: modern equipment has revealed objects well over 10,000 million light years away – perhaps not far from the very edge of the observable universe.

Selected bright galaxies in order of distance

Name or Catalog Number	Distance (thousands of light years)	Diameter (thousands of light years)	Mass* (Solar Masses)	Apparent Magnitude	Absolute Magnitude	Type
Milky Way	—	100	2×10^{11}	—	−21	Sb
Large Magellanic Cloud	170	30	1×10^{10}	0·1	−18·7	Ir I/SB?
Small Magellanic Cloud	200	16	2×10^{9}	2·4	−16·7	Ir I
Sculptor System	280	4	3×10^{6}	7	−12	E
Fornax System	560	7	2×10^{7}	7	−13	E
NGC 6822	1,500	7	3×10^{8}	8·6	−15·6	Ir
NGC 205	2,100	7	8×10^{9}	8·2	−16·3	E5
M32	2,200	4	3×10^{9}	8·2	−16·3	E2
M31, Andromeda	2,200	130	3×10^{11}	3·5	−21·1	Sb
M33, Triangulum	2,400	50	1×10^{10}	5·7	−18·8	Sc
Maffei I	3,300	?	2×10^{11}	11	−20	S0
M82	10,000	23	3×10^{10}	8·2	−19·6	Ir II
M81	10,500	100	2×10^{11}	6·9	−20·9	Sb
M51 (Whirlpool)	13,000	65	8×10^{10}	8·2	−19·7	Sc
Centaurus A	16,000	30	1×10^{12}	7	−20	E0p
M101 (Pinwheel)	20,000	200	3×10^{11}	7·5	−20·3	Sc
M83	27,000	100	$?10^{12}$	7·2	−20·6	SBc
M104 (Sombrero)	40,000	30	5×10^{11}	8·1	−22	Sa
M87 (Virgo A)	50,000	40	3×10^{12}	8·7	−22	EI

* Mass figure excludes dark extended haloes

A vast belt of fast-moving gas connects the Milky Way with its two nearest neighbor galaxies in space

Ferdinand Magellan's famous clouds

Our nearest neighbors in the Local Group of galaxies – the Large Magellanic Cloud (LMC) and the Small Magellanic Cloud (SMC) – are visible to the naked eye in the southern hemisphere. The LMC is about 170,000 light years distant, 30,000 light years in extent and contains about ten billion stars, while the SMC, at a distance of 200,000 light years, contains about a billion stars and is 16,000 light years in diameter. Both are irregular galaxies with little obvious structure.

The LMC contains a massive HII region – the Tarantula nebula – which is lit up by a cluster of more than a hundred O and B-type stars spread over a volume of space some 200 light years in diameter. The overall extent of this spectacular nebula is about 900 light years and it contains some 500,000 solar masses of gas. The IRAS satellite has shown that a vast region of star-formation lies behind the visible nebula, together with a huge cloud of neutral hydrogen. A great many old Population II stars also exist in the neighborhood of the nebula, which suggests that star-formation has been going on in this region throughout the galaxy's history. Although the Tarantula nebula lies off to one side of the main bar-like structure which contains most of the stars, some astronomers believe that it is the nucleus of this ill-defined galaxy, because it is such a massive and long-lived object.

A belt of fast-moving gas, known as the Magellanic stream, envelopes the two Magellanic clouds and stretches over the south pole of the Milky Way. This stream may be composed of gas which was dragged from the clouds when, in the relatively recent past, they made a close approach to the Milky Way system, or it may be a cloud of intergalactic gas caught in the gravitational fields of the Galaxy and the Magellanic clouds. If current ideas are correct, the Magellanic clouds and stream are all part of the massive galactic halo, but there has been a suggestion that the LMC is a separate system which has made a close approach and will eventually recede into the distance.

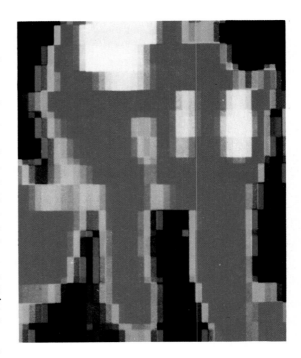

▲ *This infrared scan shows the region in the Large Magellanic Cloud which is known variously as 30 Doradus or the Tarantula nebula. Within this cloud of gas and heated dust lurks possibly the most massive and most luminous star known. Its mass has been estimated at 2,500 solar masses and its luminosity at 100 million Sun power.*

▶ *The Large Magellanic Cloud is the Milky Way's nearest neighbor galaxy; this photograph shows it in true color.*

▼ *The Small Magellanic Cloud, like its large namesake, is a splendid galaxy to view in a small telescope; but it is visible only to observers in the southern hemisphere.*

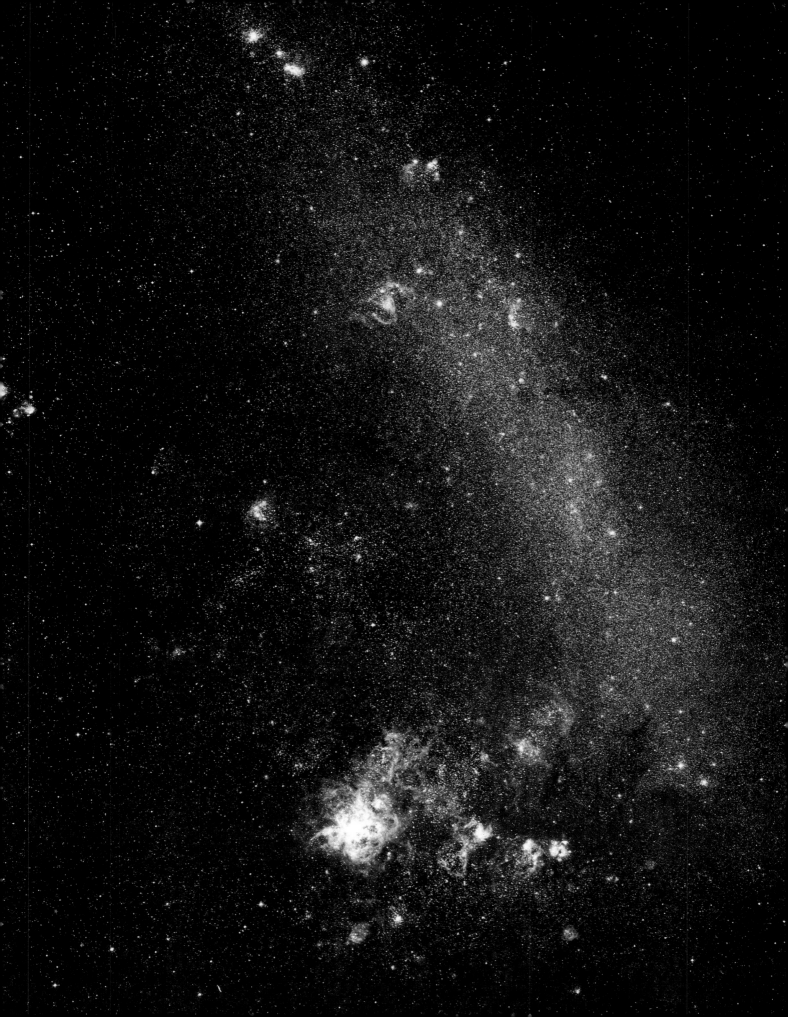

Astronomers classify galaxies by their shape, but do not really know what the different shapes indicate, nor how they evolve

The classification of galaxies

Galaxies are classified according to their shapes. Several classification schemes exist, but the simplest, due originally to Edwin Hubble, recognizes three fundamental forms – elliptical, spiral and irregular – and arranges them in a sequence known as the "tuning fork" diagram.

The letter "E" denotes elliptical galaxies, and is followed by a number between 0 and 7 according to the degree of flattening of the apparent ellipse. If "a" denotes the major axis and "b" the minor axis, the number is given by $10(a-b)/a$. For example, if the major axis is twice as long as the minor axis (that is, a = 2b), the class would be given by $10(2-1)/2 = 10/2 = 5$, and the galaxy would be of type E5. Spherical galaxies are denoted by E0, and no true ellipticals are flatter than E7.

Galaxies with spiral arms occur in two broad types – spirals (S) and barred spirals (SB). The former type have spiral arms which emerge from the nuclear bulge, while in the latter the arms emerge from the ends of what looks like a bar of stars and interstellar matter straddling the nucleus. Each type is then subdivided according to the size of the nucleus and the tightness of the spiral pattern. Of the spiral galaxies, Sa have the most tightly wound arms and the largest nuclear regions (in proportion to their overall size), Sb galaxies have a less tight spiral pattern and a relatively smaller nuclear bulge, while Sc galaxies have loose, open arms and small nuclei. Barred spirals are similarly subdivided into SBa, SBb and SBc types. Still more information may be added; for example an additional letter "s" signifies that the arms start in the nucleus, while "r" denotes that they emerge from a ring round the nucleus.

Intermediate between the ellipticals and the spirals are the SO, lens-shaped (lenticular) galaxies, which are elliptical with a narrow disk round their "equator" but no spiral arms. Irregular galaxies, which have no well-defined nucleus or structure, are designated Irr. Galaxies of type Irr I follow the tuning fork sequence in that they give the impression of spiral arms broken up into a confused jumble. Galaxies of type Irr II are completely chaotic and often highly active.

Gas, dust and hot young stars

The average content of gas, dust and hot young O and B-type stars increases along the tuning fork from the ellipticals to the Sc-types and irregulars. Typical proportions of gas and dust are less than 0.1 percent for ellipticals, up to 20 percent for spirals and 20-30 percent for irregulars, although there are exceptions with up to about 50 percent. The gas-depleted ellipticals contain a high proportion of old red Population II stars, while spirals have Population II stars in their nuclear and halo regions together with Population I disks which become progressively more dominant from Sa to Sc. Some, but not all, irregulars contain the highest proportion of blue O and B-type stars. Star formation has almost ceased in ellipticals, but not in spirals and irregulars.

Galactic masses

The masses of galaxies range from less than a million to over ten million million solar masses for ellipticals and one billion to a thousand billion solar masses for spirals, while irregulars are all less than a few tens of billions of solar masses. Apparent diameters range from less than 3,000 light years to more than 150,000 light years. These figures refer only to the visible parts of galaxies – if many of them have massive haloes and coronas of invisible matter, the figures given for size and mass are certainly underestimates.

▲ *Edwin Hubble at the Mount Wilson's 2·54m reflector.*

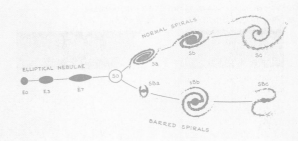

▲ *The Hubble "tuning fork" classification of galaxies.*

The pioneers of galaxy classification

Following his discovery that the "starry nebulae" really were external systems, in 1923 Hubble set to work with his colleague Humason to draw up a scale of classification. The two American astronomers were an interesting pair. Edwin Hubble (1889-1953) served in the American army during the first world war, and also became an amateur boxing champion. Milton Humason (1891-1972) had no formal training at all; his first engagement at Mount Wilson Observatory was as a mule-driver, but he joined the scientific staff in 1920 and from then on worked closely with Hubble.

The two produced a plan which included the various types of galaxy, and were tempted to suggest that these represented different stages of evolution – that an elliptical galaxy evolved into a spiral, or vice versa. However, there were serious objections. In particular, the most massive ellipticals, such as M87 in Virgo, were much more massive than the spirals, and the idea of an evolutionary sequence had to be abandoned. As with the studies relating to stellar evolution, the situation proved to be much less straightforward than astronomers had originally thought.

The classification of galaxies

NGC 1201 – Type SO

NGC 4636 – Type EO

NGC 175 – Type SBa

NGC 2811 – Type Sa

NGC 4406 – Type E3

NGC 1530 – Type SBb

NGC 3031 – Type Sb

NGC 3115 – Type E7

NGC 1073 – Type SBc

NGC 5364 – Type SC

The Local Group comprises an assortment of irregular, elliptical and spiral galaxies of various sizes

Other members of the Local Group

Most of the galaxies in the local group are rather small elliptical or irregularly-shaped systems, but there are a few larger systems, including two spirals, M33 in the constellation of Triangulum and M31 in Andromeda. M33 is a well-defined spiral with a nucleus and spiral arms, but with a more open structure than the Milky Way system. Some 2·7 million light years distant, it is smaller than our own Galaxy, and contains about 30 billion stars.

M31, the great galaxy in Andromeda, is a spiral but is nearly edge-on to the Milky Way so that its spiral structure is not easy to see. At a distance of 2·3 million light years, it is the most distant object detectable – under good conditions – to the naked eye. Only the extensive nuclear bulge is visible to the naked eye, or through small telescopes and binoculars. The whole system, comprising nuclear bulge and disk, is larger and more massive than the Milky Way system and probably contains about 300 billion solar masses. However, when the massive corona is taken into account, the Milky Way is quite possibly the most massive member of the Local Group. M31 has two smaller elliptical companion galaxies, M32 (NGC 221) and NGC 205.

The other massive galaxy in the locality is Maffei 1, one of two galaxies discovered in 1968 by the Italian astronomer Paolo Maffei. Both are in Cassiopeia, near the plane of the Milky Way, and are therefore heavily obscured by dust. Maffei 1 appears to be about 3 million light years away, making it a member of the Local Group, but being a giant elliptical system it is quite different from any other member of the group. Only about one percent of its light penetrates to the Solar System, however, making it very difficult to analyze.

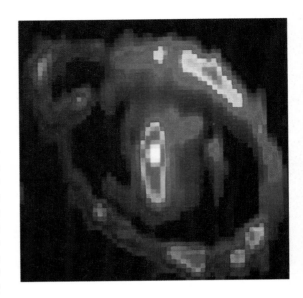

▼ *The galaxy known as M33, one of the Local Group, lies in the constellation of Triangulum. This optical photograph has enhanced colors which reveal the areas of continuing star formation (pink), regions of young stars (blue) and dust (orange) lit by older yellow stars in the center of the galaxy.*

▶ ▲ *M31, the great galaxy in Andromeda, is a massive spiral similar to the Milky Way. The true-color view (right) shows M31 and its two elliptical companions, M32 and NGC 205. Viewed at a shallow angle its spiral structure is not particularly obvious. The false-color infrared view (above) shows lanes of heated dust where stars are forming.*

Calculating the masses of the galaxies

The spectrum of a galaxy consists of the combined spectra of vast numbers of stars, and takes the form of a continuous spectrum with dark absorption lines. With a spiral galaxy, Doppler shifts in these lines and in radio emission lines (such as the 21cm radiation emitted by HI regions) can reveal the speed of rotation at different distances from its center. From this it is possible to calculate the mass of the visible disk and nuclear bulge. However, in many spirals, stars and gas clouds continue to move at high speeds at the outer perimeter of their visible disks, and this implies that they have massive haloes or coronas, so that such masses must be regarded as minimum values.

Spherical and near-spherical galaxies have very little net rotation and their stars move in a more or less random fashion, so that in any part of such a galaxy some stars are approaching and others are receding from an outside observer. Each line in the galaxy's spectrum contains contributions from receding (red-shifted) stars and approaching (blue-shifted) stars, and the effect of this is to make the spectral lines broad rather than narrow. The degree of line-broadening reveals the range of velocities, and, since the speed of stars depends on the gravitational pull to which they are subjected, this provides a clue to the total mass of that galaxy.

The evolution of galaxies

Astronomers do not know for certain how galaxies were born or how they have evolved. They think that each galaxy originated as a massive cloud of hydrogen and helium contracting under the action of gravity; and the type of galaxy into which it evolved probably depended on the amount of rotation in the cloud and the rate of star formation.

In a slowly collapsing cloud with little rotation, star formation would proceed quite rapidly, converting most of the gas into stars at an early stage and producing a spherical or elliptical galaxy. Galaxies of this type today are dominated by old red first-generation stars, since very little gas was left to form later generations of stars after the first bout of star formation. With a rapidly collapsing and faster spinning cloud, stars would begin to form while the cloud was nearly spherical, but the gas would quickly settle into a spinning disk. This kind of behavior would produce a tenuous population of old stars in the halo and a greater concentration in the ellipsoidal nucleus; within the disk, star formation would still proceed at a relatively slow rate.

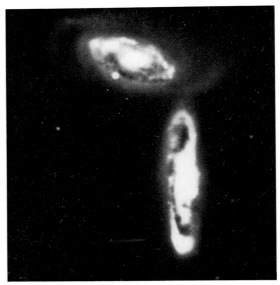

▲ *Peculiar galaxies NGC 3986/88.*

▲ *Peculiar galaxies NGC 6621/22.*

◄ *In a slowly collapsing cloud with little rotation, stars form rapidly to leave a spherical or elliptical galaxy with little gas. A faster spinning and collapsing cloud may form stars more slowly, producing a halo of old stars and a disk of gas and younger stars.*

Rapid star formation

Elliptical galaxy

Slow star formation

Spiral galaxy

Albert Einstein 1879-1955

14

"He will never make a success"...The Swiss Patent Office...Dispelling the ether...The 1905 papers on special relativity, molecular effects and radiation...The general theory of relativity...Public life and private research... PERSPECTIVE...Is there but "one science"?...Einstein's presence in literature...Technical advances based on atomic research...United States' science and immigration

The two great geniuses associated with the word "gravitation" – Newton and Einstein – though separated by over 200 years, shared a number of characteristics. For example, both began at an early age the work that led to their important discoveries and both became involved in politics later in their lives. But there are important differences, not least that Einstein's Germany underwent more drastic upheavals than Newton's England. The forces that obliged Einstein to take refuge in the United States have had a major impact on the practical application of 20th-century physics. More important, in the history of science, Einstein overturned fundamental ideas on the nature of time and space that had held sway since the time of Newton.

Early days

Albert Einstein was born in the small town of Ulm in south Germany on 14 March 1879, but his family soon moved to the nearby Bavarian capital, Munich. His father was in the electrical engineering business, so Einstein, from his early days, became acquainted with what was then the very young electrical industry. As a schoolboy, he was thought to have very little ability (it has been suggested, without much evidence, that he was dyslexic). When Einstein's father asked what career his son should follow, the headmaster replied: "It doesn't matter; he will never make a success of anything." Certainly, the young Einstein was introspective and rather isolated. His family was Jewish in an overwhelmingly Catholic city. At the same time, they took no active part in religious observances, and so were not integrated into the local Jewish community. During these years, Einstein began to discover topics that did interest him. Like Newton, he was attracted by the synthesis of classical geometry made about 300 BC by Euclid: he particularly liked its lucidity and certainty. This formed part of his growing interest in mathematics – one of the few good results he later saw in his schooling, for he quickly came to detest the regimentation of school life.

In 1894 his father's business failed, and the whole family apart from Albert moved to Italy, settling in Milan. Within six months Einstein quitted his school without taking the leaving certificate and trekked south to join his family. He found the relaxed atmosphere of Italy much more acceptable than the discipline of Germany; but his father's finances continued to be precarious, and Albert had to consider his future career. It was decided he should follow in his father's footsteps and train to become an electrical engineer. Without a school-leaving certificate, the openings for further education were limited. However, the Swiss Federal Polytechnic School in Zurich had a high reputation, and accepted students purely on the results of an entrance examination. Einstein sat the examination and failed. After a year's intensive schooling in Switzerland, he took it again and passed.

Einstein's revolution

Space and time are basic to all scientific observations, so understanding them has always been a concern of scientists. For centuries, scientists supposed that there was some kind of universal background to which relative measurements could ultimately be referred. In Aristotle's picture of the world everywhere outside the Earth was occupied by a solid transparent "aether", which could be used to describe motions. By the end of the 17th century, Newton had shown that, in order to fit the observations, any such all-pervasive ether would need to be very tenuous. Nevertheless, in the 19th century, this Newtonian ether was still widely accepted as the background against which measurements of time and space could be made.

Einstein boldly decided that the whole idea of some kind of universal framework, against which measurements could be made, was wrong – all observations are relative. He developed this idea to show that gravitation could be thought of as a distortion of the space around an object. As Faraday shifted the focus of attention from electric or magnetic bodies to the properties of the space round them, so Einstein did the same for gravitation. But Einstein was responsible for a still wider-ranging revolution. Along with Niels Bohr, he was a founder of quantum mechanics. His analysis of space, time, matter and radiation has provided the foundation of much of 20th-century physics.

▼ *Einstein at the Swiss Patent Office in Bern.*

Albert Einstein — His Life, Work and Times

Student life and after

Einstein's student years were marked again by his independent approach: he spent as much time reading the original works of the great 19th-century physicists as in attending lectures. Nevertheless, he graduated satisfactorily in 1900. By this time he was concerned with physics rather than electrical engineering, and his first hope was for a university post at Zurich. But no offer came his way – perhaps because of his independent attitude as an undergraduate. He survived on temporary teaching posts until midway through 1902, when, aided by a certain amount of influence behind the scenes, he was offered a post at the Swiss Patent Office in Berne. There he stayed, learning how to discern the basic ideas of patent applications and express them clearly, for the next seven years.

Einstein had enjoyed his student life in Switzerland. He contrasted the more democratic atmosphere there with his memories of Germany. He soon decided to transfer from German to Swiss nationality, and was so eager that he actually relinguished his German citizenship before being accepted by the Swiss. Consequently, Einstein entered the 20th century as a stateless person, and did not become Swiss until 1901.

A few months after starting work at the Patent Office, Einstein married a Hungarian, Mileva Marič, who had also been studying mathematics in Switzerland. Within a few years of graduating, he had become a married Swiss civil servant – not the most obvious background for an assault on the theoretical physics of his day. Einstein later emphasized how wrong this view was; the job provided him with the security and time he needed to come to grips with the basic problems of physics.

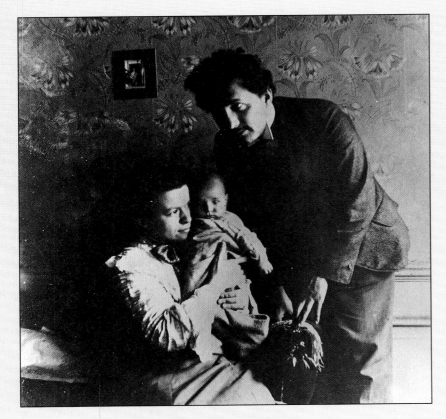

▲ *Einstein with his wife Mileva and their first son Hans Albert in 1904.*

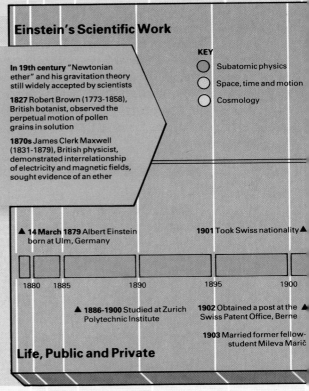

Historical Background

■ **1884** First conference of Zionist movement held in Prussia, after pogroms in Russia and Poland

Einstein's Scientific Work

In 19th century "Newtonian ether" and his gravitation theory still widely accepted by scientists

1827 Robert Brown (1773-1858), British botanist, observed the perpetual motion of pollen grains in solution

1870s James Clerk Maxwell (1831-1879), British physicist, demonstrated interrelationship of electricity and magnetic fields, sought evidence of an ether

KEY
- ⬤ Subatomic physics
- ⬤ Space, time and motion
- ⬤ Cosmology

▲ **14 March 1879** Albert Einstein born at Ulm, Germany

1901 Took Swiss nationality ▲

1880	1885	1890	1895	1900

▲ **1886-1900** Studied at Zurich Polytechnic Institute

1902 Obtained a post at the Swiss Patent Office, Berne

1903 Married former fellow-student Mileva Marič

Life, Public and Private

Scientific Background

1900 John Rayleigh (1842-1919), British physicist, tried to explain how a hot body radiates its heat: applying then acceptable physics, he failed

1900 Max Planck (1858-1947), German physicist, solved Rayleigh's problem by assuming that heat is emitted from bodies in small bursts (quanta)

⬤ **1883** Ernst Mach (1838-1916), German physicist and philosopher, suggested that Newton's ideas on space and time must be replaced

⬤ **1887** Heinrich Hertz (1857-1894), German physicist, observed effect of light on electrical properties of metal surfaces (in c. 1886 discovered radio waves)

⬤ **1887** Albert Michelson (1852-1931), US physicist, and Edward Morley (1838-1923), US chemist, failed to detect ether experimentally

⬤ **1889** George Fitzgerald (1851-1901), Irish physicist, suggested that bodies contract along the direction in which they are moving

⬤ **1892** Hendrik Lorentz (1853-1928), Dutch physicist, also suggested contraction

1897 Existence of electron ⬤ established by J. J. Thomson (1856-1940), British physicist

1899 Alpha and beta particles ⬤ discovered by Ernest Rutherford (1871-1937), New Zealand-born physicist

1875	1885	1890	1895	19

From late 19th century Rivalry increased between European powers in economic, territorial and colonial spheres

■ **1917** Revolution in Russia

■ **1914-1918** World War I

1929 Wall Street Crash heralded ■ increased economic depression worldwide

■ **1920** League of Nations inaugurated

1939-1945 World War II, "the ■ physicists' war"

1933 Nazis came to power in Germany

16 July 1945 First atomic blast, ■ followed (August) by bombs on Hiroshima and Nagasaki

■ **1945** United Nations formed

1948 State of Israel proclaimed ■

○ **1905** Paper on the quantum of light and the photoelectric effect published in *Annalen der Physik*

○ **1911** Asserted equivalence of gravitation and inertia

○ **1918** Began work on unified field theory (gravitation and the quantum combined into a single theory); continued this for rest of his life

○ **1916** Completed work on general relativity

○ **1905** Paper on Brownian motion

○ **1916** Work on the absorption and emission of radiation, including stimulated emission, the basis of lasers

○ **1924** Einstein took up Bose's work

○ **1905** Paper on special relativity, "On the Electrodynamics of Moving Bodies"

○ **1930** Produced model of the expanding Universe

▲ **1914** On outbreak of war, Einstein's attachment to pacifism increased

▲ **1925** Joined Board of Governors of Hebrew University, Jerusalem

1952 Declined request to become ▲ president of Israel

1933 Left Germany after Nazis ▲ came to power, took up post at Institute for Advanced Study, Princeton (held till 1945)

▲ **1908-1914** Taught at universities in Berne, Zurich and Prague

▲ **1919** Married cousin Elsa

18 April 1955 Died in Princeton, ▲ New Jersey

05	1910	1915	1920	1925	1930	1935	1940	1945	1950

▲ **1921** First visit to United States

▲ **1940** Became US citizen

▲ **1914-1933** Professor of physics and director of theoretical physics at Kaiser Wilhelm Institute

▲ **1921** Nobel Prize in Physics, primarily for work on photoelectric effect

1939 Wrote to President ▲ Roosevelt about the potential of atomic energy

---

● **1902** Philipp Lenard (1862-1947), German physicist, showed that electrons are released from metal by light, but in an unexpected way

● **1923** Nobel Prize won by Robert Millikan (1868-1953), US physicist, partly for work confirming Einstein's theories which he had sought to disprove

○ **1936** In *German Physics*, Lenard defended "true" science, attacked relativity theory as a Jewish conspiracy

● **1905** Lenard won Nobel prize for work on cosmic rays; also studied photoelectric effect

● **1927** Uncertainty principle relating to observation of subatomic particles, enunciated by Werner Heisenberg (1901-1976), German mathematical physicist

○ **1934** Artificial radio isotopes first produced by Irène (1897-1956) and Frédéric (1900-1958) Joliot-Curie

● **1904** Jules Poincaré (1854-1912), French mathematician, discussed the relative nature of time and motion

● **1924** Satyandra Nath Bose (1894-1974), Indian physicist, suggested method of applying statistics to subatomic particles

○ **1938** Otto Hahn (1879-1968), German chemist, and Austrian physicist Lise Meitner (1878-1968) and her nephew Otto Frisch (1904-1979) found that nuclei of uranium can be broken down by fission

○ **c. 1908** "Space-time" derived by Herman Minkowski (1864-1909), Russian-born German mathematician, from the special theory

○ **1919** Arthur Eddington (1882-1944), British astrophysicist, found observational support for general relativity at time of solar eclipse

○ **1917** Willem de Sitter (1872-1934), Dutch astronomer, showed that general relativity can lead to an expanding universe

○ **1929** Edwin Hubble (1889-1953), US astrophysicist, presented observations showing that the Universe is expanding

● **1942** Nobel laureate Enrico Fermi (1901-1954), Italian physicist, produced first sustained nuclear chain reaction, working in United States

○ **1904** Lorentz discussed how electric and magnetic forces are affected by motion

● **1913** Niels Bohr (1885-1962), Danish physicist, proposed that an atom consists of a nucleus plus electrons and that radiation is absorbed, or emitted (as a quantum), every time an electron jumps outward from, or inward to, the nucleus

1948 Dennis Gabor (1900–1979), Hungarian-born British physicist, described method of holography, but it required use of lasers to work

1965 Arno Penzias (1933–), US astrophysicist, and Robert Wilson (1936–), US radio astronomer, discovered cosmic microwave background radiation, supporting "Big Bang" theory of origin of Universe

1960 Theoretical proposals by Charles H. Townes (1915–) US physicist, Nikolai Basov (1922–) and Alexander Prokhorov (1916–), Soviet physicists, led to the development of the laser

1974 Stephen Hawking (1942–), British astrophysicist, developed the theory of black holes

● **1911** Rutherford proposed nuclear theory of the atom

● **1919** Rutherford announced first artificial disintegration of an atom

The ether and light

Like Newton, Einstein arrived early at one of the central problems he pursued throughout his life. At the age of 16 he wrote a letter to an uncle concerning the connection between electromagnetic waves and the ether. In so doing, he was touching on a matter immediately involved with his later work on relativity.

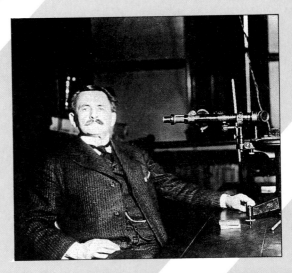

Until the latter half of the 19th century, electricity and magnetism were seen as separate things, though Michael Faraday (1791-1867) and others had shown how they could be converted into each other. However, James Clerk Maxwell (1831-1879), following up Faraday's ideas, showed theoretically that electromagnetic waves could exist in which the electrical and magnetic effects were inextricably linked together. He also showed that light represented one type of electro-magnetic wave. It seemed evident in the 19th century that, to have waves, there must be something present that could transmit them. How could you have waves at sea if you removed the sea? Maxwell

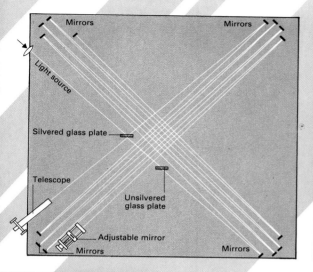

◄▲► To "dispel the ether" was not the intention of US scientists Albert Michelson (left) (1852-1931) and Edward Morley (1838-1931). But they did dispel it, in a celebrated experiment. In the tradition of Aristotle and Newton, 19th-century scientists believed in the existence of a transparent "ether" that permeated the Universe and transmitted electromagnetic waves including light. The experiment of 1887 set the interferometer devised by Michelson on a rotating table. A light beam was split into two parts moving at right angles to each other and then brought together again. Because of the Earth's motion in space, the "drag" of the ether was expected to produce a displacement of the interference fringes in the recombined beam. The experiment "failed", but this zero result began speculation that culminated in Einstein's 1905 special theory of relativity.

◄ Interference patterns occur when two (or more) coherent beams of light interact. Bright bands are seen where the amplitudes of the two waves reinforce each other and dark bands are seen where the waves cancel each other out. Because white light is made up of many colors of differing wavelengths (the spectrum), colored fringes are seen surrounding the bright bands. A slight change in phase between the two waves would result in a measurable shift of these colored fringes.

had shown that light consisted of electromagnetic waves; but, since we can see the stars, light must be able to traverse the apparently empty space between the stars and us. In the 17th century, Newton had argued that some kind of material must exist throughout all space to transmit gravitational pull from one object to another. His argument was along the lines – how can you have a tug-of-war without a rope connecting the two teams to transmit the pull? This "ether", as it was called, seemed in the 19th century what was needed to transmit electromagnetic waves.

Newton recognized that most measurement was relative. We measure the motion of a ship relative to the Earth, although we know that the Earth itself is in motion – both spinning on its axis, and moving round the Sun. We could allow for these motions, but we would then need to allow for the fact that the Sun is moving, and so on. Newton wondered if it was possible to make any measurement that was not a series of relative measurements. The ether seemed to provide an answer. If it is thought of as a kind of very tenuous jelly through which the objects move, then, instead of measuring the movement of one object relative to another, we can measure all motions relative to the ether. These would represent *absolute* measurements.

Agreeing with Newton, 19th-century physicists turned the argument round – measurements of motion should make it possible to detect the ether. However, to the physicists' surprise, however much they refined their equipment, the experiments they carried out failed to reveal the ether. These experiments depended on observing the properties of light (electromagnetic waves), so Einstein's early thoughts concerned one of the most important and puzzling problems facing physics in the early 20th century.

Einstein realized that one of the key questions concerned the nature of light itself. He asked himself, what would happen if an observer could travel as fast as a ray of light? Evidently, if the observer and a particular wave started out together, they would remain together. The wave would therefore seem to be standing still, simply oscillating up and down.

However, work by James Clerk Maxwell had indicated that a stationary wave could not correspond to light: so an observer traveling with the speed of light should see something different from our observer traveling at less than the speed of light. But why should traveling at one particular speed make the whole world look different?

The innovations of 1905 – special theory of relativity

While he was at the Swiss Patent office, Einstein found the answer to the questions he was asking about the nature of light, which he published in 1905. The speed of light, and of electromagnetic waves in general, is unique because it is the maximum permissible speed in the Universe. No ordinary body can ever reach that speed, so no observer can ever keep up with a light wave. To arrive at this conclusion Einstein had to assume that however observers moved relative to the source of the light they always found the light moving relative to themselves at the same constant speed. This assumption was at variance not only with Newton, but also with common sense. If a stone is thrown from a passing vehicle, its speed, as seen by an observer standing by, will depend both on the speed with which it is thrown and the speed of the vehicle. Why should this not be true of a ray of light?

Einstein's assertion led to even stanger results. Speed is measured in terms of distance covered per unit time, in for example, miles per hour. Hence, if speed is relative, so is distance. One consequence, Einstein deduced, was that the apparent dimensions of an object depend on the relative motion of the observer. Equally, time is relative. So the length of time something takes to happen can also depend on relative motion of the observer.

It might be expected that Einstein's contemporaries would find these striking conclusions hard to swallow. In fact, some of them had been working along other similar lines. For example, Hendrik Lorentz (1853-1928) in the Netherlands and George Fitzgerald (1851-1901) in

▲ *Hendrik Lorenz suggested that dimensions are relative.*

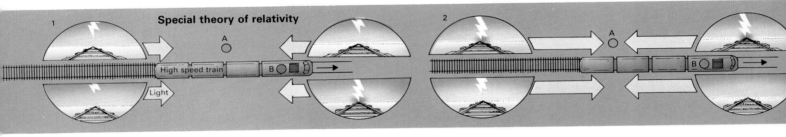

Special theory of relativity

High speed train

Light

Ireland had already suggested that a moving body might appear to contract relative to a stationary observer. This is still sometimes referred to as "Lorentz-Fitzgerald" contraction. Einstein provided a logical explanation of why this should happen. His approach is nowadays called "the special theory of relativity." The word "relativity" reflects the fact that all motion is measured relative to some observer: Einstein denied the existence of both the ether and the possibility of absolute motion. The word "special" refers to a limitation of Einstein's theory. He and his contemporaries were only talking about bodies which vary their speeds.

For physicists, the fundamental properties of a body are typically related to its size and to the amount of material it contains (that is, its mass). Shortly after publishing his ideas on the measurement of length in relativity, Einstein extended his work to include mass. One of his results represents probably the most famous equation in the world today; it says that energy is equal to mass multiplied by the square of the speed of light. This is often written: $E = mc^2$. Because the speed of light is very high, destroying a very small amount of mass can lead to the release of a very large quantity of energy. At the time, this discovery was of academic interest, but we now know it as the source of the energy of the atomic bomb.

▲ *Part of Einstein's special theory of relativity abolishes the Newtonian idea of time as an absolute. In Einstein's own "thought experiment" two bolts of lightning strike opposite ends of a railroad track and are seen by an observer "A" on the embankment and a passenger "B" on a high speed train. In situation (1), moving toward the light waves "B" sees the lightning strike the track only in front of him. In (2) "A" sees both lightning bolts striking the track simultaneously as the light waves arrives together. However "B" has yet to see the second lightning bolt strike. The light has still to arrive from that source. Which of these views is then correct? Neither. Einstein said that measurements of time depend on the frame of reference – whether the observer is moving or not.*

▶ *Einstein won the Nobel prize not for his work on relativity, but for explaining the long-standing puzzle of the photoelectric effect in 1905. If a metal surface is illuminated, electrons are given off. When the light is strengthened, more electrons are produced, as might be expected; but their energy levels are identical to those of electrons given off in dim light. The energy of the electrons depends not on the intensity of the light hitting the surface, but on its wavelength: the higher frequencies such as those from the blue end of the spectrum give higher energies than lower frequencies from the red end. Adapting Planck's idea, Einstein explained this by suggesting that radiation consists of "packets" or "quanta" of energy, each of which can be absorbed by an electron and dislodge it.*

▲ Max Planck's idea that energy is emitted in discrete "bundles" or "quanta" was taken up by Einstein and applied in his photoelectric theory. Niels Bohr used it in his model of the atom.

Atoms and the quantum

The special theory of relativity would have been enough by itself to bring Einstein fame, but again in 1905 he published other work which was equally influential. Early in the 19th century, a Scottish botanist, Robert Brown (1773-1858), had noted that pollen grains suspended in water appeared to be in constant, but irregular motion when viewed through a microscope. Various attempts were made to explain this motion, without success. Now Einstein provided a satisfactory explanation in terms of the molecules which made up the water. These molecules were always in motion because of the heat of the water, and were therefore continually striking the pollen grains from all sides. However, sometimes more water molecules would strike one side of a pollen grain than the other, so causing it to move.

Some eminent scientists of the day still did not believe that matter is composed of atoms and molecules. Einstein's explanation of molecular effects was generally accepted as clear evidence that matter is formed from tiny particles too small to be seen by the human eye.

But the work specifically cited in the eventual (1922) award to Einstein of the Nobel Prize for physics appeared in yet another paper in 1905. A major interest for physcists in the latter part of the 19th century was the way in which a hot body radiates energy into space. For example, a piece of metal heated to white heat radiates in a different way from one heated to red heat. It proved surprisingly difficult to provide a theoretical explanation of this difference. Finally, in 1900 the German physicist Max Planck (1858-1947) pointed out a possible solution. In order to fit the experimental data he found it necessary to suppose that radiation was emitted in bursts, rather than continuously. This seemed so contrary to common sense that most people saw it as just a device for the purposes of calculation, rather than as being physically meaningful. Einstein proposed that Planck's idea should be taken seriously: it actually did represent the true nature of radiation. For some purposes, light should not be thought of as waves, but as a collection of "particles", each produced by a "quantum" (i.e. discrete) change within an atom. Einstein went on to show that this approach could also explain the puzzling results of some experiments on the way in which light interacts with the surfaces of solids. His colleagues were less ready to accept this speculation than his theory of special relativity; yet, in retrospect, it represents a vital strand in the development of quantum mechanics, which along with relativity is one of the basic advances in 20th-century physics.

Photoelectric effect

High frequency light

High energy electrons

Metal plate

Low frequency light

Low energy electrons

Brownian motion

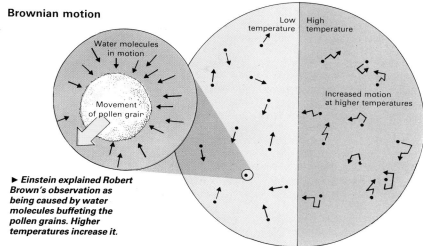

Water molecules in motion

Movement of pollen grain

Low temperature

High temperature

Increased motion at higher temperatures

► Einstein explained Robert Brown's observation as being caused by water molecules buffeting the pollen grains. Higher temperatures increase it.

Ideology and Science

"Jewish science" in Nazi Germany

Einstein's immediate fame after World War I, coupled with his pacifism, fanned antisemitic opposition to his ideas. Antisemitism had existed for centuries. What was new was the attack on "Jewish science". Most of the people involved were not well known as scientists; but one, the German Philipp Lenard (1862-1947), was a Nobel Prize winner in physics. Indeed, Einstein had earlier been influenced by Lenard's experiments on the photoelectric effect. Lenard's original objection to Einstein's dismissal of the ether was shared with many older scientists who were not anti-semitic. But Lenard soon went far beyond this, and began to claim that relativity was part of a Jewish conspiracy to subvert "true" science.

Thus, new physics, especially relativity, had developed under the influence of Jewish scientists: its purpose was to pull German scientists away from the proper Aryan thinking found in classical physics. In his four-volume treatise "German Physics" (1936-37), Lenard explained: "German physics? one asks. I might rather have said Aryan Physics or the Physics of the Nordic Species of Man. The Physics of those who have fathomed the depths of Reality, seekers after Truth, the Physics of the very founders of Science. But I shall be answered, 'Science is and remains international.' It is false. Science, like every other human product, is racial, and conditioned by blood."

But so bizarre were Nazi leaders' ideas of science that attempts to establish a "German" science in its place achieved only very limited success. Some Nazis supported a curious pseudoscientific theory of the world, popular in Germany between the wars, called the "Cosmic Ice" theory. This supposed that the Earth had been subject to a variety of catastrophes which could explain everything from the ice ages to Noah's Flood.

Communism, "idealism" and Lysenkoism

The essence of the Nazi argument, that Jewish scientists had introduced a new and unacceptable way of looking at the world, was echoed in the Soviet Union from a different viewpoint. There, much of the new physics was thought to fall into the trap of "idealism": it failed to reflect everyday reality as required in Marxist-Leninist theory.

The most striking example of this occurred not in physics, but biology. In the latter part of the 1920s, Soviet newspapers began to mention an agricultural researcher, Trofim Lysenko (1898-1977), who was attacking currently accepted theories of heredity and evolution. Lysenko was concerned with the development of cold-resistant plants. He claimed that, by exposing plants to appropriate conditions, he could produce offspring which were more resistant to cold. The history of his ideas goes back to the end of the 18th century, when the French scientist Jean Lamarck (1744-1829) concluded that changes which occurred in a plant or animal during its lifetime could be passed on to subsequent generations. In the now classic example, he argued that all giraffes must stretch their necks upward to obtain their food, and that this stretching was passed on to the next generation in the form of slightly longer necks.

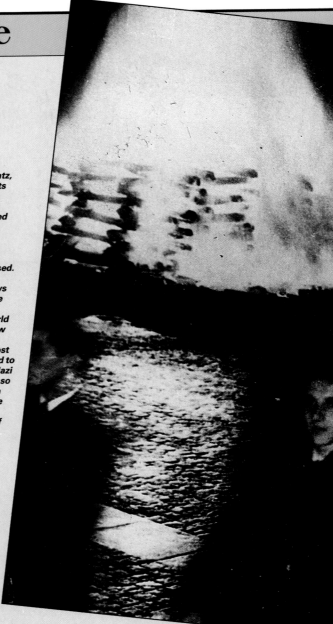

▶ 11 May 1933, Orpenplatz, Berlin: Nazis and students parade at the burning of "un-German" books. As Einstein finally abandoned Germany for the United States, scores of other academics with Jewish backgrounds either resigned or were dismissed. An April 7th law had decreed dismissal of Jews from government service and the universities.

In the face of post-World War I attacks on the "new physics" and Einstein's leading position in it, most German physicists rallied to his defense. But as the Nazi Party gained in strength so did the idea of a "Jewish science" which had to be eliminated in order to defend the superiority of the "Aryan race".

According to Charles Darwin, however, it would take some time for organisms to change, because this required an alteration to the genetic material passed from parents to offspring. If Lamarck was right, the process of change could be speeded up by exposing organisms to the appropriate environment. Translated to the realm of human society, it meant that the efforts of a community could change the characteristics of the next generation. Communist politicians, who were calling for an heroic effort to build a new society, found Lysenko's claims for Lamarck's ideas much more helpful than traditional (Darwinian) science.

During the 1930s and 1940s, Lysenko's scientific opponents were banished or interned in labor camps. One, the distinguished biologist Nikolai Vavilov (1887-?1943), died in a Siberian labor camp. Lysenko's work had been praised by Stalin and in 1948 was officially accepted by the Soviet communist party. But the sheer lack of success of Lysenkoism gradually became evident, and, as the Cold War lessened a little in intensity, Lysenko's influence declined. Not until the end of the 1960s did mainstream ideas on genetics and evolution once again figure in Russian teaching and research.

▶ In the 1930s and 1940s, scientific opponents of Trofim Lysenko (right) were eliminated by dismissal, banishment or internment: the distinguished biologist Nikolai Vavilov (1887-?1943) died in a Siberian labor camp. Lysenkoism was endorsed by the Soviet Communist Party in 1948. But with sheer lack of practical results from the Russian plant improvement programs, Lysenko's influence declined.

The uniqueness of science

Lysenkoism and Nazi attacks on "Jewish science"
provide examples of what happens when
politicians interfere with the process of scientific
research. In both cases the interference ultimately
proved to be sterile. Most scientists see this as
strong support for their belief that only one science
can exist the world over, regardless of the
prejudices of the scientists themselves.

The word "science", however, has different
meanings in different countries. Thus in some
countries history is called a science, whereas in
others it is thought to have little to do with science.

It is not always easy to draw a line between
scientific and nonscientific research fields: on
which side of the line fall attempts to study
telepathy? A second factor complicating the "one
science" picture is that, as most scientists would
accept, external influences, such as social and
economic, can determine which science develops,
at what time and to what extent. For example, the
rapid growth of nuclear physics since World War II
can certainly be linked to the production of the
atomic bomb during the war.

But virtually all scientists believe that the acid test
of any theory is not how it is developed, but
whether, once developed, it receives universal
assent. A theory which is supported only by one
national or political grouping over an extended
period of time does not satisfy this requirement.

Einstein and Literature

As Canadian humorist Stephen Leacock wrote at the time, many people believed it was near-impossible to understand Einstein's work:
"But it was Einstein who made the real trouble. He announced in 1905 that there was no such thing as absolute rest. After that there never was...Einstein explains that there is no such place as here. 'But,' you answer, 'I'm here; here is where I am right now.' But you're moving, you're spinning round as the earth spins; and you and the earth are both spinning round the sun, and the sun is rushing through space towards a distant galaxy, and the galaxy itself is beating it away at 26,000 miles a second. Now where is that spot that is here!"
In the 1700s Alexander Pope wrote of Newton:

"Nature and Nature's laws lay hid in night:
God said, 'Let Newton be!' and all was light."

Two centuries later, J.C. Squire (1884-1958) added another couplet:

"It did not last: the Devil howling 'Ho,
Let Einstein be,' restored the status quo."

Relativity has made the greatest impact on science fiction. The main problem for this genre is the limitations on travel imposed by the finite speed of light. Writers who want their characters to venture beyond the solar system immediately face the difficulty of the long travel times involved. As Kingsley Amis has pointed out:

"The fact is that to reach any but the nearest stars would take several hundred years even if one travelled at the speed of light, in the course of doing which one would, if I understand Einstein's popularisers correctly, become infinite in mass and zero in volume, and this is felt to be undesirable. A few writers simply accept this difficulty and arrange for their travellers to put themselves into some sort of deep-freeze until just before planetfall, or allow them to breed in captivity for the requisite number of generations. But most commonly, the author will fabricate a way of getting around Einstein: a device known typically as the space-warp or the hyper-drive will make its appearance, though without any more ceremony than 'He applied the space-warp,' or 'He threw the ship into hyper-drive.'"

More generally, writers' attention has been drawn to the problems of understanding space and time. In consequence, 20th-century references to space and time often carry overtones which cannot be found in earlier periods. An obvious example comes from the English poet, William Empson:

"Alas, how hope for freedom, no bars bind;
Space is like earth, rounded, a padded cell;
Plumb the stars' depth, your lead bumps you
    behind;
Blind Satan's voice rattled the whole of Hell."

The reference here to curved space-time is obvious; but even apparently straightforward references to space and time are sometimes written in the knowledge of relativity. After Freud, of 20th-century scientists, Einstein has probably most influenced nonscientists' thinking.

▶ *In stories of lasers and intergalactic travel, science fiction writing is inspired by Einstein's work*

Einstein returns to Germany

Very rarely in history has a scientist produced such an array of fundamental ideas in one year as Einstein did in 1905. (Newton's *annus mirabilis* was comparable, when in 1666 he laid the foundations of his future work on mathematics, gravitation and light.) Yet Einstein did not win immediate fame. His first application to teach in the University of Berne in 1907 was turned down; but he was accepted in the next year, and in 1909, as his reputation gradually grew, he was appointed to a post at the University of Zurich.

By this time his work was attracting particular attention in Germany. Hermann Minkowski (1864-1909), one of the leading German mathematicians, pointed out the way in which relativity mixed up space and time: measurements of distance involved time and *vice versa*. Minkowski therefore introduced the new concept of "space-time". "From now on," he declared, "space by itself and time by itself must sink into the shadows, while only a union of the two preserves independence."

In 1909 Einstein met Max Planck, author of the quantum theory, for the first time, and from then on came into increasingly close contact with German physicists. In 1911 Einstein moved to the German University in Prague, only to return to Zurich in the following year. Finally, in 1914 he moved to Berlin.

Einstein's appointment to one of the senior German academic posts, which he retained until 1933, reflected his now widely accepted eminence. He resumed his German nationality. However, though academically this position could hardly be bettered, Einstein was not totally happy.

His wife returned to Zurich with their two sons. This signaled the break up of his marriage, though the formal divorce did not come through until 1919. Moreover, he realized again how much he disliked the regimented atmosphere in Germany which had oppressed him as a boy. Almost at once this atmosphere became worse: at the outbreak of World War I, the vast majority of German scientists supported the war effort in every way they could. Einstein became increasingly at odds with the mood of his colleagues, and his attachment to pacifism increased.

General relativity

Hardly surprisingly, Einstein concentrated on his own research, examining again the basic limitation of his 1905 paper on relativity. How could this be extended to cover the case when bodies changed their speeds? People who are subject to an acceleration, for example in a car, can detect it by the presence of a force which pushes them back in their seats. As the car reaches a steady speed, this force disappears. Now the pull of gravity is also a force which we detect by the pressure it produces – on the soles of our feet when we are standing. Einstein argued that acceleration and gravity are interrelated; so, if he could generalize his theory of relativity to include acceleration, he would simultaneously have something new to say about gravity.

Einstein had been working on this extension of his theory since 1905, but his ideas came to fruition in the middle of World War I. In the paper he published in 1915 on his new "general theory of relativity" he showed that gravity, instead of being seen as a pull exerted by an object, can be viewed as a distortion of the space round the object. This distortion produces an acceleration in passing bodies, conventionally labeled "gravitational attraction".

▲ The University of Berlin, where Einstein was a professor, and director of the Kaiser Wilhelm Institute for 30 years.

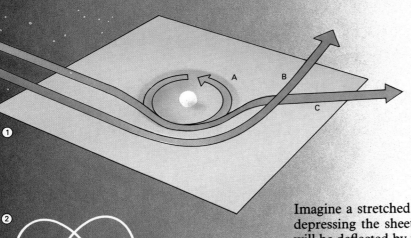

◄ (1) Space can be visualized as like an elastic sheet on which a heavy mass has produced an indentation. On encountering this, bodies follow curved paths: a relatively slow-moving body (A) deep in the well follows a closed path (like a planet round the Sun), a faster body (B) follows an open curve, while a ray of light (C) is normally deflected only very slightly. (2) Until the 1919 eclipse the only important evidence for Einstein's general theory was that it accurately predicted the slow shift of Mercury's orbit round the Sun. (3) An object moving through distorted space seems to experience a "gravitational" pull. Einstein illustrated this equivalence in terms of a passenger isolated in an elevator, who cannot tell whether he is held on the floor by the lift's acceleration or the Earth's gravity.

Imagine a stretched elastic sheet with a weight placed on the center, depressing the sheet in its vicinity. A marble rolled across the sheet will be deflected by the depression in the sheet as it passes the weight. To an observer, it will appear that the weight has attracted the marble. So, Einstein would say, the space near the Sun is distorted by its presence in such a way that the much smaller planets are deflected into orbits round the Sun.

Einstein's description of gravity is obviously different from Newton's. Newton thought gravitational pull resided in bodies, whereas Einstein saw it in the space around them. Yet this different viewpoint led initially to very few differences in the predictions the two theories made. They predicted identical results except for very high accelerations, or very massive bodies.

It was some years before the full impact of Einstein's 1915 paper on his general theory of relativity was fully comprehended felt by the scientific community. At first, the only important evidence in Einstein's favor came from a study of the path of the planet Mercury in its orbit round the Sun. Mercury is the closest planet to the relatively massive Sun, and moves more rapidly than any other planet. Hence, it is of all planets the one most likely to show deviations from Newton's predictions. The position of Mercury's elongated orbit round the Sun changes slowly with time. The reasons for this had already been partly understood by applying Newton's theory, but there was a small amount of shift in the orbit which could not be explained. Einstein was able to demonstrate that this small extra increment could be accounted for by his own theory.

"STARLIGHT BENT BY THE SUN'S ATTRACTION": THE EINSTEIN THEORY.

Confirming general relativity

Though interesting, the provision of an explanation for a small change in Mercury's orbit was hardly striking enough for Einstein's contemporaries to abandon Newton's longstanding theory. For many, the clinching evidence in favor of Einstein came from another of his predictions, which was spectacularly confirmed after the war. Newton's theory indicated that a ray of light passing near a massive object like the Sun should be deflected slightly. Einstein's theory indicated a similar effect but predicted twice as much deflection as Newton's theory. Measurement of the deflection had never been attempted: a ray of light passing near the Sun could simply not be seen in the glare of the sunlight. The way forward was explored by a British astronomer, Arthur Eddington (1882-1944), who managed, despite the war, to obtain a copy of Einstein's paper. In 1919 the Sun would be eclipsed in a part of the sky where there were a number of bright stars. Consequently, once the Moon had totally eclipsed the Sun's disk, the light from these stars would be seen from the darkened Earth close to the edge of the Sun. The light rays would be slightly deflected by the Sun, giving the impression that the stars had altered their positions in the sky. A measurement of the apparent shift in position of the stars would test Einstein's prediction. Two British expeditions were sent out to observe the eclipse: one, led by Eddington, went to the island of Príncipe off West Africa, and the other to Sobral in northeast Brazil. The findings from their observations of the eclipse on 29 May proved to be in excellent agreement with the value derived from the general theory of relativity.

▲▼ *Sir Arthur Eddington (pictured with Einstein, below) led one of the British expeditions sent in 1919, to Brazil and West Africa, to observe the solar eclipse. The apparent shift in the position of stars located in that part of the sky near to the Sun was in close accordance with that predicted by Einstein. The widely reported findings (above) verified his theory that light is subject to deflection by a massive object.*

Exploration of the Atom

Today it may seem strange that Einstein received his Nobel Prize for work on the nature of radiation, rather than for work on relativity. But his development of quantum mechanics (how atoms and subatomic particles move and interact) proved to be of fundamental importance. He was the first to point out that light can be thought of, for some purposes, as a cloud of particles – each of these being one of Max Planck's quanta. Information obtained from the study, popular in 19th-century physics, of how the atoms in a cloud of gas move could now be applied to radiation. Einstein found that this approach explained why some metals became electrically charged when exposed to light – the "photoelectric effect" employed today, for example, in camera exposure meters.

Bohr's model of the atom

In 1905 hardly anyone accepted these ideas of Einstein: it seemed ridiculous that radiation could sometimes act like a wave and sometimes like particles. Robert Millikan (1868-1953) in the United States began work on the photoelectric effect in order to show that Einstein was wrong. When he eventually won a Nobel Prize (1923), it was in part because his experiments during World War I had shown Einstein to be right. Meanwhile, just before the war, the Danish physicist Neils Bohr (1885-1962) had suggested a picture of the atom which explained why radiation appears as quanta. In his model, the atom consists of a central nucleus (with a positive electrical charge) round which electrons circle (each with a negative electrical charge, so that the atom as a whole is electrically neutral). Bohr's atom therefore looks like a tiny solar system, with the difference that planets can move at any distance from the Sun, whereas Bohr's electrons can only orbit the nucleus at certain fixed distances. If they change orbit, they do so by jumping from one "acceptable" distance to another. If they jump toward the nucleus, radiation is emitted: if they jump away from the nucleus, radiation is absorbed. For Bohr the important point was this: the electrons only changed their distances at intervals, so the radiation was not produced continuously, but in bursts – each burst of radiation corresponding to one quantum.

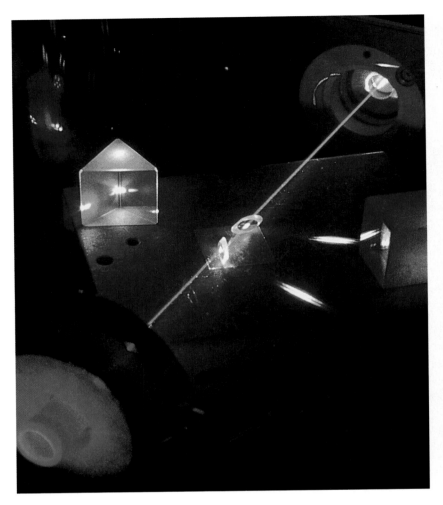

▼ *The Danish physicist Niels Bohr deep in discussion with Einstein. Bohr proposed his revolutionary theory of the atom in 1913 while he was working in Manchester with the New Zealand-born Ernest Rutherford, discoverer of alpha and beta particles.*

▲ *A laser being used in quality control of quartz "windows". Einstein's idea of stimulated emission of quanta prompted the laser's development. Lasers may be used in communications, holography, welding and cutting (e.g. surgery), and "star wars" weaponry.*

► *16 July 1945 – "Trinity", the world's first atomic bomb blast, in New Mexico. Einstein urged President Roosevelt to develop the bomb (his "one great mistake" he later called it). The range of application of physicists' work led to the war being named the "physicists' war".*

Rutherford and the atomic nucleus

Bohr managed to bring together the idea of quanta, which interested Planck and Einstein, with the picture of an atom containing a nucleus and electrons, which was then of particular interest to physicists in Britain.

At the center of this work on the structure of the atom was Ernest Rutherford (1871-1937), a New Zealander who spent much of his life in England. Bohr worked with him in Manchester. After World War I, Rutherford moved to Cambridge, and there he and his colleagues concentrated mainly on exploring the nature of the atomic nucleus. They showed that it is made up of more than one type of particle and can, under some circumstances, be made unstable. During the 1930s this work was extended in a number of laboratories, and a variety of new, and often unstable, nuclei were created.

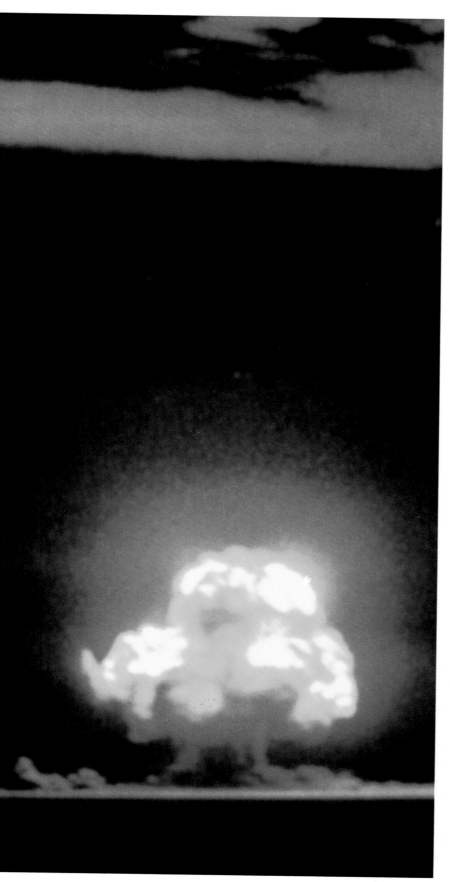

The atomic bomb

In 1938 an old friend of Einstein's, Otto Hahn (1879-1968), who was still working in Germany, found that the nuclei of the element uranium can be broken down by a newly discovered process, fission, in which the nucleus breaks down into two nearly equal fragments. It was rapidly realized by a number of physicists that fission might provide a source of tremendous energy $E = mc^2$, since there was an appreciable loss of mass during fission. With Germany obviously preparing for war, physicists in both the United States and Britain feared that German scientists might rapidly capitalize on this discovery to build an entirely new type of bomb, much more destructive than any conventional weapon. Einstein gave his very influential support to the case for pressing ahead urgently with the "Manhattan Project" and played a significant part in ensuring its start.

Einstein later regretted this: "I made one great mistake in my life – when I signed the letter to President Roosevelt recommending that atom bombs can be made." But, he added: "there was some justification – the danger that the Germans would make them." Yet the atomic bomb is the supreme example of the way in which the academic researches of Einstein and his generation of physicists became, within a few decades, applicable in ways they could never have foreseen. In fact, the range of applications of their work has sometimes led to World War II being called "the physicists' war".

Lasers and holograms

Einstein returned to the question of quanta in 1917, while he was still working on the implications of general relativity. In Bohr's theory of the atom, an electron jumping outward absorbs a quantum, whilst an electron jump inward emits a quantum. The process of absorption requires the atom to be bathed in radiation, but emission occurs spontaneously: it does not depend on what radiation is passing by the atom at the time. Einstein pointed out that if an atom is surrounded by appropriate radiation, it can be stimulated into emitting a quantum even when it would not normally do so.

This idea of "stimulated emission" lies at the heart of the modern laser ("Light Amplification by Stimulated Emission of Radiation"). Lasers use stimulated emission to produce very intense beams of radiation. Such beams have found many uses in recent years, from carrying out eye operations to projected attempts to blast enemy satellites in the United States' "Star Wars" program. Perhaps their greatest importance, however, will prove to be in transmitting messages.

Lasers have a second property of importance along with high intensity. All the waves in a laser beam are in step with each other – "coherent" radiation. It is such coherent light that is required in the new technique of holography. The laser beam is recorded as it is reflected from an object: the resultant image can be used to reconstruct a three-dimensional picture of the object. These pictures-in-the-round or "holograms" are becoming a common feature of our life.

For over twenty-five years, parallel to his public life Einstein worked in isolation for a "Grand Unified Theory"

▼ *In Brussels at the 1911 "Solvay Congress", sponsored by a Belgian industrialist, the young Einstein (second right) joins Planck, Lorentz, Curie, Rutherford and other top physicists to discuss the impact of quantum theory on the sciences.*

▲ *In 1921 Einstein and his second wife Elsa paid their first visit together to the United States (below) accompanied by the Zionist leader Chaim Weizmann. The following year they visited Japan. On both occasions Einstein was showered with honors.*

Fame and travel

Up until 1919, Einstein's name had been familiar to physicists, but not to a wider audience. The results from the observations of the eclipse that confirmed Einstein's predictions, and the acceptance that they marked the overthrow of Newton's theory, catapulted Einstein to world fame. One of those present at the meeting in London where the eclipse expeditions reported their work later recorded: "The whole atmosphere of tense interest was exactly that of the Greek drama: we were the chorus commenting on the decree of destiny as disclosed in the development of a supreme incident."

In the year of the eclipse, Einstein married again. His new bride was his cousin Elsa, whom he had known since his boyhood. She was now a widow with two daughters and they had come together again a short time before when she had nursed Einstein through a serious illness. She proved an excellent manager and protector of Einstein at home and on his travels. These soon began in earnest: in 1921 he visited both the United States and Britain for the first time, and was also awarded the Nobel Prize for physics for his work on radiation.

Einstein went to the United States primarily to raise money for the Hebrew University then being built in Jerusalem. During the preceding decade Einstein had become increasingly conscious of his Jewish background; more particularly, he had become convinced of the need for a Jewish national home. The growing antisemitism in Germany certainly played a significant role in this new awareness.

Einstein established himself as an important supporter of the Zionist cause. After World War II his old acquaintance, the Zionist leader and chemist Chaim Weizmann, became President of the new state of Israel. On Weizmann's death in 1952 Einstein was invited to succeed him. He declined on the grounds of lack of aptitude and experience, but the offer gives some indication of his standing in the Jewish world by this time.

Einstein in the United States – the latter years

Early in 1933 Hitler came to power in Germany. Einstein was in the United States at the time, and soon decided to make his home there; he had already been approached to join the new Institute for Advanced Study at Princeton, and now decided to do so. He was deprived of his German citizenship, but did not become a United States citizen until 1940. At the time of his settling in the United States, Einstein was an outspoken pacifist, but subsequent events in Germany forced him to modify his stance (◀ page 141). Einstein was by now very isolated in the world of science. The last work that involved him fully with the scientific community had stemmed from his theory of general relativity. Since this was a theory of how gravitation acted, it obviously had implications for cosmology – the study of the Universe as a whole. Einstein's initial assumption that the Universe was stationary was challenged by the observations of the American astronomer Edwin Hubble (1889-1935), who showed that the Universe is expanding.

▼ *Einstein lecturing in the United States at the California Institute of Technology, Pasadena, in 1930-1931. He undertook three such tours, the last being in 1933, when the Nazis came to power in Germany. Seven years later, having made the United States his home, Einstein was sworn in as an American citizen (below) together with his secretary Dukas and stepdaughter Margot.*

Rise of a Scientific Power

During the 20th century, and particularly in the years leading up to World War II, the immigration of scientists into the United States played a significant role in developing scientific research there. This is a recent striking example of the perennial importance of population movements in affecting the growth of ideas.

Early practical science in the United States
In the 18th and 19th centuries, scientific interest in the United States concentrated on practical or environmental concerns. Benjamin Franklin (1706-1790), for example, studied electricity partly in order to answer questions about the nature of lightning and the design of lightning conductors. George Washington (1732-1799), like a number of fellow-Americans in his rapidly expanding country, was a trained surveyor. Since surveying involved astronomical measurements, astronomy soon became a topic for study. In fact, most of the sciences cultivated during the 19th century – astronomy, geology, meteorology and biology – reflected the needs of a country where exploration and understanding of the environment were at a premium.

The experimental tradition
In 19th-century America, individual scientists who became eminent in such subjects as physics were typically practical experimenters rather than theoreticians. One such was Albert Michelson (1852-1931), the first American to win a Nobel Prize for physics. Michelson was an immigrant to the United States: born in Poland, of Jewish descent, his family came to the country when he was about three years old. The results of the experiment he conducted with Edward Morley (1838-1923), to test the effects of the ether on the speed of light, were subsequently realized to be strong evidence in favor of Einstein's theory of special relativity (◀ page 131).

By the end of the 19th century the old connection between astronomy and surveying had essentially ceased: astronomers increasingly concentrated on the physical properties of distant, and therefore faint, objects. Such work required large telescopes which could collect large amounts of light. American scientists pioneered the building of these telescopes; they had the advantage of skilled mechanics, good observing sites and wealthy patrons who provided the money. By the early 20th century, American observers had become world leaders in astronomy. When Einstein's first model of the universe based on general relativity was finally discarded, it was on the basis of observations made at Mount Wilson in California.

The position in physics was different. In terms of Nobel Prizes, only three awards were made to American physicists up to the mid-1930s, even though, by this time, universities had created physics departments which could provide good research training. (In the 19th century, American scientists had gone to Germany to develop their research skills). However, the emphasis remained on experiment – all the Nobel Prizes in physics awarded to Americans up to World War II were for experimental work.

The new influx of Europeans
This situation changed as the political conditions in Europe worsened during the 1930s. In addition to Einstein arriving in Princeton, an array of other European physicists came to the United States. Not all were Germans. Perhaps the most eminent after Einstein was the Italian, Enrico Fermi (1901-1954), who came to the United States in 1938 directly from the ceremony in Sweden where he received the Nobel Prize for physics. Fermi was an outstanding experimental physicist – his group at Chicago produced the first nuclear energy generator in 1942. But he was also a highly competent theoretician who emphasized the importance of this type of work for the United States. Hans Bethe

▲ Ben Franklin demonstrated the electrical nature of lightning, and invented the lightning conductor, Franklin stove and bifocal lenses.

▼ Prominent among the many physicists who came to the United States from troubled Europe in the 1930s was Italian Enrico Fermi.

▼ Germany was a world leader in scientific and technological research before World War II. It remained ahead in rocket development until the end of the war. The Americans and Russians then captured German researchers and used them to develop rocketry in their countries. Wernher von Braun and others helped launch American space exploration – shown here by an astronaut "space-walking".

(born 1906), who had briefly worked with Fermi in Rome, was even more influential in this respect. Ejected from his post in Germany because his mother was Jewish, he established a research group in theoretical physics in the United States, ultimately receiving a Nobel Prize for his work. Bethe published some very influential teaching material on theoretical physics and, like Fermi, was closely involved in the atomic bomb project (♦ page 141).

The impact on American physics

The first, and more obvious consequence of this emigration of European physicists to the United States was the stimulation and leadership it gave to work on the atomic bomb. American preeminence in nuclear physics after the war would have stemmed from this alone. But for the physicist community an equally important factor was the creation of theoretical groups who could work alongside, and on equal terms with, the experimental groups. A glance at the list of American postwar Nobel Prize winners quickly reveals how many were immigrants; but it also shows that there is now a fairly equal balance between experimenters and theoreticians. Immigration has not simply helped world leadership in physics to shift from Germany to the United States: it has also led to a more balanced and cohesive physics research program.

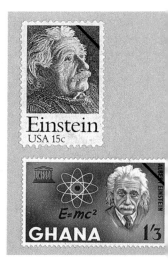

▲ *A baggy sweater and the famous equation E = mc² (equivalence of mass and energy), recurrent motifs in stamps celebrating a giant of the 20th century.*

◄ *"I will a little tink." For ten years after his retirement from the Institute for Advanced Study at Princeton, New Jersey, Einstein continued his quest for a "unified field theory" bringing together quantum mechanics and gravitation theory.*

▼ *Einstein featured on an Israeli banknote, and being visited by Prime Minister Ben-Gurion in 1951. A year later Einstein declined a request to become President of Israel.*

The Dutch astronomer Willem de Sitter (1872-1934), who had been responsible for informing Eddington of Einstein's work, had already shown that general relativity, when applied to the Universe, favored the idea of an expanding universe. Edwin Hubble's work confirmed this view. In 1930 Einstein declared his agreement with de Sitter in a paper that can be regarded as one of the foundation documents of modern cosmology.

From this point on, Einstein's concern was with something even wider and more fundamental. His research had dealt with two of the main areas of 20th-century theoretical physics, gravitation and quantum mechanics, but they had been treated quite separately. Einstein spent the last decades of his life trying to bring together into a unified theory these two basic aspects of modern physics, one dealing with very large amounts of matter and the other with very small amounts. Nowadays there is great interest amongst physicists in what are known as GUTs (Grand Unified Theories), but Einstein's contemporaries considered his attempts to be premature. In consequence, he came to have less and less contact with the world of physics. He had already accepted, some time before his death on 18 April 1955, that he was not going to reach his hoped-for goal: "As to my work, it no longer amounts to much. I don't get many results any more and have to be satisfied with playing the Elder Statesman and the Jewish Saint."

Glossary

This Glossary contains entries about prominent stars and constellations, and other phenomena observed in the skies (and some observed in Earth's atmosphere), as well as concepts used in astronomy and cosmology.

A

Aberration of light
In astronomy, a displacement between a star's observed and true position caused by the Earth's motion about the Sun and the finite nature of the velocity of light. The effect is similar to that observed when you walk in the rain: though the rain is in fact falling vertically, because of your motion it appears to be falling at an angle. The maximum aberrational displacement is 20.5″ of arc; stars on the ECLIPTIC appear to move to and fro along a line of 41″; stars 90° from the ecliptic appear to trace out a circle of radius 20.5″; and stars in intermediate positions ellipses of major axis 41″.

Adonis
Asteroid about one kilometer in diameter with a highly eccentric ORBIT. Its perihelion is within the orbit of Venus, its aphelion beyond that of Mars. It was discovered in 1936.

Albedo
The ratio between the amount of light reflected from a surface and the amount of light incident upon it. The term is usually applied to celestial objects within the SOLAR SYSTEM: the Moon reflects about 7% of the sunlight falling upon it, and hence has an albedo of 0.07.

Aldebaran
Alpha Tauri, the 14th brightest star in the night sky and the brightest star in TAURUS. At a distance of 21pc, it has an absolute magnitude varying about −0.3 and an apparent magnitude varying about 0.85.

Algol
Beta Persei, second brightest star in the constellation PERSEUS. It is a multiple star of at least three but probably four components, two of which form an eclipsing binary (see VARIABLE STARS) causing a 10h diminution of brightness every 69h.

Alpha Centauri
Multiple star in the constellation CENTAURUS, comprising a DOUBLE STAR around which orbits at a distance of 10,000AU a red dwarf, Proxima Centauri, which is the nearest star to the Solar System, being 1.33 parsecs distant.

Altair
Brightest star in the constellation AQUILA and the twelfth brightest in the night sky (apparent magnitude +0.77). It has an extremely rapid rotation and is 5.1 parsecs from the Earth.

Andromeda
Constellation in the N Hemisphere. The Great Andromeda Nebula (M31) is the most distant object visible to the naked eye in N skies. It is the nearest external GALAXY to our own, a larger spiral (49kpc across), and about 670kpc away.

Antares
Alpha Scorpii, a DOUBLE STAR comprising a red supergiant 480 times larger than the Sun and a blue star of unknown type 3 times larger than the Sun (apparent magnitudes +1.23 and +5.5). It is 100pc from the Earth.

Antimatter
A variety of matter differing from the matter that predominates in our part of the UNIVERSE in that it is composed of antiparticles rather than particles. Individual antiparticles, many of which have been found in cosmic ray showers or produced using particle accelerators, differ from their particle counterparts in that they are oppositely charged (as with the antiproton-proton pair) or in that their magnetic moment is orientated in the opposite sense with respect to their spin (as with the antineutrino and neutrino). In our part of the Universe antiparticles are very short-lived, being rapidly annihilated in collisions with their corresponding particles, their mass-energy reappearing as a gamma-ray photon. (The reverse is also true: a high-energy gamma ray sometimes spontaneously forms itself into a positron-electron pair.) However, it is by no means inconceivable that regions of the Universe exist in which all the matter is antimatter, composed of what are to us antiparticles. The first antiparticle, the positron (antielectron), was discovered by C.D. Anderson in 1932.

Apsides, Line of
The imaginary straight line connecting the two points of an elliptical ORBIT that represent the orbiting body's greatest (higher apsis) and least (lower apsis) distances from the body around which it is revolving.

Aquarius
The Water Bearer, a large but faint constellation on the ECLIPTIC; the 11th sign of the ZODIAC.

Aquila
The Eagle, a large autumn constellation in the N Hemisphere, lying in the plane of the Milky Way. (See also ALTAIR.)

Arcturus
Alpha Boötis, a red giant star 11pc distant. It has a very high PROPER MOTION and an apparent magnitude of −0.04.

Aries
The Ram, first constellation of the ZODIAC. In N skies it is a winter constellation.

Aries, First Point of
The vernal equinox, a point of intersection of the equator and the ECLIPTIC used as the zero of celestial longitude. Owing to PRECESSION, the First Point of Aries is currently in PISCES.

Asteroids
The thousands of planetoids or minor planets, ranging in diameter from a few meters to 1000km (CERES), most of whose orbits lie in the Asteroid Belt between the orbits of Mars and Jupiter. Vesta is the only asteroid visible to the naked eye, though Ceres was the first to be discovered. Their total mass is estimated to be 0.001 that of the Earth. A second asteroid belt beyond the orbit of Pluto has been postulated. The "Apollo" asteroids are those that cross the orbit of the Earth; of these, Phaethon passes nearest the Sun. Chiron's orbit passes from inside that of Saturn to just beyond Uranus. (See also METEOR; SOLAR SYSTEM.)

Astrolabe
An astronomical instrument dating from the Hellenic period, used to measure the altitude of celestial bodies and, before the introduction of the sextant, as a navigational aid. It consisted of a vertical disk with an engraved scale across which was mounted a sighting rule or "alidade".

Astrology
The art and science of divining the future from the study of the heavens. Originating in ancient Mesopotamia as a means for predicting the fate of states and their rulers, the astrology that found its way into Hellenistic culture applied itself also to the destinies of individuals. Together with the desire to devise accurate CALENDARS, astrology provided a key incentive leading to the earliest systematic ASTRONOMY and was a continuing spur to the development of astronomical techniques until the 17th century. The majority of Classical and medieval astronomers, Ptolemy and Johannes Kepler among them, practiced astrology, often earning their livelihoods thus. Astrology exercised its greatest influence in the Greco-Roman world and again in Renaissance Europe (despite the opposition of the Church) and, although generally abandoned after the 17th century, it has continued to excite a fluctuating popular interest down to the present.

Astronomical Unit (AU)
A unit of distance equal to the semi-major axis of the Earth's orbit (approximately the mean distance of the Earth from the Sun), used for describing distances within the Solar System. Its value is 149.6Gm.

Astronomy
The study of the heavens. At the crossroads of agriculture and religion, astronomy, the earliest of the sciences, was of great practical importance in ancient civilization. Before 2000 BC, Babylonians, Chinese and Egyptians all sowed their crops according to calendars computed from the regular motions of the Sun and Moon.

Although early Greek philosophers were more concerned with the physical nature of the heavens than with precise observation, later Greek scientists returned to the problems of positional astronomy. The vast achievement of Greek astronomy was epitomized in the writings of Claudius Ptolemy. His *Almagest*, passing through Arabic translations, was eventually transmitted to medieval Europe and remained the chief authority among astronomers for over 1400 years.

Throughout this period the main purpose of positional astronomy had been to assist in the casting of accurate horoscopes, the twin sciences of astronomy and ASTROLOGY having not yet parted company. The structure of the Universe meanwhile remained the preserve of (Aristotelian) physics. The work of Nicolas Copernicus represented an early attempt to harmonize an improved positional astronomy with a true physical theory of planetary motion. Against the judgment of antiquity that Sun, Moon and planets circled the Earth as lanterns set in a series of concentric transparent shells, in his *de Revolutionibus* (1543) Copernicus argued that the Sun lay motionless at the center of the planetary system.

Although the Copernican (or heliocentric) hypothesis proved to be a sound basis for the computation of navigators' tables (the need for which was stimulating renewed interest in astronomy), it did not become unassailably established in astronomical theory until Isaac Newton published his mathematical derivation of KEPLER's LAWS in 1687. In the meantime Joannes Kepler, working on the superb observational data of Tycho Brahe, had shown the orbit of Mars to be elliptical and not circular, and Galileo had used the newly invented telescope to discover SUNSPOTS, the phases of Venus and four moons of Jupiter.

Since the 17th century the development of astronomy has followed on successive improvements in the design of telescopes. In 1781 William Herschel discovered Uranus, the first discovery of a new PLANET to be made in historical times. Measurement of the parallax of a few stars in 1838 first allowed the estimation of interstellar distances. Analysis of the FRAUNHOFER LINES in the spectrum of the Sun gave scientists their first indication of the chemical composition of the STARS.

In the present century the scope of observational astronomy has extended to electromagnetic radiation emitted by celestial objects from the shortest wavelengths (gamma rays) to the largest (radio), taking in X-rays, ultraviolet, optical and infrared. As the Earth's atmosphere absorbs most of these radiations from space, telescopes have been launched by rockets and carried on satellites. Thus, astronomers have discovered QUASARS, PULSARS and neutron stars, and have been able to show in detail the faintest parts of distant galaxies and nebulae. In their turn, these discoveries have enabled cosmologists to develop more self-consistent models of the UNIVERSE. (See also COSMOLOGY; OBSERVATORY.)

Atmosphere

The envelope of gas, vapor and aerosol particles surrounding the earth, retained by gravity and forming a major constituent in the environment of most forms of terrestrial life, protecting it from the impact of METEORS, COSMIC RAY particles and harmful solar radiation. The composition of the atmosphere and most of its physical properties vary with altitude, certain key properties being used to divide the whole into several zones, the upper and lower boundaries of which change with latitude, the time of day and the season of the year. About 75% of the total mass of atmosphere and 90% of its water vapor and aerosols are contained in the troposphere, the lowest zone. Excluding water vapor, the air of the troposphere contains 78% nitrogen, 20% oxygen, 0.9% argon and 0.03% carbon dioxide, together with traces of the other noble gases; and methane, hydrogen and nitrous oxide. The water vapour content fluctuates within wide margins as water is evaporated from the oceans, carried in clouds and precipitated upon the continents. The air flows in meandering currents, transferring energy from the warm equatorial regions to the colder poles. The troposphere is thus the zone in which weather occurs, as well as that in which most air-dependent life exists. Apart from occasional inversions, the temperature falls with increasing altitude through the troposphere until at the tropopause (altitude 7km at the poles, l6km on the equator) it becomes constant (about 217K), and then slowly increases again into the stratosphere (up to about 48km). The upper stratosphere contains the ozone layer, which filters out the dangerous ultraviolet radiation incident from the SUN. Above the stratosphere, the mesosphere merges into the ionosphere, a region containing various layers of charged particles (ions) of immense importance in the propagation of radio waves, being used to reflect signals between distant ground stations. At greater altitudes still, the ionosphere passes into the exosphere, a region of rarefied helium and hydrogen gases, in turn merging into the interplanetary medium. In all, the atmosphere has a mass of about 5.2×10^{18}kg, its density being about 1.23kg/m at sea level. Its weight results in its exerting an average air pressure of 101.3kPa (1013mbar) near the surface, this fluctuating greatly with the weather and falling off rapidly with height. The other PLANETS of the SOLAR SYSTEM (with the possible exception of PLUTO), though only two of their SATELLITES, all have distinctive atmospheres, though none of these contains as much life-supporting oxygen as does that of the Earth.

Atmosphere refraction

The refraction of light rays passing through the atmosphere because of variations in its density and temperature, which produce corresponding variations in its refractive index. Under standard conditions, rays of light passing through the atmosphere are slightly curved so that the apparent positions of celestial bodies are displaced toward the ZENITH by a small amount; ie celestial bodies appear slightly higher above the horizon than their true positions. The effect is greater close to the horizon. Unusual density variations may produce mirages, shimmer and other deceptive effects.

Auriga

The Charioteer, winter constellation of N skies, containing CAPELLA, Alpha Aurigae, the sixth brightest star in the night sky.

Aurora (polar lights)

Striking display of lights seen in night skies near the Earth's geomagnetic poles. The *aurora borealis* (northern lights) is seen in Canada, Alaska and N Scandinavia, the *aurora australis* (southern lights) is seen in Antarctic regions. The auroras are caused by the collision of air molecules in the upper atmosphere with charged particles from the Sun that have been accelerated and "funneled" by the Earth's magnetic field. Particularly intense auroras are associated with high solar activity. Night-time airglow is termed the permanent aurora.

Azimuth

In navigation and astronomy, the angular distance measured from 0-360° along the horizon eastward from an observer's north point to the point of intersection of the horizon and a great circle (see CELESTIAL SPHERE) passing through the observer's ZENITH and a star or planet.

B

Baily's Beads

Named for Francis Baily (1774-1844), the apparent fragmentation of the thin crescent of the Sun just before totality in a solar ECLIPSE, caused by sunlight shining through mountains at the edge of the lunar disk.

Betelgeuse

Alpha Orionis, second brightest star in ORION. An irregularly variable red supergiant (see VARIABLE STARS) with a variable radius some 300 times that of the Sun, it is over 150pc from Earth.

Black hole

A region of space into which matter has fallen and within which the gravitational field is so powerful that nothing, not even electromagnetic radiation (including light), can escape. The matter that has formed the black hole becomes infinitely compressed in a central point known as a SINGULARITY. A black hole may be formed by the total gravitational collapse of a massive star that has run out of nuclear fuel and can no longer support itself. The minimum mass of material that can collapse in this way, in the present-day Universe, is about three solar masses, but it has been suggested that very much smaller masses could have been compressed into tiny "primordial" black holes during the big bang. At the other end of the scale, supermassive black holes of millions or even billions of solar masses may exist in the cores of active galaxies.

Because no electromagnetic radiation can escape from black holes, they may be detected only through their gravitational influence on other bodies or through the emission of X- and gamma rays by infalling matter, which becomes violently heated close to their boundaries (see EVENT HORIZON).

Blink comparator (blink microscope)

Astronomical instrument used to detect differences between apparently similar star pictures, viewed as in a stereoscope, by rapidly obscuring each alternately. Anything that has moved flickers. The planet PLUTO was discovered this way. It can also detect variable stars and those of large proper motion.

Boötes

The Herdsman, a constellation of the N Hemisphere, containing the star ARCTURUS.

Brown dwarf

A STAR of such low mass (probably less than 0.08 of the Sun's mass) that thermonuclear reactions never get started in its core. Brown dwarfs are expected to be very cool and dim, shining mainly at infrared wavelengths as a result of the heat generated by their contracting from interstellar gas clouds. Because they are so faint only a few have been discovered so far, but they may exist in large numbers. An example is the companion to the star Van Biesbroeck 8, which is about 21 light years from Earth.

C

Calendar

A system for reckoning the passing of time. The principal problem in drawing up calendars arises from the fact that the solar day, the lunar month and the tropical year – the most immediate natural time units – are not simple multiples of each other. In practice a solution is found in basing the system either on the phases of the Moon (lunar calendar) or on the changing of the seasons (solar calendar). The difficulty that the days eventually get out of step with the Moon or the seasons is solved by adding in (intercalating) one or more extra days or months at regular intervals in an extended cycle of months or years.

Years are commonly numbered in Western societies from the birth of Christ – as computed by a 6th-century monk. Years since that epoch are labeled AD, years before, BC. There is no year 0, AD 1 following directly from 1 BC. Astronomers, on the other hand, figure years BC as negative numbers one less than the date BC and include a year 0 (=1 BC). The astronomers' year -10 is thus the same as 11 BC.

Cancer

The Crab, a spring constellation in the N Hemisphere, the fourth sign of the ZODIAC. At the time the zodiacal system was adopted, Cancer marked the northernmost limit of the ECLIPTIC. A hazy object near the center of Cancer is a cluster of stars named Praesepe, the Beehive.

Canis Major

The Great Dog, a constellation of the S Hemisphere visible during winter in Northern skies. It contains SIRIUS, the brightest star in the night sky. Mythologically, Canis Major and CANIS MINOR were ORION's hunting dogs.

Canis Minor

The Little Dog, a constellation on the celestial equator (see CELESTIAL SPHERE) visible in Northern skies during winter. It contains the binary star PROCYON (see DOUBLE STAR).

Canopus

Alpha Carinae, the second brightest star in the sky, with an apparent magnitude of −0.72. It is 210 times larger than the Sun and 360pc from Earth.

Capella

Alpha Aurigae, the sixth brightest star in the night sky. It is a DOUBLE STAR, 13.8pc distant, each component having apparent magnitude +0.85, with possibly two further dim components.

Capricornus

The Sea Goat, a fairly inconspicuous constellation of the S Hemisphere, lacking any bright stars, and the tenth sign of the ZODIAC. Lying between the constellations of AQUARIUS and SAGITTARIUS, Capricornus in ancient times lay at the southernmost limit of the ECLIPTIC.

Cassiopeia

In astronomy, a Northern circumpolar constellation (see CIRCUMPOLAR STARS) whose five principal stars form a prominent "W".

Castor

Alpha Geminorum, second brightest star of GEMINI. About 14.4pc from Earth, it has at least six components: a binary, each component of which is itself a binary, is orbited at distance by a third binary (see DOUBLE STAR).

Celestial sphere

In ancient times, the sphere to which it was believed all the stars were attached. In modern times, an imaginary sphere of indefinite but very large radius upon which, for purposes of angular computation, celestial bodies are considered to be situated. The celestial poles are defined as those points on the sphere vertically above the terrestrial poles, and the celestial equator by the projection of the terrestrial equator onto the sphere. (See also ECLIPTIC.) Astronomical coordinate systems are based on these great circles (circles whose centers are also the center of the sphere) and, in some cases, on the observer's celestial horizon. In the most frequently used, the equatorial system, terrestrial latitude corresponds to declination – a star directly overhead in New York City will have a declination of +41° (S Hemisphere declinations are preceded by a minus sign), New York City having a latitude of 41°N and terrestrial longitude to right ascension, which is measured eastward from the FIRST POINT OF ARIES. Right ascension is measured in hours, one hour corresponding to 15° of longitude.

Centaurus
The Centaur, a constellation in the S Hemisphere. (See ALPHA CENTAURI; PROXIMA CENTAURI.)

Cepheid variables
Stars whose brightness varies regularly with a period of 1-60 days. They are pulsating stars that fluctuate in size and temperature during each cycle. The length of their cycle is directly proportional to their absolute magnitude, making them useful "mileposts" for computing large astronomical distances. (See VARIABLE STAR.)

Ceres
Largest of the ASTEROIDS (1000km in diameter) and the one first discovered (by Giuseppe Piazzi, 1801). Its orbit was first computed by K.F. Gauss and found to satisfy Bode's Law. Its "year" is 1681 days and its maximum apparent magnitude is +7.

Circumpolar stars
The stars that can be seen every night of the year from any particular latitude, and that appear to circle the celestial pole (see CELESTIAL SPHERE).

Comet
A nebulous body that orbits the Sun. In general, comets can be seen only when they are comparatively close to the Sun, though the time between their first appearance and their final disappearance may be as much as years. As they approach the Sun, a few comets develop tails (some comets develop more than one tail) of lengths of the order 1-100Gm, though at least one tail 300Gm in length – more than twice the distance from the Earth to the Sun – has been recorded. The tails of comets are always pointed away from the Sun, so as the comet recedes into space its tail precedes it. There are two principal types of tail, the dust tail and the ion (or plasma) tail. The tiny dust particles that make up the dust tail are blown from the head of the comet by radiation pressure, while the ionized gas of the plasma tail is driven out by the SOLAR WIND.

The head of the comet contains the nucleus. Nuclei may be as little as 100m or possibly as much as 100km in radius, and are thought to be composed primarily of frozen gases and ice mixed with smaller quantities of meteoritic material. The nucleus of HALLEY'S COMET measures about 16×8×8km. Most of the mass of a comet is contained within the nucleus, though this may be less than 0.000,001 that of the Earth. Surrounding the nucleus is the bright coma, possibly as much as 100Mm in radius, which is composed of gases and small particles erupting from the nucleus.

Cometary orbits are usually very eccentric ellipses, with some perihelions (see ORBIT) closer to the Sun than that of MERCURY, aphelions as much as 100,000AU from the Sun. The orbits of some comets take the form of hyperbolas, and it is thought that these have their origins altogether outside the SOLAR SYSTEM, that they are interstellar travelers.

In Greco-Roman times it was generally believed that comets were phenomena restricted to the upper atmosphere of the Earth. In the late 15th and 16th centuries it was shown by Michael Mästlin (1550-1631) and Tycho Brahe that comets were far more distant than the Moon. Isaac Newton interpreted the orbits of comets as parabolas, deducing that each comet was appearing for the first time. It was not until the 17th century that Edmund Halley showed that some comets returned periodically.

Conjunction
This occurs when the Earth, the Sun and a planet are in a straight line (as projected onto the plane of the Solar System). A planet on the far side of the Sun is in superior conjunction, a planet between Earth and Sun in inferior conjunction (see also OPPOSITION). Planets may be in conjunction with each other (see ASTROLOGY).

Constellation
A group of stars forming a pattern in the sky, though otherwise unconnected. In ancient times the patterns were interpreted as pictures, usually of mythical characters. The ECLIPTIC passes through twelve constellations, known as the zodiacal constellations (see ZODIAC).

Corona
The outer atmosphere of the SUN or other STAR. The term is also used for the halo seen around a celestial body, due to diffraction of its light by water droplets in thin clouds of the Earth's ATMOSPHERE. Around high voltage terminals a faint glow appears due to the ionization of the local air. The result of this ionization is an electrical discharge known as corona discharge, the glow being called a corona.

Cosmic rays
Charged particles, mainly the nuclei of hydrogen and other atoms, that isotropically bombard the Earth's upper ATMOSPHERE at velocities close to that of light. These primary cosmic rays interact with molecules of the upper atmosphere to produce what are termed secondary cosmic rays, which are considerably less energetic: they are subatomic particles that change rapidly into other types of particles. Initially, secondary cosmic rays, which pass frequently and harmlessly through our bodies, were detected by use of the geiger counter and the cloud chamber, though now many other kinds of detector are used in studies of cosmic rays. It is thought that cosmic rays are produced by SUPERNOVAS, though some may be of extragalactic origin.

Cosmogony
The science or pseudoscience of the origins of the UNIVERSE.

Cosmology
The study of the structure and evolution of the Universe. Ancient and medieval cosmologies were many, varied and imaginative, usually oriented around a stationary, flat Earth at the center of the Universe, surrounded by crystal spheres carrying the Moon, Sun, planets and stars, though Aristarchus understood that the Earth was spherical and circled the Sun. With increasing sophistication of observational techniques and equipment, more realistic views of the Universe emerged. Modern cosmological theories take into account Albert Einstein's Theory of relativity and the recession of galaxies shown by the RED SHIFT in their spectra.

The most important of the evolutionary theories is the Big Bang theory resulting from Edwin Hubble's observations of the galaxies. This theory proposes that the Universe began by exploding from a hot, superdense state some 10 to 20 billion years ago. As the expanding mixture of matter and radiation cooled and diluted, it eventually condensed to form galaxies and stars. An alternative model, the Steady State theory of Hermann Bondi, Fred Hoyle and Thomas Gold, put forward in 1948, proposed that the Universe had existed and will exist forever in its current form. This required the continuous creation of new matter so that the average density and appearance of the Universe remain the same at all times.

In 1965 Arno Penzias and Robert Wilson discovered that the Universe possesses an inherent radio "background noise", and it was suggested by R. Dicke that this was the relic of the radiation produced by the Big Bang. Further researches have indicated the probability that space is filled with uniform blackbody thermal radiation corresponding to a temperature of around 3K. This supports an evolutionary theory, and the Steady State theory was largely abandoned.

The Big Bang theory also accounts neatly for the observed amounts of helium, deuterium and lithium in the Universe by proposing that these elements were formed by fusion reactions everywhere in the expanding fireball of matter and radiation during the first few minutes of the history of the Universe. However, the Big Bang theory leaves several unanswered questions, the most important of which is why the Universe should be so uniform – eg matter is distributed evenly through the Universe, and background radiation has the same strength from all directions in space. A possible solution to this and other questions has been a theoretical development called inflation. The inflationary Universe describes a phase of exponential expansion inflating a tiny seed of the Universe by a factor of 10^{50} or more during the first instant of the Big Bang. Just as a surface of a balloon expanded by a similar amount would look like the surface of a flat plane, so this rapid expansion of the Universe would smooth out the inhomogeneities. The inflationary Universe is an active area of research, and new developments are likely.

Considerable contemporary debate centers on whether the Universe is "open" or "closed". If the Universe is open it will expand forever; if it is closed it will eventually cease to expand and thereafter will collapse until it reaches a superdense state again. The oscillating Universe theory suggests that this collapse may trigger a new Big Bang, and that the Universe expands and contracts in a cyclical fashion. Whether or not the Universe continues to expand forever depends on its mean density. If the mean density of the Universe exceeds a value known as the critical density (equivalent to about three hydrogen atoms per cubic meter of space), then gravity will eventually halt the expansion and the Universe will be closed. However, if the mean density is less than this value, the Universe is open. The inflationary hypothesis requires that the mean density be almost precisely equal to the critical density. At present it is not certain whether the Universe is open or closed. (See also ASTRONOMY; BLACK HOLE; PULSAR; QUASAR.)

Crab nebula
M1, a bright NEBULA in the constellation TAURUS, the remnants of the SUPERNOVA of 1054. It is about 2000pc from the Earth and is associated with a PULSAR.

Cygnus
The Swan, a large, approximately cruciform constellation of the N Hemisphere containing Deneb (absolute magnitude −7) and the fine binary Albireo.

Cygnus X-1
An X-ray emitting binary system (see DOUBLE STAR) that consists of a blue supergiant STAR, HDE 226868, and an invisible companion (itself estimated to have a mass 9-11 times that of the SUN), which is widely believed to be a BLACK HOLE. The X-ray emission is believed to come from a disk of high-temperature gas, drawn from

the visible star and circulating around the black hole.

Day
Term referring either to a full period of 24 hours (the civil day) or to the (usually shorter and varying) period between sunrise and sunset when a given point on the Earth's surface is bathed in light rather than darkness (the natural day). Astronomers distinguish the sidereal day from the solar day, depending on whether the reference location on the Earth's surface is taken to return to the same position relative to the stars or to the Sun. The civil day is the mean solar day, some 168 seconds longer than the sidereal day, ie the sideral day is equivalent to 23 hours 56 minutes 04.1 seconds of mean time. The sidereal day itself is subdivided into 24 hours of sidereal time. In most modern states the day is deemed to run from midnight to midnight, though in Jewish tradition the day is taken to begin at sunset.

Declination
The angular distance of a celestial body from the celestial equator (see CELESTIAL SPHERE) along the MERIDIAN through the body. Bodies north of the equator have positive declinations, those south, negative. Together with right ascension, declination defines the position of a body in the sky.

Delphinus
The Dolphin, a small summer constellation in N skies. Four of its stars form a diamond sometimes known as Job's Coffin.

Dorado
The Swordfish or Goldfish, a S Hemisphere constellation containing the Large Magellanic Cloud (see MAGELLANIC CLOUDS).

Double star (binary star)
A pair of stars revolving around a common center of gravity. Less frequently the term "double star" is applied to two stars that merely appear close together in the sky, though in reality at quite different distances from the Earth (optical pairs), or to two stars whose motions are linked but that do not orbit each other (physical pair). About 50% of all stars are members of either binary or multiple star systems, in which there are more than two components. It is thought that the components of binary and multiple star systems are formed simultaneously. Visual binaries are those that can be seen telescopically to be double. There are comparatively few visual binaries, as the distances between components are small relative to interstellar distances, but examples are CAPELLA, PROCYON, SIRIUS and ALPHA CENTAURI. Spectroscopic binaries, though they cannot be seen telescopically as doubles, can be detected by RED and blue SHIFTS in their spectra, their orbit making each component alternately approach and recede from us. Eclipsing binaries are those whose components, due to the orientation of their orbit, periodically mutually eclipse each other as seen from the Earth.

Draco
The Dragon, a large N Hemisphere constellation. Alpha Draconis was the pole star c3000 BC (see PRECESSION). Gamma Draconis is the second magnitude star Eltanin. Draco also contains the planetary NEBULA NGC 6543.

E

Eclipse
The partial or total obscurement of one celestial body by another; also the passage of the Moon through the Earth's shadow. The components of a binary star (see DOUBLE STAR) may eclipse each other as seen from the Earth, in which case the star

is termed an eclipsing binary. The Moon frequently eclipses stars or planets, and this is known as OCCULTATION.

A lunar eclipse occurs when the Moon passes through the umbra of the Earth's shadow. This happens usually not more than twice a year, as the Moon's orbit around the Earth is tilted with respect to the ECLIPTIC. The eclipsed Moon is blood-red in color because some of the Sun's light is refracted by the Earth's atmosphere into the umbra. A partial lunar eclipse occurs when only part of the umbra falls on the Moon.

In a solar eclipse the Moon passes between the Sun and the Earth. A total eclipse occurs when the observer is within the umbra of the Moon's shadow: the disk of the Sun is covered by that of the Moon, and the solar corona (see SUN) becomes clearly visible. The maximum possible duration of a total eclipse is about 7½ min. Should the observer be outside the umbra but within the penumbra, or should the Earth pass through only the penumbra, a partial eclipse will occur.

An annular eclipse is seen when the Moon is at its farthest from the Earth, its disk not being large enough totally to obscure that of the Sun. The Moon's disk is seen surrounded by a brilliant ring of light.

Ecliptic
The great circle traced out on the CELESTIAL SPHERE by the apparent motion of the Sun during the year, corresponding to the motion of the Earth around the Sun. The ecliptic passes through 12 constellations, known as the constellations of the ZODIAC.

Epicycle
A circle whose center lies on the circumference of a larger circle. In geocentric cosmologies, such as that of Ptolemy, the planets were thought to move around epicycles, the centers of which lay on larger deferent circles centered on the Earth.

Equinoxes
(1) The two times each year when day and night are of equal length. The spring or vernal equinox occurs in March, the autumnal equinox in September.
(2) The two intersections of the ECLIPTIC and equator (see CELESTIAL SPHERE). The vernal equinox is in PISCES (see also ARIES, FIRST POINT OF), the autumnal between VIRGO and LEO.

Eridanus
The River; large, long CONSTELLATION of the S celestial hemisphere. Of particular interest is Epsilon Eridani: this, at 3.31 pc, is the closest star to us to resemble our Sun.

Eros
An ASTEROID measuring roughly 35×16×8km discovered in 1898 by G. Witt. Eros' eccentric orbit brings it close to Earth every seven years, sometimes within 22 million km. Its orbital period is 643 days.

Event horizon
The boundary of a BLACK HOLE beyond which an outside observer can detect nothing.

F

Fireball
A particularly bright METEOR, brighter than MAGNITUDE −5. The term is also applied to lightning of globular form.

Flare, Solar
A temporary brilliance in the SUN's chromosphere associated with a sunspot or group of sunspots. Large flares may last for as long as an hour or more, small ones only a few minutes. A flare results in the emission of electromagnetic radiation ranging from gamma rays and X-rays to radio waves, and of atomic particles – electrons,

protons and alpha particles. Flares are believed to be produced by the release of magnetic energy stored in the magnetic fields of complex sunspot groups or active regions.

Foucault pendulum
A pendulum comprising an iron ball at the end of a long steel wire which, on being set swinging, maintains its direction of swing while the Earth rotates beneath it. When one was demonstrated by J.B.L. Foucault in 1851, it provided the first direct evidence for the rotation of the Earth.

Fraunhofer lines
Dark lines that appear in the spectrum of the SUN. They are due to the absorption of the radiation of particular frequencies (and thus energies) by atoms in the outer layers of the solar atmosphere. Analysis of the solar spectrum thus leads to the identification of these atoms. The lines were first accurately mapped by J. Von Fraunhofer. The more prominent are denoted by letters: A and B are due to terrestrial oxygen; C to hydrogen; D to sodium; E to iron; and so on.

G

Galactic clusters
Clusters of stars lying in or near the galactic plane, each of which contains a few hundred stars. Because of their irregular shape they are also termed open clusters. The best-known galactic cluster in N skies is the PLEIADES.

Galaxy
The largest individual conglomeration of matter, containing stars, gases, dust and planets. Galaxies are classified according to their shapes, the three basic types being elliptical, spiral and irregular. Elliptical galaxies contain predominantly old stars and little or no gases. A typical spiral galaxy consists of a central nucleus, where stars are relatively densely grouped together, surrounded by a disk of gases and younger stars concentrated into a pattern of spiral arms. Spiral galaxies have arms that emerge directly from the nucleus, while barred spirals have arms that emerge from a bar of stars and interstellar matter that straddles the nucleus. Irregular galaxies have no discernible structure. Irregulars usually contain the highest proportion of gases, and ellipticals the least. It seems likely that whether a galaxy becomes elliptical, spiral or irregular depends on the amount of rotation present in the gas cloud from which it formed, and on the rate of star formation within it. In the remote future, when the available gas is used up, star formation in galaxies will cease. It is thought that a significant fraction of the matter in a galaxy will eventually collapse into a BLACK HOLE.

The masses of galaxies range from about 10E6 solar masses to several times 10E12 solar masses. Recent observations of the rotation rates of spiral galaxies indicate that they are immersed within extensive haloes of dark matter amounting to up to ten times as much mass as their visible stars and gas clouds. Our own galaxy, the Milky Way system, is a spiral with a diameter (measured across the visible disk) of about 30,000 parsecs, and contains about 10E11 stars.

Galaxies emit radiation of all kinds, but in differing proportions. While an ordinary spiral like the Milky Way emits mainly at optical wavelengths, radio galaxies emit most strongly at radio wavelengths. Active galaxies are those that show signs of violent activity. They are usually characterized by highly luminous compact nuclei and by relatively rapid variability. Many have jets of matter emanating from their cores, and extensive radio-emitting clouds extending far beyond their visible confines. Radio galaxies, Seyfert galaxies (spiral galaxies with compact active nuclei named for the US astronomer Carl Seyfert (1911-

1960)) and – according to most astronomers – QUASARS are examples of active galaxies.

Galaxies are generally located within groups or clusters, containing from a few to a few thousand members. Superclusters are even larger, loose groupings of galaxies and clusters that contain several thousand galaxies and span regions of space up to 100 megaparsecs in diameter. The Milky Way galaxy is part of the Local Group, which comprises about thirty member systems. (See also ANDROMEDA).

Gamma-ray astronomy
The study of gamma rays emitted by celestial objects. Because the wavelength of gamma rays is so short, astronomers use scintillation counters or spark chambers to obtain directional observation. Of particular interest are gamma-ray bursts – intense blasts lasting from a tenth of a second to tens of seconds – which occur several times a year from sources widely distributed over the sky. Twenty or so gamma-ray stars have been identified in the Milky Way that other techniques have not yet identified.

Gemini
The Twins, a constellation on the ECLIPTIC named after its two brightest stars, Castor and Pollux. The third sign of the ZODIAC, Gemini gives its name to the Geminid METEOR shower.

Globular clusters
Apparently ellipsoidal, densely packed clusters of up to a million stars orbiting a GALAXY. The MILKY WAY and the ANDROMEDA galaxy each has about 200 such clusters. They contain high proportions of cool red stars and RR Lyrae VARIABLE STARS. Study of the latter enables the distances of the clusters to be calculated.

Great Bear
Ursa Major, a large N Hemisphere constellation containing the seven bright stars known as the Plow or Big Dipper. Two of these, the Pointers, form roughly a straight line with POLARIS and are thus of navigational importance. Five stars of the Plow are, with SIRIUS, members of a widely separated GALACTIC CLUSTER.

H

Halley's comet
The first periodic comet to be identified (by E.Halley, late 17th century) and the brightest of all recurring comets. It has a period of about 76 years. Records of every appearance of the comet since 240 BC, except that of 163 BC, are extant; and it is featured on the Bayeux tapestry. The comet's reappearance in 1986 provided the first opportunity to investigate a comet at close quarters. Five spacecraft successfully investigated the comet – the two Japanese probes, Sakigake and Suisei, from long range; the two Soviet probes, Vega 1 and Vega 2, from less than 10,000km; and the European probe, Giotto, which passed by the nucleus at a range of 605km. Water ice was proved to be the major constituent of the nucleus, which measured about 15×8×8km. The nucleus was seen to be covered by an extremely dark crust, probably made of compacted dust and perhaps only a centimeter thick, through which jets of gas and dust erupted. Features as small as 100m across were resolved. The dust, gases, plasma and magnetic fields associated with the comet were investigated in detail.

Halo
A luminous ring or series of arcs sometimes seen around the Sun or Moon, the result of refraction or reflection or both of their light by crystals of ICE in high, thin clouds. Commonest is the 22° halo, of angular radius 22° and centered on the Sun or Moon. (See also CORONA.)

Harvest moon
The full moon occurring nearest to the autumnal equinox (about 23 September) in the N Hemisphere. For several nights the full moon rises at closely similar times (about sunset), and may be bright enough for harvesting to continue into the night. In the S Hemisphere this occurs around the spring equinox (see EQUINOXES).

Hercules
A large N Hemisphere constellation containing a superb GLOBULAR CLUSTER, M13, of about 500,000 stars, and which is just visible to the naked eye.

Hubble's constant
Ratio between the distance of a GALAXY and the rate at which it is receding from us. Edwin Hubble first calculated this as about 500km/s per Mpc (megaparsec); however, he used incorrect estimates of the distances of the galaxies, and current revised estimates of its value are in the range 50-100km/s per Mpc.

Hydra
The Water Monster, a large S Hemisphere constellation containing the bright star Alphard and a cluster of galaxies over 30Mpc distant.

I

Implosion
A bursting inward, as opposed to explosion, a bursting outward. Implosion due to gravitational collapse is an important end-stage in the lives of STARS (see also BLACK HOLES).

Infrared astronomy
The study of infrared radiation emitted by celestial objects. By placing an infrared telescope in space, the IR background can be reduced a million times. IR sources include cool dust clouds and warm dust around young stars in our GALAXY, in addition to nearby galaxies, active galaxies and quasars.

Interstellar matter
Thinly dispersed matter, in the form of gases and dust, between the stars. The dust grains scatter and absorb starlight, causing distant stars to appear fainter than they otherwise would do. The amount of extinction due to the dust is greater at shorter wavelengths, so that blue light is affected more than red; consequently, distant stars appear redder in color than they really are (interstellar reddening). Dense dust clouds show up as dark patches (see NEBULA) against the background stars. Gas clouds containing high-temperature stars show up as luminous patches (emission nebulae). The interstellar gas also reveals its presence by the absorption lines (interstellar lines) that it superimposes on the SPECTRA of stars. Neutral hydrogen gas emits radio waves at a wavelength of 21cm (ie a frequency of 1420MHz). Radio astronomers can also detect emission lines from a variety of species of molecules, many of which are organic in nature, which exist mainly in dense, cool molecular clouds.

Ion propulsion (ion drive)
Drive proposed for spacecraft on interstellar or longer interplanetary trips. The vaporized propellant (liquid cesium or mercury) is passed through an ionizer, which strips each atom of an electron. The positive ions so formed are accelerated rearward by an electric field. The resultant thrust is low but in the near vacuum of space may be used to build up huge velocities by constant acceleration over a long period of time. The drive has been tested in orbit around the Earth.

J,K

Jupiter
The largest and most massive planet in the Solar System (diameter about 143Mm, mass 317.8 times that of Earth), fifth from the Sun. Jupiter is larger than all the other planets combined and, with a mean solar distance of 5.20AU and a "year" of 11.86 Earth years, is the greatest contributor to the Solar System's angular momentum. Its atmosphere consists mainly of hydrogen, helium and hydrogen compounds such as methane and ammonia. Its disk is marked by prominent cloud-belts paralleling its equator, these being occasionally interrupted by turbulences, and particularly by the Great Red Spot, an elliptical area 40Mm long and 13Mm wide in the S Hemisphere that seems to be an anticyclonic high-pressure feature rotating counterclockwise in a period of six days. Another long-term feature, the South Tropical Disturbance, was first observed in 1901 and disappeared in 1939. The nature of these features is not yet known. When Voyager 1 detected two rings of particles, Jupiter became the third planet to be shown to have one or more rings. Jupiter's day is about 9.92h and this high rotational velocity causes a visible flattening of the poles: the equatorial diameter is some 6% greater than the polar diameter. Jupiter has 16 moons, the two largest of which, Callisto and Ganymede, are larger than MERCURY: Io has violently active volcanoes on its surface. Jupiter radiates twice as much heat as it receives from the Sun. The poles are as warm as the equator.

Kepler's Laws
Three laws formulated by Johannes Kepler to describe the motions of the planets in the Solar System. (1) Each planet orbits the Sun in an ellipse of which the Sun is at one focus. (2) The line between a planet and the Sun sweeps out equal areas in equal times: hence the planet moves faster when closer to the Sun than it does when farther away. (3) The square of the time taken by a planet to orbit the Sun is proportional to the cube of its mean distance from the Sun.

L

Leo
The Lion, a constellation on the ECLIPTIC and fifth sign of the ZODIAC. It contains the bright star REGULUS (apparent magnitude +1.35). Leo gives its name to the annual Leonid METEOR shower.

Libra
The Scales, an average sized constellation on the ECLIPTIC, the seventh sign of the ZODIAC.

Light year
In ASTRONOMY, a unit of distance equal to the distance traveled by light in a vacuum in one sidereal year, equal to 9461Tm (about 6 million million miles). The unit has largely been replaced by the PARSEC (1 ly=0.3069pc).

Little Dipper
Ursa Minor (the Little Bear), N Hemisphere circumpolar constellation containing POLARIS, the N polestar.

Lyra
The Lyre, a medium-sized N Hemisphere constellation containing VEGA and the Ring Nebula (M57), a fine planetary NEBULA some 700pc from the Earth.

M

Magellanic clouds
Two irregular GALAXIES that orbit the MILKY WAY, visible in S skies. The Large Magellanic Cloud (Nubecula Major), about 9kpc in diameter, has a well-marked axis suggesting that it may be an embryonic spiral galaxy. The Small Magellanic Cloud (Nubecula Minor) is about 5kpc across. Both are rich in CEPHEID VARIABLES. Their distances are about 50kpc (LMC) and 60kpc (SMC).

The Large Magellanic Cloud contains a giant NEBULA, the Tarantula nebula, near to which a SUPERNOVA explosion occurred in 1987.

Magnetosphere
The region of space around a body in which the magnetic field of that body is dominant.

Magnitude, Stellar
A measure of a star's brightness. The foundations of the system were laid by Hipparchus (c120 BC), who divided stars into six categories, from 1 to 6 in order of decreasing brightness. Later the system was extended to include fainter stars that could be seen only by telescope, and brighter stars, which were assigned negative magnitudes (eg Sirius, −1.5). Five magnitudes were defined as a 100-times increase in brightness. These apparent magnitudes depend greatly on the distances from us of the stars. Absolute magnitude is defined as the apparent magnitude a star would have were it at a distance of 10pc from us: Sirius then has magnitude +1.4. Absolute magnitudes clearly tell us far more than do apparent magnitudes. Stars are also assigned bolometric and photographic magnitude, and magnitudes measured at particular wavebands in the invisible and infrared regions of the spectrum.

Mars
The fourth planet from the Sun with a mean solar distance of 228Gm (about 1.52AU) and a "year" of 687 days. During the Martian day of about 24.62h the highest temperature at the equator is about 10°C, the lowest just before dawn being about −100°C. Mars has a mean diameter of 6775km, with a small degree of polar flattening, and at its closest to Earth (see CONJUNCTION) is some 56Gm distant. Its tenuous atmosphere is believed to consist mainly of carbon dioxide, nitrogen and noble gases, and the distinctive Martian polar caps are thought to be composed of frozen carbon dioxide and ice.

Telescopically, Mars appears as an ocher red disk marked by extensive dark areas: these latter have in the past been erroneously termed *maria* (seas). Several observers have reported sighting networks of straight lines on the Martian surface – the famous canals. However, photographs sent back by the Mariner probes revealed a network of subsidiary valleys. The Mariner scientists attributed these as dried river beds, but they are not the same as the "canals" seen by earlier observers. Mars is spotted with craters, rather as is the MOON. The Viking spacecraft, which landed in 1976, detected no evidence of living organisms on Mars, but it has been suggested that such organisms might be able to survive near the edges of the polar ice caps. This remains to be tested. Mars has two moons, Phobos and Deimos.

Mercury
The planet closest to the Sun, with a mean solar distance of 58Gm. Its highly eccentric ORBIT brings it within 46Gm of the Sun at perihelion and takes it 70Gm from the Sun at aphelion. Its diameter is about 4880km, its mass about 0.054 that of the Earth. It goes around the Sun in just under 88 days and rotates on its axis in about 59 days. The successful prediction by Albert Einstein that Mercury's orbit would be found to advance by 43″ per century is usually regarded as a confirmation of the general theory of relativity. Night surface temperature is thought to be about 100K, midday equatorial temperature over 700K. The planet's average density indicates a high proportion of heavy elements in its interior. Mercury has little or no atmosphere and no known moons.

Meridian
On the celestial sphere, the great circle passing through the celestial poles and the observer's ZENITH. It cuts the observer's horizon N and S.

(See also CELESTIAL SPHERE; TRANSIT.) The term is also used for a line of terrestrial longitude.

Mesosphere
The atmospheric zone immediately above the stratosphere, in which the temperature decreases with increasing altitude from about −10°C at 50km to a minimum of about −90°C at 85km. (See ATMOSPHERE.)

Meteor
The visible passage of a meteoroid (a small particle of interplanetary matter) into the Earth's atmosphere. Because of friction it burns up, showing a glowing trail of ionized gas in the night sky. The velocity on entry lies in the range 11-72km/s.

Meteoroids are believed to consist of asteroidal and cometary debris. Although stray meteoroids reach our atmosphere throughout the year, for short periods at certain times of year they arrive in profuse numbers, sharing a common direction and velocity. In 1866 Giovanni Schiaparelli showed that the annual Perseid meteor shower was caused by meteoroids orbiting the Sun in the same orbit as a comet observed some years before; moreover, as their period of orbit is unrelated to that of the Earth, the meteoroids must form a fairly uniform "ring" around the Sun for the shower to be annual. Other comet-shower relationships have been shown, implying that these streams of meteoroids are cometary debris.

Meteors may be seen by a nighttime observer on average five times per hour: these are known as sporadic meteors or shooting stars. Around twenty times a year, however, a meteor shower occurs and between 20 and 35,000 meteors per hour may be observed. These annual showers are generally named for the constellations from which they appear to emanate, eg Perseids (PERSEUS), Leonids (LEO). Large meteors are called FIREBALLS, exploding ones are bolides.

Meteorites are larger than meteors, and are of special interest in that, should they enter the atmosphere, they at least partially survive the passage to the ground. Many have been examined. They fall into two main categories: "stones", whose composition is not unlike that of the Earth's crust; and "irons", which contain about 80%-95% iron, 5%-20% nickel and traces of other elements. Intermediate types exist. Irons display a usually crystalline structure, which implies that they were initially liquid, cooling over long periods of time. Sometimes large meteorites shatter on impact, producing large craters like those in Arizona and Wolf Creek, Australia.

Milky Way
A hazy, milk-like band of stars encircling the night sky. Irregular dark patches are caused by intervening clouds of gas and dust. Its appearance is due to the view of the disk of our GALAXY, which we see from the Sun's location within it. The term is also used to name our Galaxy. It is a disk-shaped spiral galaxy containing some 100 billion stars, and has a radius of about 15kpc. Our SOLAR SYSTEM is one of the spiral arms and is just over 9kpc from the galactic center, which lies in the direction of SAGITTARIUS. The Galaxy slowly rotates about a roughly spheroidal nuclear bulge (radius about 4.5kpc), though not at uniform speed; the Sun circles the galactic center about every 230 million years. The Galaxy is surrounded by a spheroidal halo some 50kpc in diameter, composed of gases, dust, occasional stars and GLOBULAR CLUSTERS. This, in turn, seems to be immersed within an extended halo of dark matter, which cannot be seen directly but whose gravitational influence seems necessary to account for the high speeds at which gas and stars in the outer regions of the Galaxy are moving.

Missing mass
Matter that is not directly visible but is inferred to exist in order to provide sufficient gravitational attraction to account for several aspects of the large-scale motion of matter in COSMOLOGY. Stars and gas clouds in the outer regions of spiral galaxies (see GALAXY) move faster than would be the case if all their mass were contained in visible stars. Likewise, clusters of galaxies can hold themselves together only if they contain at least ten times as much mass as is visibly present in their member galaxies. If the Universe is closed (see COSMOLOGY), well over 90% of its total mass must consist of dark matter.

Month
Name of several periods of time, mostly defined in terms of the motion of the MOON. The synodic month (lunar month or lunation) is the time between successive full moons; it is 29.531 DAYS. The sidereal month, the time taken by the Moon to complete one revolution about the Earth relative to the fixed stars, is 27.322 days. The anomalistic month, 27.555 days, is the time between successive passages of the Moon through perigee (see ORBIT). The solar month, 30.439 days, is one twelfth of the solar YEAR. Civil or calendar months vary in length through the year, lasting from 28 to 31 days (see CALENDAR), though in popular usage the (lunar) month refers to 28 days.

Moon
A SATELLITE, in particular the Earth's largest natural satellite. The Moon is so large relative to the Earth (it has a diameter two-thirds that of MERCURY) that Earth and Moon are sometimes regarded as a double planet. The Moon has a diameter of 3476km and a mass 0.0123 that of the Earth; its escape velocity is around 2.4km/s. The orbit of the Moon defines the several kinds of MONTH. The distance of the Moon from the Earth varies between 363Mm and 406Mm (perigee and apogee) with a mean of 384.4Mm. The Moon rotates on its axis every 27.322 days, hence keeping the same face constantly toward the Earth; however, in accordance with KEPLER's second LAW, the Moon's orbital velocity is not constant and thus there is exhibited the phenomenon known as libration: to a particular observer on the Earth, marginally different parts of the Moon's disk are visible at different times. There is also a very small physical libration due to slight irregularities in its rotational velocity.

The Moon is covered with craters, whose sizes range up to 250km diameter. These are sometimes seen in chains up to 1Mm in length. Other features include rilles, trenches a few kilometers wide and a few hundred kilometers long; the *maria* or great plains; the bright rays that emerge from the large craters, and the lunar mountains. There are also lunar hot spots, generally associated with those larger craters showing bright rays: these remain cooler than their surrounds during lunar daytime, warmer during the lunar night.

It is widely believed that the majority of craters and *mare* basins were formed by the impacts of meteorites and asteroidal-sized bodies, but some, too, may be the result of internal volcanic activity. Most of the giant impacts that formed the *maria* occurred between 4.5 and 3.8 billion years ago, and the basins so produced were subsequently filled by volcanic magma. Analysis of samples brought back to Earth by the Apollo missions has shown that lunar rocks contain a higher proportion of refractory elements (those with a high boiling point, such as titanium) and are depleted in volatiles (those with low boiling point), compared to terrestrial rocks. There is no consensus about how the Moon was formed; one theory suggests that Earth and Moon were formed simultaneously in close proximity.

N

Nadir
The point on the CELESTIAL SPHERE directly opposite an observer's ZENITH.

Nebula
An interstellar cloud of gas or dust. The term was originally used to denote any fuzzy celestial object, including external GALAXIES: this practice has now been abandoned.

Emission nebulae are gas clouds that shine because they absorb ultraviolet radiation from very hot, highly luminous stars embedded within them. They are also known as HII regions because their hydrogen gas is ionized by the illuminating stars. Reflection nebulae are seen when light from a high-luminosity star is reflected, or scattered, from nearby dust. Dark nebulae, such as the Coal Sack or the Horsehead nebula, are due to relatively dense clouds of dust that obscure background stars; thus they show up as dark patches against the starry background. Star formation takes place within interstellar clouds of gas and dust. Heated cocoons of dust surrounding newly forming stars can be detected by infrared observations.

Planetary nebulae are shells of gas expelled from stars that are approaching their final stages of evolution. The central star is often visible and is usually a small, very hot object with a surface temperature of about 100,000K, probably representing the exposed core of a red giant that, after expelling its outer envelope of gas, is evolving to become a white dwarf (see STAR). The Ring Nebula (M57) is an outstanding example.

Nebular hypothesis
Theory accounting for the origin of the Solar System put forward by Pierre Simon Laplace. It suggested that a rotating NEBULA had formed gaseous rings that condensed into planets and moons, the nebula's nucleus forming the Sun.

Neptune
The fourth largest planet in the SOLAR SYSTEM and the eighth in position from the Sun, with a mean solar distance of 30.07AU. Neptune was first discovered in 1846 by J.G. Galle using computations by Urbain Leverrier based on the perturbations of URANUS' orbit. The calculation had been performed independently by John Couch Adams in England, but vacillations on the part of the then Astronomer Royal had precluded a rigorous search for the planet. Neptune has two moons, Triton and Nereid, the former having a circular, retrograde orbit (see RETROGRADE MOTION), the latter having the most eccentric orbit of any moon in the Solar System. Neptune's "year" is 164.8 times that of the Earth, its day being about 18h. Its diameter is about 50 Mm and its mass 17.2 times that of the Earth. Observations when Neptune passed in front of a star in 1984 suggest that Neptune too may have rings (see SATURN), but this is not confirmed. Like Jupiter and Saturn, Neptune emits more heat than it receives from the Sun. Its internal structure is believed to comprise a rocky metallic core surrounded by an ice mantle and a deep, hydrogen-rich atmosphere. The Voyager spaceprobe will no doubt reveal more of Neptune's structure and constitution on its 1989 fly-by.

Nova
A star that over a short period (usually a few days) increases in brightness by 100 to 1,000,000 times. This is thought to be due to the star undergoing a partial explosion: that is to say, part of the star erupts, throwing out material at a speed greater than the Escape velocity of the star. A nova is believed to occur in a binary system (see DOUBLE STAR) in which one component is a white dwarf (or, exceptionally, a neutron star). Material dumped from the larger star onto the compact one eventually undergoes explosive nuclear "burning" to produce the nova outburst. The initial brightness fades rapidly, though it is usually some years before the star returns to its previous luminosity, having lost about 0.0001 of its mass. At that time a rapidly expanding planetary NEBULA may be seen to surround the star. Recurrent novae are stars that flare up at irregular periods of a few decades. Dwarf novae are subdwarf stars that suffer nova-like eruptions every few weeks or months. Novae have been observed in other galaxies besides the MILKY WAY. (See also SUPERNOVA.)

Nutation, Astronomical
Irregularities in the PRECESSION of the equinoxes owing to variations in the torque produced by the gravitational attractions of the Sun and Moon on the Earth.

O

Oblate spheroid
A spheroid that has two of its axes of symmetry of equal length greater than that of the third. The Earth, in common with the other planets of the SOLAR SYSTEM, is oblate, its polar diameter being some 45km greater than that of its equator. A prolate spheroid is one with two axes of symmetry equal in length and shorter than the third.

Observatory
Place from which a variety of astronomical observations are made. Ancient observatories such as Stonehenge were used to predict SOLSTICES and EQUINOXES. With Tycho Brahe and the advent shortly after his death of the telescope, the modern observatory was born. Apart from the telescope, modern instruments used by observatories include the spectroscope, the transit instrument and the meridian circle (used to measure the right ascension and declination of stars: see CELESTIAL SPHERE), the coelostat and the coronagraph (for observing the Sun), the photometer (for measuring stellar brightnesses) and, in RADIO ASTRONOMY, the RADIO TELESCOPE. The basic instruments are complemented by electronic instrumentation for the detection and analysis of radiation. Computers play an increasingly important part in the control of the instruments, in image processing and in data analysis.

Occultation
The covering up of one celestial body by another. The term is usually applied to the passage of planets in front of stars or of the Moon in front of stars or planets.

Opposition
In ASTRONOMY, the situation in which the Earth lies directly between another planet (or the Moon) and the Sun.

Orbit
The path followed by one celestial body revolving under the influence of gravity about another. In the SOLAR SYSTEM the planets orbit the Sun, and the moons the planets, in elliptical paths, though Triton's orbit of NEPTUNE is as far as can be determined perfectly circular. The point in the planetary, asteroidal or cometary orbit closest to the Sun is called its perihelion; the farthest point is termed aphelion. In the case of a moon or artificial satellite orbiting a planet or other moon, the corresponding terms are perigee and apogee. (See also APSIDES, LINE OF; KEPLER'S LAWS.) Celestial objects of similar masses may orbit each other, particularly DOUBLE STARS.

Orion
The Hunter, a large constellation on the celestial equator that is visible during winter in N skies, containing RIGEL, BETELGEUSE and the Orion NEBULA.

P

Parsec (pc)
In astronomy, the distance at which 1 ASTRONOMICAL UNIT would subtend an angle of 1 second. Originally defined as the distance of a star with a parallax of 1″ viewed from Earth and Sun, the parsec was introduced to replace the LIGHT YEAR. 1 pc=3.258 ly=206,265AU.

Pegasus
The Winged Horse, a large N Hemisphere constellation noticeable for its Great Square, formed by four bright stars. Pegasus contains a GLOBULAR CLUSTER (M15).

Perseus
Large N Hemisphere constellation containing the eclipsing binary (see DOUBLE STAR) ALGOL, two GALACTIC CLUSTERS, one of which is a double cluster, and the bright star Mirfak. It gives its name to the Perseid METEOR shower.

Perturbation
In the elliptical orbit of one celestial body around another, an irregularity caused by the gravitational attraction of a third.

Photosphere
A layer of gas on the Sun, 125-190km thick, visible to us as the Sun's apparent surface, emitting most of the Sun's light. Its temperature is estimated at 6000K.

Pisces
The Fishes, a large, faint constellation on the ECLIPTIC, the 12th sign of the ZODIAC. The vernal EQUINOX now lies in Pisces.

Planet
In the SOLAR SYSTEM, one of the nine major celestial bodies orbiting the Sun; by extension, a similar body circling any other star. The possible presence of massive planets around a few nearby stars has been inferred from small periodic irregularities in their PROPER MOTIONS. For example, Barnard's Star may have at least two planets comparable in mass to Jupiter. In 1983 the IRAS infrared satellite discovered infrared radiation from disks of cool dust, possibly planet-forming material, surrounding several stars, including VEGA, Fomalhaut and Beta Pictoris. In 1984 the Beta Pictoris disk was detected at optical wavelengths. These observations imply that planets are by no means unique to the Sun.

Planetarium
An instrument designed to represent the relative positions and motions of celestial objects. Originally a mechanical model of the SOLAR SYSTEM the planetarium of today is an intricate optical device that projects disks and points of light representing Sun, Moon, planets and stars on to the interior of a fixed hemispherical dome. The various cyclic motions of these bodies as seen from a given latitude on Earth can be simulated. The first modern planetarium, built in 1923 by the firm of Carl Zeiss, is still in use at the Deutsches Museum, Munich, West Germany.

Planetesimal hypothesis
A discarded theory proposed by T.C. Chamberlin and F.R. Moulton (1872-1952) to explain the formation of PLANETS. It states that a passing star drew matter out of the Sun, some of which condensed to form small solid particles (planetesimals), which in turn coalesced to form planets. The term "planetesimal" is now applied to the kilometer-sized, or larger, bodies that according to the accretion theory of planetary formation were formed by the hierarchical accretion of smaller particles, and subsequently themselves coalesced to form planets.

Pleiades
A GALACTIC CLUSTER in the constellation TAURUS. Seven of the stars, named for the seven daughters

of Atlas, can be seen by the naked eye. The Pleiades are about 153pc from the Sun and are surrounded by faint reflection nebulosity (see NEBULA).

Pluto
The ninth planet of the SOLAR SYSTEM, orbiting the Sun at a mean distance of 39.44AU in 247.7 years. Pluto was discovered in 1930 following observations of PERTURBATIONS in NEPTUNE's orbit. Pluto has one moon, Charon, which is larger in relation to its parent planet than any other in the Solar System. Because of its distance from us, little is known of Pluto, though the changes of light in a series of eclipses between Pluto and Charon during 1985-90 should reveal more about its size and diameter. At present, its mass is believed to be 0.002 that of Earth and its diameter about 2500km. Its surface is highly reflective, and its low density suggests that it is composed mostly of water ice and frozen gases. Pluto's orbit is very eccentric: indeed, it currently lies closer to the Sun than Neptune, and will do so until 1999. Because of its smallness and unusual orbit, some astronomers suggest that Pluto should be reclassified as an asteroid.

Polaris
Alpha Ursae Minoris, a CEPHEID VARIABLE star in the LITTLE DIPPER. Because of its close proximity to the N celestial pole (see CELESTIAL SPHERE), Polaris is also known as the Polestar or North Star, and has been used in navigation for centuries: owing to PRECESSION, Polaris is moving away from the N celestial pole.

Precession
The gyration of the rotational axis of a spinning body, such as a gyroscope, describing a right circular cone whose vertex lies at the center of the spinning body. Precession is caused by the action of a torque (spinning force) on the body. Precession of the equinoxes occurs because the Earth is not spherical but bulges at the equator, which is at an angle of 23.5° to the ECLIPTIC. Because of the gravitational attraction of the Sun, the Earth is subject to a torque that attempts to pull the equatorial bulge into the same plane as the ecliptic, therefore causing the planet's poles, and hence the intersections of the equator and ecliptic (the equinoxes), to precess in a period of about 26,000 years. The Moon (see NUTATION) and planets similarly affect the direction of the Earth's rotational axis.

Procyon
Alpha Canis Minoris, a visual DOUBLE STAR; the brightest star in CANIS MINOR (absolute magnitude +2.7) and 3.53pc distant.

Proper motion
The rate of motion at right angles to our line of sight of a star, measured in seconds of arc per year. (See RADIAL VELOCITY.)

Proxima Centauri
The closest star to the Sun (1.33pc distant), a red dwarf star orbiting ALPHA CENTAURI.

Pulsar
Short for pulsating radio star, a celestial radio source emitting brief, extremely regular pulses of electromagnetic radiation (normally at radio frequency, apart from a few examples detectable at X-ray or optical frequencies). Each pulse lasts a few hundredths of a second and the period between pulses is of the order of one second or less. Though the pulse frequency varies from pulsar to pulsar, for each pulsar the period is highly regular, in some cases as regular as can be measured. The first pulsar was discovered in 1967 by Antony Hewish and S.J. Bell. The fastest pulsar yet observed has a period of 0.0016s. It is likely that there are some 10,000 pulsars in the MILKY WAY, though less than 400 have as yet been discovered. It is believed that pulsars are the neutron STAR remnants of SUPERNOVAE, rapidly spinning and radiating through loss of rotational energy.

Quasar
Short for quasi-stellar object, a telescopically star-like celestial object whose spectrum shows an abnormally large RED SHIFT. The largest quasar red shift so far measured is 4.01. Quasars are widely believed to be extremely distant objects, receding from us at high velocities, though some research suggests that their red shifts may not be entirely due to their sharing in the expansion of the Universe, in which case they may not be as distant as they seem.

Quasars show variability in light and radio emission (although the first quasars were discovered by RADIO ASTRONOMY, not all are radio sources), which indicates that they are comparatively small objects less than 0.3pc across. If quasars are as remote as their red shifts imply, they must be 100-10,000 times more luminous than a normal galaxy such as the Milky Way system. The most popular hypothesis is that a quasar is the compact hyperactive nucleus of a galaxy, so luminous that in most cases it completely swamps the light from the surrounding galaxy within which it is embedded, but not all astronomers accept this view. If this picture is correct, the central "energy machine" may be a supermassive BLACK HOLE accreting material from its surroundings.

Radar astronomy
The study of celestial objects and the Earth's atmosphere by radar pulses. It includes tracking meteors and radar pulses reflected from the Moon and planets.

Radial velocity
The component of the motion of a celestial body in the direction of the line of sight; that is, toward or away from the observer.

Radio astronomy
The study of the electromagnetic radiation emitted or reflected by celestial objects in the approximate wavelength range 1mm-30m, usually by use of a RADIO TELESCOPE. The science was initiated accidentally in 1932 by Karl Jansky, who found an interference in a telephone system he was testing: the source proved to be the MILKY WAY. In 1937 an American, Grote Reber, built a 9.5m radio telescope in his backyard and scanned the sky at a wavelength around 2m. After WWII the science began in earnest. Investigation of the sky revealed that clouds of hydrogen gas in the Milky Way were radio sources, and mapping of these confirmed our Galaxy's spiral form (see GALAXY).

The sky is very different for the radio astronomer than for the optical astronomer. Bright stars are not radio objects (our Sun is one solely because it is so close), while many radio objects are optically undetectable. Radio objects include QUASARS, PULSARS, SUPERNOVA remnants (eg the CRAB NEBULA) and other galaxies. The work of Martin Ryle in the 1960s and 1970s has enabled radio galaxies that are possibly at the farthest extremities of the Universe to be mapped. The Universe also has an inherent radio "background noise" (see COSMOLOGY).

Radio telescope
The basic instrument of RADIO ASTRONOMY. The receiving part of the equipment consists of a large parabola, the big dish, which operates on the same principle as the parabolic mirror of a reflecting telescope. The signals that it receives are then amplified and examined. In practice, it is possible to build radio telescopes effectively far larger than any dish could be by using several connected dishes; this is known as an array.

Red shift
An increase in wavelength of the light from an object, usually caused by its rapid recession. The red shift is determined by measuring the difference between the wavelength of a given line in the spectrum of a star or galaxy and the laboratory wavelength of that line. The red shift is equal to the ratio between that difference and the laboratory wavelength of the line; for speeds that are a small fraction of the speed of light, the red shift is also equal to the ratio between the speed of recession of the source and the speed of light. The spectra of distant GALAXIES show marked red shifts, and this is interpreted as implying that they are rapidly receding from us.

Regulus
Alpha Leonis, the brightest star in LEO. Its apparent magnitude is +1.35 and its distance from the Sun 26pc. It is a visual triple star.

Retrograde motion
The apparent backward (ie westward) motion of a PLANET due to the Earth's own motion (see ORBIT): also, the motion of any SOLAR SYSTEM body rotating or orbiting in the opposite (clockwise as viewed from the N celestial pole) direction to the majority.

Rigel
Beta Orionis, a blue supergiant which is the brightest star in ORION. A quadruple star consisting of a visual binary and a spectroscopic binary (see DOUBLE STAR), it is 276pc distant.

S

Sagittarius
The Archer, a constellation on the ECLIPTIC lying in the direction of the galactic center (see MILKY WAY). Sagittarius is the ninth sign of the ZODIAC.

Satellite
In astronomy, a celestial object that revolves with or around a larger celestial object. In our SOLAR SYSTEM this includes PLANETS, COMETS, ASTEROIDS and meteoroids (see METEOR), as well as the moons of the planets, though the term is usually restricted to this last sense. Of the 58 known moons, the largest is Ganymede (JUPITER III), the smallest Leda (Jupiter XIII). The MOON is one of the largest known satellites relative to its parent planet; indeed, the Earth-Moon system is sometimes considered a double planet.

Satellites, Artificial
Manmade objects placed in orbit as SATELLITES. First seriously proposed in the 1920s, they were impracticable until large enough rockets were developed. The first artificial satellite, Sputnik I, was launched by the USSR in October 1957, and was soon followed by a host of others, mainly from the USSR and the US, but also from the UK, France, Canada, West Germany, Italy, Japan and China. They have many scientific, technological and military uses. Astronomical observations (notably X-RAY ASTRONOMY) can be made unobscured by the ATMOSPHERE. Studies can be made of the radiation and electromagnetic and gravitational fields in which the Earth is bathed, and of the upper atmosphere. Experiments have been made on the functioning of animals and plants in space (with zero gravity and increased radiation). Artificial satellites are also used for reconnaissance, surveying, meteorological observation, as navigation aids (position references and signal relays), and in communications for relaying television and radio signals.

Saturn
The second largest planet in the SOLAR SYSTEM n

and the sixth from the Sun. Until the discovery of URANUS (1781) Saturn was the outermost planet known. It orbits the Sun in 29.46 years at a mean distance of 9.54AU. Saturn does not rotate uniformly: its period of rotation at the equator is 10.23h, rather longer toward the poles. This rapid rotation causes a noticeable equatorial bulge: the equatorial diameter is 120.6Mm, the polar diameter 108.1Mm. Saturn has the lowest density of any planet in the Solar System, less than that of water, and may contain over 60% hydrogen by mass. Its total mass is about 95 times that of the Earth. Saturn has at least 21 moons. The largest, Titan, about the same size as MERCURY, is known to have an atmosphere. Of the other moons, four have diameters greater than 1000km, nine greater than 100km, and the rest are very small. The most striking feature of Saturn is its ring system, seven or more rings. The major rings are subdivided into thousands of ringlets, grooves and ripples. Until recently Saturn was thought to be the only ringed planet in the Solar System, but rings have since been identified around URANUS, JUPITER and possibly NEPTUNE. Rings may be a characteristic of the outer planets, representing partially consolidated material left over from their accretion.

Schwarzschild radius
The radius of the sphere into which a given body of known mass must be compressed in order to become a BLACK HOLE.

Scorpius
The Scorpion, a medium-sized constellation on the ECLIPTIC; the eighth sign of the ZODIAC. Scorpius contains the bright star ANTARES.

Sidereal time
Time referred to the rotation of the Earth with respect to the fixed stars. The sidereal DAY is about four minutes shorter than the solar day, as the Earth moves each day about 1/365 of its orbit about the Sun. Sidereal time is used in astronomy when determining the locations of celestial bodies.

Singularity
In astronomy, the point or ring within a BLACK HOLE at which the gravitational field is of infinite strength.

Sirius
Alpha Canis Majoris (the Dog Star), the brightest STAR in the night sky, with an apparent magnitude of −1.46. It is 2.7pc distant, 20 times more luminous than the Sun, and has absolute magnitude +1.4. A DOUBLE STAR, its major component is twice the size of the Sun; its minor component (the Pup), the first white dwarf star to be discovered, has a diameter only 50% greater than that of the Earth, but is extremely dense, with a mass just less than that of the Sun.

Solar energy
The energy given off by the SUN as electromagnetic radiation. In one year the Sun emits about 1.2×10^{34}J of energy, of which half of one-billionth (6×10^{24}J) reaches the Earth. Of this, most is reflected away, only 35% being absorbed. The power reaching the ground is at most 1.2kW/m², and on average 0.8kW/m². Solar energy is naturally converted into wind power and into the energy of the hydrologic cycle, increasingly exploited as hydroelectric power. Plants convert solar energy to chemical energy by photosynthesis, normally at only 0.1% efficiency; the cultivation of algae in ponds can be up to 0.6% efficient, and is being developed to provide food and fuel. Solar heat energy may be used directly in several ways. Solar evaporation is used to convert brine to salt and distilled water. Flat-plate collectors – matt black absorbing plates with attached tubes through which a fluid flows to collect the heat – are beginning to be used for domestic water heating, space heating, and to run air-conditioning

systems. Focusing collectors, using a parabolic mirror, are used in solar furnaces, which can give high power absorption at high temperatures. They are used for cooking, for high-temperature research, to power heat engines for generating electricity, and to produce electricity more directly by the Seebeck effect. Solar energy may be directly converted to electrical energy by solar cells.

Solar system
The Sun and all the celestial objects that move in ORBIT around it, including the nine known planets (MERCURY; VENUS; EARTH; MARS; JUPITER; SATURN; URANUS; NEPTUNE; PLUTO), their 58 known moons, the ASTEROIDS, COMETS, meteoroids (see METEOR) and a large quantity of gas and dust. The planets all move in their orbits in the same direction and, with the exceptions of Venus and Uranus, also rotate on their axes in this direction: this is known as direct motion. Most of the Moons of the planets have direct orbits, with the exception of four of Jupiter's minor moons, the outermost moon of Saturn and the inner moon of Neptune, whose orbits are retrograde (see RETROGRADE MOTION). Most of the planets move in elliptical, near circular orbits, and roughly in the same plane. The origin of the Solar System is not known, though various theories have been proposed (see NEBULAR HYPOTHESIS; PLANETESIMAL HYPOTHESIS). The most popular current theory suggests that the Sun and planets formed from the same cloud of gas and dust, which, as it contracted, formed a central condensation (the Sun) surrounded by a disk of matter that broke up to form the planets. It would not appear to be unique among the stars (see BETA PICTORIS; PLANET; VEGA).

Solar wind
The electrically charged material, mostly electrons and protons, thrown out by the Sun at an average speed of 400km/s. The "quiet" component is a continuous stream to which is added an "active" component produced by bursts of activity on the Sun's surface. The solar wind affects the magnetic fields of the planets, and causes the tails of COMETS.

Solstices
The two times each year when the Sun is on the points of the ECLIPTIC farthest from the equator (see CELESTIAL SPHERE). At the summer solstice in late June the Sun is directly overhead at noon on the Tropic of Cancer; at winter solstice, in late December, it is overhead at noon on the Tropic of Capricorn.

Southern Cross
Crux, a small, bright constellation about 30° distant from the S celestial pole. The four bright stars forming the cross are Acrux (alpha), Mimosa (beta), Gacrux (gamma) and Delta Crucis.

Space exploration
At 10.56pm EDT on 20 July 1969 Neil Armstrong became the first man to set foot on the MOON. This was the climax of an intensive US space program sparked off by the successful launch of the Russian artificial SATELLITE Sputnik 1 in 1957, and accelerated by Yuri Gagarin's flight in Vostok 1, the first manned spacecraft, in 1961. Later that year Alan Shepard piloted the first American manned spacecraft, and President Kennedy set the goal of landing a man on the Moon and returning him safely within the decade. On 20 February 1962 John Glenn orbited the Earth three times in the first Mercury craft to be boosted by an Atlas rocket, but it was Valery Bykovsky who set the one-man endurance record with a five-day mission in June 1963. His Vostok 5 craft was accompanied in orbit for three days by Vostok 6, which carried Valentina Tereshkova, the first woman cosmonaut. Alexei Leonov completed the

first spacewalk in March 1965, but then it was the turn of the Gemini missions to break all records. Astronauts from both countries died, on the ground and in space. Unmanned probes such as Orbiter, Ranger and Surveyor were meanwhile searching out Apollo landing sites, while Russian Luna and Lunokhod craft were also studying the Moon. In 1968 Apollo 7 carried out an 11-day Earth-orbit flight, and at Christmas Apollo 8 made 10 lunar orbits. The lunar landing craft was tested on the Apollo 9 and Apollo 10 missions, leaving the way clear for the triumphant landing of Apollo 11. Apollo 12 was equally successful, landing only 550m from the lunar probe Surveyor 3, but the Apollo 13 mission was a near disaster: an explosion damaged the craft on its way to the Moon, and re-entry was achieved only with great difficulty. Apollo 14 had no such problems in visiting Fra Mauro, and on the Apollo 15 mission a lunar Roving Vehicle allowed collection of a very wide range of samples. Apollo 16 brought back over 90kg of moon rock; in December 1972 Apollo 17 made the last lunar landing. In 1973 the Skylab missions returned attention to the study of world resources from space, and movements toward cooperation in this field were demonstrated by the joint Apollo-Soyuz mission in 1975. Exploration of the planets has been carried out by unmanned probes: the Mariner series to Mars, Venus and Mercury; the Pioneer and Voyager missions to outer space, and a number of Soviet contributions, such as Venera, the Zond bypass probe to Venus and Mars soft-landing craft. Results from the two American Viking probes that soft-landed on Mars in 1976 did not reveal the existence of life there. By 1986 all the known planets, apart from Neptune and Pluto and two comets, Giacobini-Zinner and HALLEY'S, had been inspected at close range by spacecraft. Voyager 2 is scheduled to encounter Neptune in 1989.

The launch of the first test flight space shuttle in 1981 saw the introduction of reusable spacecraft. In 1982, two satellites were launched into orbit from the first operational shuttle, and the following year a shuttle flight carried the first American woman, Sally Rider, into space. In 1984 shuttle astronauts set a new record for working in space when they captured and repaired the faulty Solar Maximum Satellite.

Spacelab, a manned, reusable space laboratory built by the European Space Agency, took its first flight in the cargo bay of a shuttle in 1983. It proved that a scientist can carry out experiments in space, including processing materials in microgravity and high-vacuum conditions.

The shuttle program brought a change in emphasis from exploration to operation in space. The intention is for crews, consisting of astronauts, and mission and payload specialists, routinely to launch and repair satellites and to carry out research. The program received a tragic set-back in January 1986 when the shuttle Challenger exploded after liftoff, killing all seven crew.

Both Russia and America are now working toward permanently manned space stations. The Soviets launched their program in 1971, with the Salyut series of space stations. They are equipped for Earth, solar and astronomical observations and material processing experiments and, although not permanently manned, are visited regularly by crews flown up in Soyuz spacecraft. Some crews have stayed on Salyut for over 6 months at a time. The most recent version of the space station, Mir, has been enlarged by add-on modules to provide a basis for what may become a permanently manned facility.

The US space station program for the 1990s will

use shuttles to ferry modules into orbit, where they can be assembled. Permanently manned in low orbit, the space station will consist of living quarters, solar power sources, computer, work space and docking bay. Space stations could be used for processing materials that are difficult to manufacture on Earth, launching and servicing satellites, space telescopes, building spacecraft, and launching missions to outer space.

The next century could see permanently occupied outposts on the Moon to mine minerals for manufacturing satellites, space stations and planetary probes, and a manned mission to Mars. Another possibility is electricity generated in geostationary orbit by large arrays of solar cells, and transmitted back to Earth.

Space factories
Envisaged to process materials in space. These would take advantage of microgravity and atmospheric pressure to manufacture materials and products, on a large scale, that are difficult or impossible to produce on Earth; eg pharmaceuticals, electronics, optics and advanced alloys. Some preliminary investigations have taken place on Salyut space stations and space shuttles (see also SPACE EXPLORATION.)

Space-time
A way of describing the geometry of the physical Universe arising from Albert Einstein's special theory of relativity. Space and time are considered as a single 4-dimensional continuum rather than as a 3-dimensional space with a separate infinite 1-dimensional time. Time thus becomes the "fourth dimension". Events in space-time are analogous to points in space, and invariant space-time intervals to distances in space.

Star
A large incandescent ball of gases held together by its own gravity. The SUN is a fairly normal star in its composition, parameters and color. The lifespan of a star depends upon its mass and luminosity: a very luminous star may have a life of only one million years, the Sun a life of ten billion years, the faintest main sequence stars a life of ten thousand billion years. Stars are divided into two categories, Populations I and II. The stars in Population I are slower moving, generally to be found in the spiral arms of GALAXIES, and believed to be younger. Population II stars are faster moving and mainly to be found in the spheroidal halo of stars around a galaxy and in the GLOBULAR CLUSTERS. Compared to Population I stars they have a smaller proportion of metals in their composition. Many stars are DOUBLE STARS.

It is believed that stars originate as condensations out of INTERSTELLAR MATTER. In certain circumstances a protostar will form, slowly contracting under its own gravity, part of the energy from this contraction being radiated, the remainder heating up the core: this stage may last several million years. At last the core becomes hot enough for thermonuclear reactions (see FUSION, NUCLEAR) to be sustained, and stops contracting. Eventually the star as a whole ceases to contract, and radiates entirely by the thermonuclear conversion of hydrogen into helium: it is then said to be on the main sequence. When all the hydrogen in the core has been converted into helium, the now purely helium core begins to contract while the outer layers continue to "burn" hydrogen: this contraction heats up the core and forces the outer layers outward, so that the star as a whole expands for some 100-200 million years until it becomes a red giant star. Although the outer layers are comparatively cool, the core has become far hotter than before, and thermonuclear conversions of helium into carbon begin. The star contracts once more when its nuclear "fuels" become exhausted, and ends its life as a white dwarf star. It is thought

that more massive stars become neutron stars, whose matter is so dense that its protons and electrons are packed together to form neutrons; were the Sun to become a neutron star, it would have a radius of less than 20km. Finally, when the star can no longer radiate through thermonuclear or gravitational means, it ceases to shine. Some high-mass stars may at this stage undergo ultimate gravitational collapse to form BLACK HOLES. (See also CEPHEID VARIABLES; CONSTELLATION; COSMOLOGY; GALACTIC CLUSTER; MAGELLANIC CLOUDS; MILKY WAY; NEBULA; NOVA; PULSAR; QUASAR; SOLAR SYSTEM; STAR CLUSTER; SUPERNOVA; UNIVERSE; VARIABLE STAR.)

Star cluster
A cluster of stars sharing a common origin. There are two distinct types of star cluster: see GALACTIC CLUSTER; GLOBULAR CLUSTER.

Sun
The star about which the Earth and the other planets of the SOLAR SYSTEM revolve. The Sun is an incandescent ball of gases, by mass 69.5% hydrogen, 28% helium, 2.5% carbon, nitrogen, oxygen, sulfur, silicon, iron and magnesium altogether, and traces of other elements. It has a diameter of about 1393Mm, and rotates more rapidly at the equator (24.65 days) than at the poles (about 34 days). Although the Sun is entirely gaseous, its distance creates the optical illusion that it has a surface: this visible edge is called the PHOTOSPHERE. It is at a temperature of about 6000K, cool compared to the center of the Sun (15,000,000K) or the corona (1,000,000K); the photospheres of other stars may be at temperatures of less than 2000K or more than 500,000K. Above the photosphere lies the chromosphere, an irregular layer of gases between 1.5Mm and 15Mm in depth. It is in the chromosphere that FLARES and prominences occur: these last are great plumes of gas that surge out into the corona and occasionally off into space. The corona is the sparse outer atmosphere of the Sun. During solar ECLIPSES it may be seen to extend several thousand megameters and be as bright as the full Moon, though in effect it extends beyond the orbit of NEPTUNE. The Earth lies within the corona, which at this distance from the Sun is termed the SOLAR WIND. The Sun is a very normal STAR, common in its characteristics though rather smaller than average. It lies in one of the spiral arms of the MILKY WAY.

Sunspots
Apparently dark spots visible on the face of the SUN, regions about 2000K cooler than the adjacent photosphere that appear dark merely by contrast with their surroundings. Single spots are known, but mostly they form in groups or pairs. They are never seen at the Sun's poles. They are associated with concentrated localized magnetic fields, but their precise cause is not fully understood. Their prevalence reaches a maximum about every 11 years.

Supernova
A catastrophic stellar explosion in which a substantial fraction of the star's mass is blown out into space, or in some cases in which the star is completely destroyed. During the event, the star's luminosity may increase by a factor of millions or even billions, so that it may shine briefly as brightly as several billion suns. There are two principal types of supernova, Type I and Type II. Type I supernovae are typically about ten times more luminous than Type II; Type II supernovae show hydrogen lines in their spectra, while Type I supernovae do not. A Type I event is widely believed to occur in a binary system within which one star has dumped sufficient material onto the surface of a white dwarf companion to cause it to be squeezed and heated gravitationally to such an

extent that explosive thermonuclear reactions blow the white dwarf to pieces. A Type II event is believed to involve a massive Population I star that has exhausted the nuclear fuel in its core. The core is thought to collapse to form a neutron star; the rest of the star (the envelope) is blasted into space to form an expanding supernova remnant such as the CRAB NEBULA. Supernovae are rare events; on average only about three supernovae per century occur in a typical galaxy. The most recent supernova in the Milky Way Galaxy occurred in 1604. The most recent naked-eye supernova occurred in the Large MAGELLANIC CLOUD in 1987.

T

Taurus
The Bull, a large constellation on the ECLIPTIC; the second sign of the ZODIAC. It contains the CRAB NEBULA, the GALACTIC CLUSTERS the Hyades and PLEIADES, and the bright star Aldebaran.

Transit
The passage of a star across an observer's meridian (the great circle on the CELESTIAL SPHERE passing through his/her ZENITH and the north point of his horizon). The term is also applied to the passage of the inferior planets, Mercury and Venus, across the disk of the Sun.

U

Ultraviolet astronomy
The study of ultraviolet radiations emitted by celestial objects. As UV radiation above 310nm can penetrate to the Earth's surface, the sky in the longer UV can be studied with optical telescopes. UV astronomy is therefore taken to be the study of wavelengths between 10 and 310nm, with UV telescopes on balloons, rockets and satellites. A star that is hotter than 10,000K shines most brightly at UV wavelengths, and it is these young, hot stars that UV telescopes see.

Universe
The system of all that exists or happens. In COSMOLOGY, the term is applied to our Universe, ie all that we can observe and the presumably homogeneous and isotropic extension thereof. It is possible that other universes may exist or that, if we inhabit an oscillating universe, there may have been prior universes and there may be subsequent universes.

Uranus
The third largest planet in the SOLAR SYSTEM and the seventh from the Sun. Physically very similar to NEPTUNE, but rather larger (equatorial diameter 52Mm) it orbits the Sun every 84.02 years at a mean distance of 19.2AU, rotating in about 17h. The plane of its equator is tilted 98° to the plane of its orbit, such that the rotation of the planet and the revolution of its five moons, which orbit closely parallel to the equator, are retrograde (see RETROGRADE MOTION). In March 1977 an occultation of a star by Uranus led to the discovery of a series of rings similar to SATURN's. Voyager 2's fly-by in January 1986 greatly enhanced our knowledge of Uranus revealing faint atmospheric cloud belts, a magnetic field tilted by 55° to the rotation axes, and 15 moons.

V

Van Allen radiation belts
The belts of high-energy charged particles, mainly protons and electrons, surrounding the Earth, named for James Alfred Van Allen, who discovered them in 1958. They extend from a few hundred to about 50,000km above the Earth's surface, and radiate intensely enough to make it

essential for astronauts to be specially protected from them. The particles are trapped in these regions by the Earth's magnetic field.

Variable stars
Stars that vary in brightness. There are two main categories. Extrinsic variables are those whose variation in apparent brightness is caused by an external condition, as in the case of eclipsing binaries (see DOUBLE STAR). Intrinsic variables vary in absolute brightness owing to physical changes within them. They may vary either regularly or irregularly: most intrinsic variables are pulsating or eruptive in nature. Pulsating variables, which vary in size, are the most common type of variable star: they include the RR Lyrae stars, with periods from 1.5h to a little over a day, W Virginis stars and RV Tauri stars (all three types appearing principally in GLOBULAR CLUSTERS); long period and semiregular variables, which are red giants, and the CEPHEID VARIABLES. Types of variable stars whose periods are known to have a relationship to their absolute brightness are especially important in that they can be used to determine large astronomical distances. Eruptive variables include flare stars (UV Ceti stars), faint red stars that suddenly flare up by one or two magnitudes in brightness once or twice a day. NOVAE and SUPERNOVAE involve much more extreme eruptions.

Vega
Alpha Lyrae, the fourth brightest star in the night sky (apparent magnitude 0.03, absolute magnitude +0.5). It is 8pc distant, and 58 times as bright as the Sun. The InfraRed Astronomical Satellite (IRAS) discovered infrared radiation near Vega in 1983, suggesting that planetary material is orbiting the star. If this proves correct, it is the first evidence of a SOLAR SYSTEM forming apart from our own.

Venus
The planet second from the Sun, about the same size as the Earth. Its face is completely obscured by dense clouds containing sulfuric acid, though the USSR's Venera probes and the orbiter of the Venus Pioneer program in 1978 produced images of broadscale topography of the planet, revealing that two-thirds of the planet was covered by rolling plains, with larger craters. The American Pioneer Probe has indicated that Venus has active volcanoes. Venus revolves about the Sun at a mean distance of 0.72AU in 225 days, rotating on its axis in a retrograde direction (see RETROGRADE MOTION) in 243 days. Its diameter is 12.1Mm, its atmosphere is 97% carbon dioxide, and its surface temperature is about 750K. It has no moons, and almost certainly supports no life.

Virgo
The Virgin, a large constellation on the ECLIPTIC; the sixth sign of the ZODIAC. It contains the bright spectroscopic binary (see DOUBLE STAR) Spica and a cluster of galaxies.

W,X,Y

Weak nuclear force
The force underlying the beta type of radioactivity, and which is fundamental to the burning of stars like the SUN. At the quantum level it is described by the exchange of W and Z bosons.

X-ray astronomy
The study of the X-RAYS emitted by celestial objects. As the Earth's atmosphere absorbs most X-radiation before it reaches the surface, observations are made from high altitude balloons, satellites and rockets. X-rays are normally emitted from regions of superhot gas; X-ray sources include the solar corona, solar flares, compact stars in binary systems, quasars and intergalactic gas.

Year (yr)
Name of various units of time, all depending on the revolution of the Earth about the Sun. The sidereal year (365.25636 mean solar DAYS) is the average time the Earth takes to complete one revolution measured with respect to a fixed direction in space. The tropical year (365.24220 mean solar day), the year measured by the changing seasons, is that in which the mean longitude of the Sun moves through 360°. The anomalistic year (365.25964 mean solar days) is the average interval between successive terrestrial perihelions (see ORBIT). The civil year is a period of variable duration, usually 365 or 366 days (leap year), depending on the type of CALENDAR in use.

Z

Zenith
In astronomy, the point on the CELESTIAL SPHERE directly above an observer and exactly 90° from the celestial horizon. It is directly opposite to the NADIR.

Zodiac
The band of the heavens whose outer limits lie 9° on each side of the ECLIPTIC. The 12 main CONSTELLATIONS near the ecliptic, corresponding to the 12 signs of the zodiac, are ARIES; TAURUS; GEMINI; CANCER; LEO; VIRGO; LIBRA; SCORPIUS; SAGITTARIUS; CAPRICORNUS; AQUARIUS; PISCES. The orbits of all the planets except Pluto lie within the zodiac and their positions, as that of the Sun, are important in ASTROLOGY. The 12 signs are each equivalent to 30° of arc along the zodiac.

Zodiacal light
A hazy band of light, usually to be seen in the W after sunset or the E before sunrise, but in fact extending all along the ECLIPTIC. Associated is the Gegenschein, a circular patch of light on the ecliptic directly opposite to the Sun. Both phenomena are caused by the reflection of sunlight on clouds of interplanetary dust.

Credits

Key to abbreviations: AAT Anglo Australian Telescope Board; BBC HPL Hulton Picture Library, London; NASA National Aero Space Administration, Washington; RAS Royal Astronomical Society, London; SPL Science Photo Library, London. b bottom; bl bottom left; br bottom right; c center; cl center left; cr center right; t top; tl top left; tr top right l left; r right.

7 Patrick Moore 10tr Mansell Collection, London 10br BBC HPL 11t from Tycho Brahe: *Astronomiae Instaurate Mechanica*, photo Bodleian Library, Oxford 11tr Mansell Collection, London 11br from Tycho Brahe: *Astronomiae Instaurate Mechanica*, photo Bodleian Library, Oxford 14t Equinox Archives, Oxford 14c Lowell Observatory 14b Equinox Archives, Oxford 22 BBC HPL 24t,b NASA, Washington 25 NASA 26 NASA 27 Private Collection, Leamington Spa, photo Mark Fiennes 28t Space Frontiers Ltd. 28b NASA 29 SPL 30t Patrick Moore 30-31 NASA 31br Mansell Collection 32-33t Michael Kobrick/NASA 32c,b Sovfoto, NY 33l NASA 33r D.B. Campbell, Arecibo Observatory, Cornell University (The Arecibo Observatory is part of the National Astronomy and Ionopshere Center which is operated by Cornell University under contract with the National Science Foundation) 34-35 NASA 36tr SPL 36b Michael Kobrick/NASA 37t NASA 37c US Geological Survey 37bl,r NASA 38t Mansell Collection, London 38c Lowell Observatory 38b photo: Bodleian Library, Oxford 40t artwork reference courtesy *Scientific American* 43b artwork reference courtesy C.F. Capen and *Sky and Telescope* 43c Charles Capen, Lowell Observatory 44-45t NASA 44br NASA 45bc SPL 45tr NASA 45c NASA 45br SPL/NASA 48

NASA 53 SPL 52-53 NASA 58t NASA 58cl Patrick Moore 58cr NASA 60 NASA 61tl SPL/NASA 61 NASA 64-65 NASA 66tr Huygensmuseum "Hofwijck", Voorburg 67 NASA 68-69 NASA 70tr W.M. Sinton, Institute of Astronomy, University of Hawaii 70bc CCD Hawaii/Patrick Moore 70br Lowell Observatory 71c BBC HPL 71b Archiv Gerstenberg, Wietze 72tl D. R. Roddy 72br Paul Brierley 73bl Paul Brierley, Harlow. 74bl Patrick Moore 75tr BBC HPL 75c Sovfoto, NY 76c,b SPL/Dr. D. Klinglesmith/NASA 76tr Royal Society, London, photo: Eileen Tweedie 76tr Michael Holford 77bl Scala, Florence 77br Patrick Moore 78tr Science Museum, London, photo Butler 78br CF Capan Planetary Library, Institute for Planetary Research Observatories 79b Mansell Collection 82b Patrick Moore 85t BBC HPL 86c Harvard University Archive 86b Harvard College Observatory 87t © 1974 AURA Inc./Kitt Peak National Observatory 87c Prof. Hanbury Brown/University of Sydney 87b Lick Observatory, University of California 103tl Mount Wilson Observatory Photograph/E.P. Hubble Oct. 5/6 1923; reproduction J. Bedlie 103bl Harvard College Observatory 104 Kitt Peak National Observatory/Cerro Tololo Inter-American Observatoy 105bl Patrick Moore/Smithsonian Institution 105tr SPL/Leicester University 105br SPL/Dr. Kris Davidson 106tr Patrick Moore 110t Dept. of Applied Mathematics and Theoretical Physics, Cambridge 111tr,cr RAS/photo Eileen Tweedie 112tl SPL/Max-Planck Institut 112b Lund Observatory 113c European Space Agency 113b Rutherford-Appleton Laboratory, Oxon 114tr Harvard College Observatory 114cr RAS/Hale Observatory 196l D.F. Malin/AAT 119tr Mount

Wilson Observatory © Carnegie Institute of Washington 120tr Iain Nicolson 120b, 121 Royal Observatory, Edinburgh 122tr Huntington Library, California 122cr Mount Wilson Observatory 123tl,tr,cl,bl Mount Wilson and Las Campanas Observatory 123 tc, ct, cb, br California Institute of Technology/Palomar Observatory photograph 123cr 123b Kitt Peak National Observatory/CTIAO 124tr Iain Nicolson 124b SPL/Dr. Jean Lorre 125 SPL/Mt. Palomar Observatory 126tr,cr Kitt Peak National Observatory/CTIAO 127,128 With permission of the Hebrew University of Jerusalem, Israel 130t The Bettmann Archive Inc 131 Mount Wilson & Las Campanas Observatories 132 Archiv für Kunst und Geschichte 133 Mrs Otto Frisch 134-35 The Photosource 135b Novosti Press Agency 136-37 MEPL 138t Bildarchiv Preussischer Kulturbesitz 139t Royal Observatory, Greenwich 139c Illustrated London News 140t SPL/Photo Researchers Inc 140b AIP Niels Bohr Library 141 SPL/US Army 142t AIP Niels Bohr Library 143-3 Institut Internationale de Physique Solvay 143t Brown Brothers 143b Werner Wolff/Time Magazine 144t Philadelphia Museum of Art: The Mr & Mrs Wharton Sinkler Collection 144-5 Daily Telegraph Colour Library 144b Brown Brothers 146t Magnum/Haas 146c AM 146b AIP Niels Bohr Library

Artists Robert Burns; Kai Choi; Paul Doherty; Chris Forsey; Mick Gillah; Kevin Maddison; Coral Mulah; Mick Saunders.
Art assistant Frankie Macmillan
Indexer John Baines
Media conversion and typesetting Peter MacDonald, Ron Barrow
Production Joanna Turner

Index